AMATEUR RADIO THEORY COURSE

by

MARTIN SCHWARTZ
Formerly Instructor at American Radio Institute

Published by
AMECO PUBLISHING CORP.
275 Hillside Avenue
Williston Park, New York 11596

AMATEUR RADIO THEORY COURSE

PRINTED 1976
ALL MATERIAL IN THIS BOOK UP TO DATE

Copyright 1974
by the
Ameco Publishing Corp.

Library of Congress Catalog No. 73-91927

Printed in the United States of America

EXPLANATION OF COURSE

This Radio Communications Course has been written for the purpose of preparing you for the FCC Amateur examinations. The material contained in this course covers the written examination requirements for the Novice, Technician, General and Conditional classes of licenses. This course, together with the Advanced Class License Guide and the Extra Class License Guide (both published by the Ameco Publishing Corp.), cover the examination requirements for the Advanced and Extra Classes of licenses respectively.

The course is divided into three sections. The first section consists of three lessons on basic DC and AC theory. Some of the AC theory is not required for the amateur exams, but was given to provide you with a solid theoretical background in order to understand the lessons that follow. Section II discusses vacuum tubes, solid-state diodes and transistors. Section III takes up transmitters, receivers, antennas and the FCC rules and regulations.

After each section, there is a Study Guide that assists you by pointing out the important information in each lesson. You should read this Study Guide before and after each section.

There are a number of practice questions at the end of each lesson. These will check your knowledge of the material in the lesson. After each section there is an examination that tests your knowledge of the important points of the section. The correct answers to these questions will be found in Appendix 6.

There are two sample FCC-type exams at the end of the course. The first is a General exam on Page 282; the second is a Novice exam on Page 289. Under new regulations promulgated in July 1976, General and Technician applicants must take both the Novice exam (Element 2) and the General exam (Element 3). The Novice applicant must take only the Novice exam (Element 2). The correct answers to the final exams will be found in Appendix 6.

Most of the questions in this course are of the multiple choice type because this type of question is used exclusively by the FCC.

It is suggested that you study the entire course, regardless of which exam you are preparing for. This will give you an excellent background in radio communications. However, if you are strongly interested in obtaining your Novice license in a hurry, you can read only those parts that cover the necessary information for the Novice exam. Appendix 5 lists the paragraphs and questions that the prospective Novice operator must study.

In addition to the rules and regulations in Lesson 14, other important rules are given in Appendix 7 on Page 316. The prospective amateur should be familiar with these additional rules.

GOOD LUCK!

TABLE OF CONTENTS

INTRODUCTION TO RADIO

Let us begin by defining communication as a means or system by which we exchange our thoughts, opinions, information and intelligence with others. We are all familiar with the various methods of communication in use today. These methods may be simple and direct or highly developed technically. For example, people engaged in conversation, either directly or by using a telephone, illustrate the most common and simple means of exchanging ideas. Or the system may be more complex, as in radio transmission and reception between two radio amateur operators.

Before the discovery and development of electricity and radio, people used simple and crude methods for transmitting intelligence. The early Indians used smoke signals and drum beats to convey messages from one tribe to another. Although these sound and sight systems of transmitting messages were adequate for early man, they proved to be more and more archaic as man moved upward on the ladder of civilization. As mankind progressed into modern times, the invention of the telegraph and telephone became milestones in the history of the progress of communication. The telegraph and telephone were then radically different from any previous communication system in that they used electrical devices for both the sender and the receiver, and a wire or cable as the medium for the transmission. It thus became possible to communicate between any two points on the face of the earch which could be bridged by a cable or wire.

The next significant stage in the progress of message transmission was the development of a system of communication called the WIRELESS. The wireless was superior to the telegraph and telephone since it used the air as a transmission medium rather than a wire or cable. Today, wireless transmission is known as RADIO COMMUNICATIONS. And you, the prospective Amateur Radio Operator, will study in this course all of the technical aspects of a basic Radio Communications System so that you will be well equipped to operate your own radio transmitting station.

Let us, at this point, consider briefly a basic radio communications system as illustrated in block diagram form in Figure 1. The basic operation of this system is as follows: Someone speaks into the microphone which changes sound energy into electrical energy. This electrical energy is fed into the sender or TRANSMITTER. The transmitter generates electrical vibrations which, together with the energy output of the microphone, are fed to the transmitting antenna.

The transmitting antenna radiates the electrical vibrations out into space in the form of electrical radio waves. These radio waves travel outward from the antenna in a manner similar to the outward motion of ripples from a central point of disturbance in a pool of water.

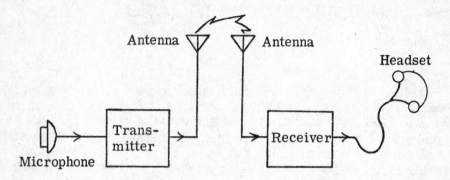

Figure 1. Block diagram of basic radio communications system.

At the receiving end of the radio communications system, the receiving antenna intercepts the radio waves and sends them into the receiver. The receiver converts the radio waves into electrical vibrations which energize the earphones. The earphones then convert the electrical energy back into the original sound that was spoken into the microphone attached to the transmitter. This brief description gives you a basic, non-technical picture of how a Radio Communications System operates.

Your Amateur Radio Course will first consider the basic principles of electricity and radio. After you have analyzed these principles, you will study the functions of the numerous circuits which are basic to an understanding of radio. The course then concludes with a detailed study of a complete radio transmitter from beginning to end.

SECTION I – LESSON 1
DIRECT CURRENT THEORY

1-1 MATTER AND ELECTRICITY

Matter is a general term used to describe all the material things about us. Matter includes all man-made structures, woods, metals, gases, etc.; in other words, everything tangible. All matter, regardless of its size, quality or quantity, can be broken down fundamentally into two different types of particles. These particles, which are too small to be seen under a powerful microscope, are called ELECTRONS and PROTONS. Electrically, we say that the ELECTRON is NEGATIVELY charged and the PROTON is POSITIVELY charged. Also, the proton is about 1800 times as heavy as the electron.

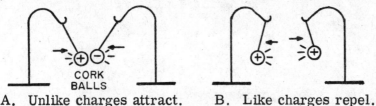

A. Unlike charges attract.   B. Like charges repel.

Figure 1-1. Attraction and repulsion.

1-2 THE LAW OF ELECTRIC CHARGES

Any object, such as a piece of glass, normally has a neutral or zero charge; that is, it contains as many electrons as protons. If this piece of glass can be made to have an excess of electrons, it is said to be negatively charged. Conversely, if the piece of glass can somehow be made to have a deficiency of electrons, the protons will predominate, and it is then said to be positively charged.

If a positively charged body is brought near a negatively charged body, the two objects will be drawn together. On the other hand, if two positively charged bodies or two negatively charged bodies are brought near each other, they will try to move away from each other. This reaction is the basis for our first law of electricity - the LAW OF ELECTRIC CHARGES. The law states "like charges repel, unlike charges attract". This law is illustrated by Figures 1-1A and 1-1B. In Figure 1-1A, a positively charged ball of cork is suspended by a piece of string near a negatively charged ball of cork. The two bodies swing toward each other since they attract each other. Figure 1-1B illustrates the two positively charged balls repelling each other.

1-3   DIFFERENCE OF POTENTIAL

If we were to connect a copper wire between the negative and the positive balls of cork, an electron flow would result. This is illustrated in Figure 1-2. The excess electrons from the negative ball would flow onto the positive ball where there is an electron deficiency and therefore, an attraction for the electrons. This flow continues until the deficiency and excess of electrons has disappeared and the balls become neutral or uncharged. This flow of electrons between the two differently charged bodies is caused by the difference in charge. A difference in charge between two objects will always result in the development of an electrical pressure between them. It is this electrical pressure that causes a current flow between these two bodies when they are connected by a piece of copper wire. This electrical pressure is defined as a DIFFERENCE OF POTENTIAL. The words "POTENTIAL" and "CHARGE" have similar meanings.

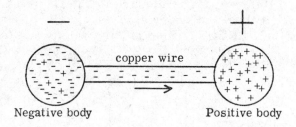

Figure 1-2.   Flow of electrons.

1-4   CONDUCTORS AND INSULATORS

Materials through which current can easily flow are called CONDUCTORS. Most metals are good conductors. Conductors incorporate a large number of free electrons in their atomic structure. These free electrons are not held tightly and will move freely through the conductor when stimulated by external electrical pressure. Examples of good conductors, in the order of their conductivity, are silver, copper, aluminum and zinc.

Those materials through which current flows with difficulty are called INSULATORS. The electrons are tightly held in the atomic structure of an insulator and, therefore, cannot move about as freely as in conductors. Examples of insulators are wood, silk, glass and bakelite. In electronics, a distinction is made between insulators which are good enough only for power frequencies, and those which can be used for radio frequencies. Examples of good radio frequency insulators are: quartz, pyrex, mycalex and polystyrene. Wood, silk, glass and bakelite can be used for power frequencies, but not for radio frequencies. We will discuss the differences between power and radio frequencies in a later section.

1-5   RESISTANCE

The ability of a material to oppose the flow of current is called

RESISTANCE. All materials exhibit a certain amount of resistance to current flow. In order to compare the resistances of various materials, we require some standard unit of resistance measurement. The unit of resistance that was adapted for this purpose was the OHM, and the Greek letter Ω is its symbol. (For a list of common radio abbreviations, refer to Appendix 1). One ohm is defined as the amount of resistance inherent in 1,000 feet of #10 copper wire. For example, 5,000 feet of #10 copper wire would have a resistance of 5 ohms, 10,000 feet of #10 copper wire would have 10 ohms, etc. Although the ohm is the basic unit, the MEGOHM, meaning 1,000,000 ohms, is frequently used. The instrument used to measure resistance is the OHMMETER.

There are four factors which determine the resistance of a conductor. They are:

1. Length. The resistance of a conductor is directly proportional to its length. The longer the conductor, the greater is its resistance. The current has to flow through more material in a longer conductor and therefore, meets more total opposition.

2. Cross-sectional area. The resistance of a conductor is inversely proportional to the cross-sectional area. This means that the resistance becomes smaller as the thickness or area becomes larger. For example, if we double the cross-sectional area of a conductor of a given length, the resistance will be cut in half. If we triple the area, the resistance will be cut to one-third of its original resistance. The current will flow through a conductor of larger cross-sectional area with greater ease because of its wider path. If we decrease the cross-sectional area of the conductor, less electrons can squeeze through. Hence, we have a greater resistance.

3. Temperature. In practically all conductors, witn the exception of carbon, the resistance varies directly with the temperature. As the temperature of a conductor rises, its resistance increases; as the temperature drops, the resistance decreases.

4. Material make-up. The resistance of a conductor depends upon the material of which it is made. Because of their material structure, some conductors have more resistance than others. For example, silver has a very low resistance, whereas nichrome has a high resistance.

1-6　RESISTORS

The resistor is a common radio part with a built-in specific amount of resistance. Resistors which are made of mixtures of carbon and clay are called carbon resistors. Carbon resistors are used in low power circuits. Wire wound resistors, which contain special resistance wire, are used in high power circuits. Figure 1-3 illustrates several types of fixed resistors which are used in radio circuits, together with the symbol which is used to represent them in circuit diagrams. When it becomes necessary to vary the amount of resistance in a circuit, we use adjustable and VARIABLE RESISTORS

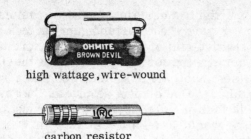
high wattage, wire-wound

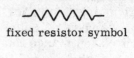
fixed resistor symbol

carbon resistor

precision resistor

Figure 1-3. Fixed resistors.

The adjustable resistor is usually wire-wound, and has a sliding collar which may be moved along the resistance element to select any desired resistance value. It is then clamped in place. Figure 1-4A shows an adjustable resistor.

Variable resistors are used in a circuit when a resistance value must be changed frequently. Variable resistors are commonly called potentiometers or rheostats, depending upon their use. The resistance is varied by sliding a metal contact across the resistance in such a way so as to get different amounts of resistance. The volume control in a radio is a typical example of a variable resistor. Figure 1-4 B shows a potentiometer used as a volume control for a radio receiver; Figure 1-4 C shows a potentiometer wound of heavier wire for use in a power supply circuit.

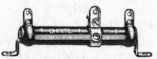

variable resistor symbol.

A. adjustable power resistor.

B. volume control potentiometer.   C. power supply rheostat.

Figure 1-4. Variable resistors.

1-7   CONDUCTANCE
    The reciprocal or the opposite of resistance is called CONDUCTANCE.

$$(1-1) \quad \text{conductance} = \frac{1}{\text{resistance}}$$

Conductance is the ability of an electrical circuit to pass or conduct electricity. A circuit having a large conductance has a low resistance; a circuit having a low conductance has a high resistance. The unit of conductance is the MHO. A resistance of one ohm has a conductance of one mho; a resistance of 10 ohms has a conductance of .1 mho (1/10 = 0.1). In other words, to determine the conductance, we divide the number 1 by the amount of resistance in ohms. We frequently use the term MICROMHO, meaning one millionth of a mho.

1-8   VOLTAGE AND CURRENT

Voltage is another term for the difference of potential or electrical pressure which we spoke about in a preceding paragraph. It is the force which pushes or forces electrons through a wire, just as water pressure forces water through a pipe. Some other terms used to denote voltage are EMF (electro-motive force), IR DROP and FALL OF POTENTIAL. The unit of voltage is the VOLT and the instrument used to measure voltage is the VOLTMETER. The KILOVOLT is equal to 1000 volts.

Current is the flow of electrons through a wire as a result of the application of a difference of potential. If a larger amount of electrons flow past a given point in a specified amount of time, we have a greater current flow. The unit of current is the AMPERE; it is equal to 6,300,000,000,000,000,000 electrons flowing past a point in one second. MILLIAMPERE and MICROAMPERE are terms used to denote one-thousandth and one-millionth of an ampere, respectively. Current is measured by an AMMETER. A meter whose scale is in milliamperes is called a MILLIAMMETER, and a meter that reads microamperes is called a MICROAMMETER.

We have one more important term to define and that is the COULOMB. The coulomb is the unit of electrical quantity. The coulomb is the number of electrons contained in one ampere. One coulomb flowing past a point in one second is equal to one ampere. Many people confuse the COULOMB with the AMPERE. The difference is this: The ampere represents the RATE OF FLOW of a number of electrons, whereas the coulomb represents only the quantity of electrons, and has nothing to do with the rate of flow or movement of the electrons.

1-9   THE DRY CELL

Several methods are used to produce current flow or electricity. A common method is the dry cell, which is used in the ordinary flashlight. The dry cell contains several chemicals combined to cause a chemical reaction which produces a voltage. The voltage produced by all dry cells, regardless of size, is 1-1/2 volts. A battery is composed of a number of cells. Therefore, a battery may be 3 volts, 6 volts, 7-1/2 volts, etc., depending upon the number of cells it contains. The fact that a cell is larger than another one indicates that the larger cell is capable of delivering current for a longer period of time than the smaller one. Figure 1-5 illustrates a typical 1-1/2 volt cell and a 45 volt battery. The 45 volt battery contains 30 cells.

Every cell has a negative and a positive terminal. The electrons leave the cell at the negative terminal, flow through the circuit

Fig. 1-5A. 1-1/2 v. flashlight cell.   Fig. 1-5B. 45 v. "B" battery.

and return to the cell at the positive terminal. This type of current flow is known as DIRECT CURRENT (DC). Direct current flows only in ONE direction.

1-10 ELECTRICAL CIRCUITS

Figure 1-6A is a diagram of a complete electrical circuit. The arrows indicate the direction of the current flow. As long as we can trace the current from the negative point of the cell, all around the circuit and back to the positive point, we have a complete circuit. The important thing to remember is that current will only flow through a complete circuit.

The necessary parts for a complete circuit are:

(1) A source of voltage - the dry cell in Figure 1-6A.

(2) Connecting leads - the copper wire conductors in Figure 1-6A.

(3) A load - the bulb in Figure 1-6A.

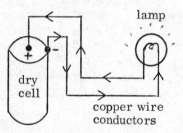 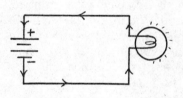

Fig. 1-6A. Complete electrical circuit. Fig. 1-6B. Schematic diagram.

If a break occurred in the connecting leads, or in the wire of the bulb, no current would flow and the bulb would go out. We would then have an OPEN CIRCUIT. Figure 1-7A illustrates the open circuit condition.

If we place a piece of wire directly across the two cell terminals, no current will flow through the bulb. This condition is illustrated in Figure 1-8A. The current by-passes the bulb and flows through the path of least resistance, which is the piece of wire. This condition is known as a SHORT CIRCUIT; it is to be avoided because it causes a severe current drain which rapidly wears the battery down.

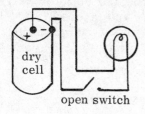

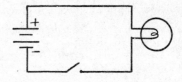

Fig. 1-7A. Open circuit. Fig. 1-7B. Schematic diagram.

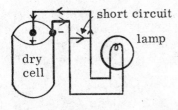

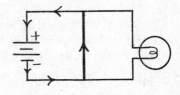

Fig. 1-8A. Short circuit. Fig. 1-8B. Schematic diagram.

1-11 SCHEMATICS

In drawing an electrical circuit on paper, we find it impractical to draw the actual battery or lamp as was done in Figures 1-6A, 1-7A and 1-8A. Instead, we use simple symbols to represent the various electrical parts. For instance:

A cell is shown as

A battery is shown as

A resistor is shown as

You will find a complete table of radio symbols in Appendix II. Figures 1-6A, 1-7A and 1-8A can now be redrawn in the manner shown in Figures 1-6B, 1-7B and 1-8B. Note that we indicate the negative battery terminal by a short line and the positive terminal by a long line.

1-12 OHM'S LAW

We have discussed the significance of voltage, current and resistance. Now we shall further study the important relationships that exist between these three factors. If we were to increase the battery voltage of Figure 1-6A, more electrons would flow through the circuit because of the greater electrical pressure exerted upon them. If we were to decrease the voltage, the flow of electrons would decrease. On the other hand, if the resistance of the circuit were made larger, the current would decrease because of greater opposition to current flow. If the resistance were made smaller, the current would increase by the same reasoning. These relationships are formulated

13

into a law known as OHM'S LAW which is stated as follows: The current is directly proportional to the voltage and inversely proportional to the resistance. Ohm's Law, mathematically stated, says that the current, in amperes, is equal to the voltage, in volts, divided by the resistance, in ohms.

The three formulas of Ohm's Law are:

(1-2) $I = \dfrac{E}{R}$ (1-3) $E = IR$ (1-4) $R = \dfrac{E}{I}$

"I" stands for the current in amperes.
"E" is the voltage in volts.
"R" is the resistance in ohms.

It is obvious that it is quicker to use letters such as I, E and R than to actually write out the words. Also, note that IR means I multiplied by R. If two out of the three factors of Ohm's Law are known (either E, I or R), the unknown third factor can be found by using one of the above three equations. Several examples will clarify the use of Ohm's Law:

Problem: (1) Given: Current is .75 amperes
　　　　　　　　　　　Resistance is 200 ohms
　　　　　　　Find:　The voltage of the battery.

Solution: Since we are interested in finding the voltage, we use formula 1-3 because it tells us what the voltage is equal to. We then substitute the known values and solve the problem as follows:

(1)　E = IR
(2)　E = .75 x 200
(3)　E = 150V.

$$\begin{array}{r} 200 \\ \times\,.75 \\ \hline 1000 \\ 1400 \\ \hline 150.00 \end{array}$$

Problem: (2) Given: Battery voltage is 75 volts.
　　　　　　　　　　　Resistance of bulb is 250 ohms.
　　　　　　　Find:　Current in circuit.
Solution: Use formula 1-2 to find the current.

(1) $I = \dfrac{E}{R}$　　(2) $I = \dfrac{75}{250}$　　(3) $I = .3$ amp.　$250\overline{)75.0}$ .3 750

Problem: (3) Given: Current in circuit is 2 amp.
　　　　　　　　　　　Battery voltage is 45 volts.
　　　　　　　Find:　Resistance of circuit.
Solution: Use formula 1-4 and substitute for E and I to find R.

(1) $R = \dfrac{E}{I}$　　(2) $R = \dfrac{45}{2}$　　(3) $R = 22.5$ ohms.

1-13 RESISTANCES IN SERIES

If two or more resistances are connected end to end as shown in Figure 1-9A, any current flowing through one will also flow through the others. The arrows indicate the direction of current flow. The

14

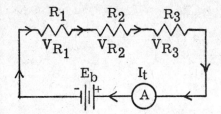 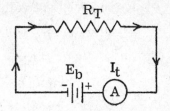

Figure 1-9A. Series circuit.   Figure 1-9B. Equivalent circuit.

above circuit is called a SERIES CIRCUIT. Since the same current flows through each resistor, the CURRENT IS THE SAME AT EVERY POINT IN A SERIES CIRCUIT. Similarly, the total current is the same as the current in any part of the series circuit. To put it mathematically:

$$(1-5) \quad I_{(total)} = I_{R_1} = I_{R_2} = I_{R_3}$$

It is important to note that the current in Figure 1-9A will remain unchanged if the separate series resistors are replaced by a single resistor whose resistance value is equal to the sum of the three resistors. Figure 1-9B illustrates the equivalent circuit of Figure 1-9A.

THE TOTAL RESISTANCE IN A SERIES CIRCUIT IS EQUAL TO THE SUM OF THE INDIVIDUAL RESISTANCES.

(1-6) $R_T = R_1 + R_2 + R_3$, etc.   where R_T is total resistance

Whenever current flows through a resistance in a circuit, a part of the source voltage is used up in forcing the current to flow through the particular resistance. The voltage that is used up in this manner is known as the VOLTAGE DROP or fall of potential across that particular resistor. The voltage drop is equal to the current through the part multiplied by the resistance of the part.

If we add up the voltage drops across all the parts of a series circuit, the sum would be equal to the source or battery voltage.

(1-7) $E_B = V_{R_1} + V_{R_2} + V_{R_3}$, etc.

where E_B is the battery voltage
V_{R_1} is the voltage across R_1
V_{R_2} is the voltage across R_2, etc.

Problem: Find the resistance of R_2 in Figure 1-9C.

Solution: (1) Since we know the total current and the battery voltage, we can use Ohm's Law to find the total resistance.

$$R_T = \frac{E}{I} = \frac{100}{.5} = 200 \text{ ohms}$$

(2) Since the total resistance in this series circuit is 200 Ω and $R_1 = 75\Omega$, then $R_2 = R_T - R_1$

(3) $R_2 = 200 - 75$ (4) $R_2 = 125$ ohms

Fig. 1-9C.
Problem.

15

Problem: Find the voltage across R1 and R2 in Figure 1-9C.

Solution: Since E = IR, the voltage across R1 is:

$$E_{R1} = .5 \times 75 = 37.5 \text{ V.}$$

The voltage across R2 is:

$$E_{R2} = .5 \times 125 = 62.5 \text{ V.}$$

Note that the total voltage divides itself across the resistors in proportion to the resistance of each resistor.

1-14 INTERNAL RESISTANCE OF BATTERY

A battery has a certain amount of resistance, just as any other device has. We refer to the resistance of the battery as its "internal resistance". The current, flowing in a circuit, flows through the internal resistance of the battery in the same manner as it flows through the resistance of the load. The internal resistance of the battery is in series with the rest of the circuit. It is represented by "Ri" in Figure 1-10. The total resistance of Figure 1-10 is equal to Ri plus the load resistance.

If the battery is in good condition, Ri is small and is usually ignored.

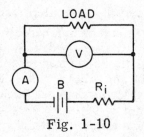

B - Battery.
Ri - Internal resistance of battery.
A - Ammeter.
V - Voltmeter.

Fig. 1-10

1-15 RESISTANCES IN PARALLEL

The circuit in Figure 1-11A is called a PARALLEL CIRCUIT. R_1 and R_2 are in parallel with each other. The current in the circuit now has two paths to flow through from the negative end of the battery to the positive end. If we remove resistor R_1 or R_2 from the circuit, the current has only one path to flow through from the negative to the positive end of the battery. Since it is easier for the current to flow through two paths instead of one, the total resistance of a parallel combination is less than the resistance of either resistor in the circuit. The more resistors we add in parallel, the less becomes the total resistance. This is because we increase the number of paths through which the current can flow. An analogy for this would be to consider the number of people that can pass through one door in a given time, compared to the number of people that can pass through several doors in the same time.

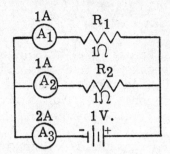
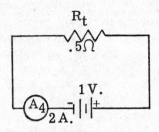

Fig. 1-11A. Parallel circuit.   Fig. 1-11B. Equivalent circuit.

If the resistors in Figure 1-11A were equal, it would be twice as easy for the current to pass through the parallel combination than it would be for it to pass through either one of the resistors alone. The total parallel resistance would, therefore, be one-half of either one of the resistors. Figure 1-11B shows the equivalent circuit of Figure 1-11A.

In Figure 1-11B, R_T is the total resistance of R_1 and R_2 in parallel. The current flowing in the equivalent circuit must be equal to the total line current of Figure 1-11A.

The total resistance of <u>any TWO</u> resistors in parallel may be found by using the following formula:

$$(1-8) \quad R_T = \frac{R_1 \times R_2}{R_1 + R_2}$$

For example, if R_1 and R_2 of Figure 1-11A were 3 and 6 ohms respectively, the total resistance would be:

$$(1) \quad R_T = \frac{R_1 \times R_2}{R_1 + R_2} \qquad (2) \quad R_T = \frac{3 \times 6}{3 + 6} = \frac{18}{9} = 2 \text{ ohms.}$$

The total resistance of <u>ANY NUMBER</u> of resistors in parallel may be found by applying the following formula:

$$(1-9) \quad R_T = \frac{1}{\dfrac{1}{R_1} + \dfrac{1}{R_2} + \dfrac{1}{R_3}} \text{ etc.}$$

For example, if three resistors of 5, 10 and 20 ohms were connected in parallel, the total resistance would be:

$$(1) \quad R_T = \frac{1}{\dfrac{1}{R_1} + \dfrac{1}{R_2} + \dfrac{1}{R_3}} \qquad (2) \quad R_T = \frac{1}{\dfrac{1}{5} + \dfrac{1}{10} + \dfrac{1}{20}} \quad \text{(least common denominator is 20)}$$

$$(3) \quad \frac{1}{\dfrac{4 + 2 + 1}{20}} = \frac{1}{\dfrac{7}{20}} \qquad (4) \quad 1 \times \frac{20}{7} = 2\frac{6}{7} \text{ ohms.}$$

1-16 CHARACTERISTICS OF A PARALLEL CIRCUIT

1) The total resistance of several resistors hooked in parallel is less than the smallest resistor.

2) The amount of current flowing through each branch depends upon the resistance of the individual branch. The total current drawn from the battery is equal to the sum of the individual branch currents.

3) The voltage across all the branches of a parallel circuit is the same; in Figure 1-11A the voltage across R_1 is the same as the voltage across R_2.

An example will illustrate the above principles. Refer to Figure 1-11C.

Given: Current through R_1 is 0.2 A.
           R_1 = 50 ohms. R_2 = 200 ohms.

Find: 1) Current through R_2.
           2) Total current.

Solution: Since we know the resistance of R_1 and the current through R_1, we can find the voltage across R_1 by using Ohm's law.

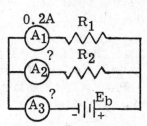

Fig. 1-11C.
Problem.

(1) $E_{R_1} = I_{R_1} \times R_1$

(2) $E_{R_1} = .2 \times 50$

(3) $E_{R_1} = 10V$

Since R_1 is in parallel with R_2, the voltage across R_2 is the same as that across R_1. Therefore, $E_{R_2} = 10V$ also.

Knowing the resistance of R_2 (given) and the voltage across it, we can find the current through R_2:

$$I_{R_2} = \frac{E_{R2}}{R_2} = \frac{10}{200} = .05 \text{ amp. current through } R_2$$

In a parallel circuit, the total current is equal to the sum of the individual branch currents; therefore:

(1) $I_T = I_{R_1} + I_{R_2}$ (2) $I_T = .2A + .05A = .25$ amp.
                                                   total current

1-17 SERIES-PARALLEL CIRCUITS

Circuits A and B of Figure 1-12 are called SERIES-PARALLEL CIRCUITS. In circuit A, the 10 ohm resistors are in parallel with each other. But this parallel combination is in series with the 20 ohm resistor. The total resistance of circuit A is computed as follows:

First find the resistance of the two 10 ohm parallel resistors using formula 1-8.

$$R_T = \frac{R_1 \times R_2}{R_1 + R_2} = \frac{10 \times 10}{10 + 10} = \frac{100}{20} = 5 \text{ ohms.}$$

Since the parallel resistors are in series with the 20 ohm re sistor, then the total resistance of this combination is:

5 + 20 or 25 ohms.

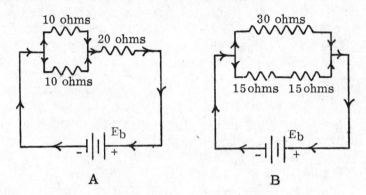

Figure 1-12.   Series-parallel circuits.

In diagram B, the two 15 ohm resistors are in series with each other. This series combination is in parallel with the 30 ohm resistor. The total resistance of series-parallel circuit B is computed as follows:

The resistance of the two 15 ohm resistors in series is 15 + 15 or 30 ohms. Since this 30 ohms is in parallel with the 30 ohm resistor, the total resistance of the combination is:

$$R_T = \frac{30 \times 30}{30 + 30} = \frac{900}{60} = 15 \text{ ohms}$$

1-18 POWER

Whenever current flows through a resistance, there is friction between the moving electrons and the molecules of the resistor. This friction causes heat to be generated, as does all friction. We could also say that electrical energy is changed to heat energy whenever current flows through a resistor. The unit of energy is the JOULE. The rate at which the heat energy is generated is the power that the resistor consumes. This power consumption in the form of heat represents a loss because we do not make use of the heat generated in radio circuits.

We should know how much heat power a resistor is consuming or dissipating. This is important because a resistor will burn up if it cannot stand the heat that is being generated by current flow. Resistors are, therefore, rated, not only in ohms, but in the amount of power that they can dissipate without overheating. The unit of electrical power is the WATT. A resistor rated at 5 watts is one which can safely dissipate up to 5 watts of power. If this resistor is forced to dissipate 10 watts, by increased current flow, it will burn up.

Exactly how much power is dissipated in a particular circuit, and upon what factors does the power dissipation depend? Since the power is the result of friction between the flowing electrons and the resistance in the circuit, the actual power dissipated depends upon the current and the resistance. The more current that flows, the more electrons there are to collide with the molecules of the resistance material. Also, the greater the resistance, the greater is the resulting friction. The actual power dissipated in a resistor can be found by the following formula:

(1-10) $P = I^2 \times R$

(I^2 means I x I)

where: P is the power in watts
I is the current in amperes
R is the resistance in ohms

Problem: Find the power dissipated in a 2000 ohm resistor with 50 milliamperes flowing through it.

Solution: First change milliamperes to amperes. This is done by moving the decimal three places to the left. Thus 50 milliamperes equals .05 ampere. Then substitute the values given in formula 1-10.

(1) $P = I^2 \times R$
(2) $P = .05 \times .05 \times 2000$
(3) $P = 5$ watts

$$(1)\quad \begin{array}{r} .05 \\ \times\ .05 \\ \hline .0025 \end{array} \qquad (2)\quad \begin{array}{r} .0025 \\ \times\ 2000 \\ \hline 5.0000 \end{array}$$

By using Ohm's law and algebraically substituting in formula 1-10, we can arrive at two more formulas for obtaining power dissipation.

(1-11) $P = E \times I$

(1-12) $P = \dfrac{E^2}{R}$

where: P is the power in watts,
E is the voltage in volts,
I is the current in amperes and
R is the resistance in ohms.

Formula 1-11 states that the power is equal to the product of the voltage across the resistor and the current through the resistor.

The Wattmeter is the instrument that is used to measure power. The Watt-hour meter is the instrument that is used to measure energy.

PRACTICE QUESTIONS - LESSON 1

(For answers, refer to Appendix 6)

1-1* The unit of power is the:
    a. ampere   b coulomb   c. watt   d. joule

1-2* The instrument used to measure resistance is:
    a. the wattmeter   c. the ammeter
    b. the ohmmeter   d. the voltmeter

1-3* The resistance of two equal resistors connected in parallel is:
    a. the sum of the two resistors

b. one-half of one of the resistors
c. one-quarter of one of the resistors
d. the average value of the resistors

1-4* The unit of electrical quantity is the:
    a. ohm   b. watt   c. joule   d. coulomb

1-5 A kilovolt is:
    a. 100 volts   c. 1000 volts
    b. one-thousandth of a volt   d. one-millionth of a volt

1-6 The total current in a parallel circuit is:
    a. the same in each branch
    b. equal to the sum of the individual branch currents.
    c. equal to the current in each branch multiplied by two
    d. none of the above

1-7 Which of the following factors does not influence the resistance of a conductor?
    a. length   b. diameter   d. temperature   d. color

1-8* Of the following formulas, pick out the incorrect one:
    a. $I = \dfrac{E}{R}$ b. $E = RI$ c. $R = \dfrac{I}{E}$ d. $P = I^2 R$

1-9 The total current in a series circuit is equal to:
    a. the current in any part of the circuit
    b. the sum of the currents in each part
    c. the total resistance divided by the voltage
    d. the sum of the IR drops

1-10 A short circuit:
    a. is found in every good electrical circuit
    b. causes a heavy current to be drained from the electrical source
    c. prevents current from flowing
    d. decreases the conductance of the circuit

1-11* Find the power dissipated by a 2500 ohm resistor that is carrying 75 milliamperes.

1-12* Find the source voltage of the circuit shown:

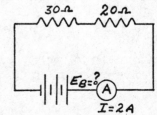

21

1-13 A 20 ohm resistor, a 15 ohm resistor and a 30 ohm resistor are all hooked in parallel. What is their total resistance?

1-14* What is the total current in the circuit shown?

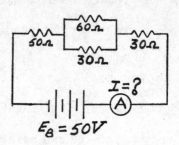

1-15* What is the voltage across the 50 ohm resistor in question 1-14?

1-16* The unit of energy is:
    a. watt   b. joule   c. coulomb   d. electron

1-17* The instrument used to measure power is the:
    a. ohmmeter   c. wattmeter
    b. power meter   d. wavemeter

1-18* Assuming that the internal resistance of the battery of question 1-12 above is one ohm, what is the total resistance of the circuit?
    a. 50 ohms   c. 12 ohms
    b. 51 ohms   d. 13 ohms

1-19* Another term for voltage is:
    a. flow of electrons   c. EI drop
    b. electromotive force   d. electrical energy

1-20* The unit of current is:
    a. ampere   c. joule
    b. coulomb   d. ohm

1-21* Direct current is obtained from a
    a. dry cell   c. motor
    b. generator   d. conductor

1-22* What is the power consumed by the 20 ohm resistor of Question 12 above?
    a. 40 watts   b. 100 watts   c. 25 watts   d. 80 watts

1-23* Which of the following is not a good conductor?
    a. silver   b. gold   c. pyrex   d. zinc

SECTION I – LESSON 2
MAGNETISM

2-1   THE MAGNET
    We are all familiar with the effects of magnetism. A horseshoe magnet will attract and pull to it iron filings. A powerful crane electromagnet will pick up heavy pieces of iron. A compass needle will point to the North Pole. A magnet, therefore, is any object which has the ability of attracting to itself, magnetic materials such as iron or steel. Figure 2-1 shows a horseshoe magnet attracting particles of iron filings.

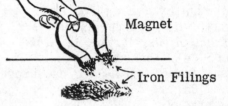

Figure 2-1.
Magnet's attraction power.

Magnet

Iron Filings

    When a magnetized bar of iron is suspended from a string tied around its center so that it is free to rotate, it will come to rest with one end pointing almost directly north. The end that points north is called the NORTH POLE, and the opposite end of the magnetized bar of iron is called the SOUTH POLE.

2-2   LAW OF MAGNETIC POLES
    If the North Pole end of one magnet is brought near the North Pole end of another magnet, the magnets will repel each other. The same reaction of REPULSION will occur if two South Pole ends are brought close to each other. However, if a North Pole end and South Pole end are brought close to each other, the magnets will attract each other. The reason that the North Pole of a suspended magnet points to the earth's North geographical pole is that the earth itself is a magnet. The earth's South magnetic pole is located near the North geographical pole. A compass points to the North geographical pole because the compass needle is a magnet and the pointer is its North pole.
    The results of experiments in magnetic attraction and repulsion were formulated into the law of poles which states that OPPOSITE POLES ATTRACT EACH OTHER, WHEREAS LIKE POLES REPEL EACH OTHER. Figure 2-2 illustrates this principle.

2-3   MAGNETIC LINES OF FORCE
    We cannot see the forces of repulsion or attraction which exist between the pole pieces of two magnets. We must assume that the North Pole of one magnet sends out some kind of invisible force which

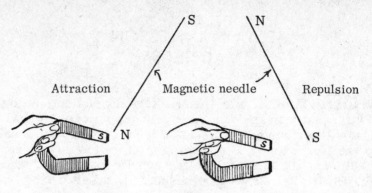

Figure 2-2. Attraction and repulsion.

has the ability to act through air and pull the South Pole of the other magnet to it. If we had unique vision, we would be able to see certain lines leaving the North Pole of one magnet and crossing over to the South Pole of the other magnet. These lines are known as magnetic lines of force, and as a group are called a MAGNETIC FIELD or FLUX. Figure 2-3 illustrates the magnetic field as it exists around a bar magnet.

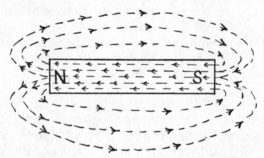

Figure 2-3. Magnetic lines of force.

Notice that the lines of force leave the magnet at the North Pole and return to the magnet at the South Pole. Note, also, that the magnetic field continues flowing inside the magnet from the South to the North Pole. The complete path of the magnetic flux is called the magnetic circuit.

One way to show magnetic lines of force is to sprinkle iron fil-

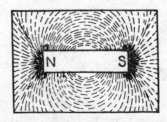

Figure 2-4. Picture of iron filings.

24

ings on a piece of paper under which we place a bar magnet. The result is shown in Figure 2-4. The iron filings arrange themselves so as to look like the lines of force that surround the magnet.

Figure 2-5 illustrates the magnetic field of attraction as it exists between the North and the South Pole of two separate magnets. Notice that the magnetic field appears to be actually pulling the two pole ends together.

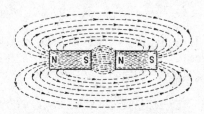

Figure 2-5.   Unlike poles attract.

Figure 2-6 illustrates the magnetic field of repulsion between two like poles. Notice that the magnetic fields are actually pushing each other away.

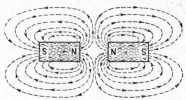

Figure 2-6.   Like magnetic poles repel.

2-3A THE MAGNETIC CIRCUIT

Magnetic flux flowing in a magnetic circuit is analogous to electric current flowing in an electrical circuit. The magnetic flux has a direction of flow, as well as a given strength or amplitude. Just as a current will flow only when the electrical circuit is complete, similarly, a magnetic flux can exist only if there exists a complete magnetic path.

2-4 SHIELDING

If a non-magnetized object, such as a tennis ball, were placed in the path of a magnetic field, as shown in Figure 2-7, the lines of force would pass right through the ball just as light shines through a piece of glass. However, if the tennis ball is covered up with a thick layer of soft iron, the lines of force will take the path of least magnetic resistance, as illustrated in Figure 2-8.

Notice that the area in the center of the ball is now free of magnetic flux. The above example illustrates the principle of magnetic shielding which is so extensively used in electronic circuits.

People who work near strong magnetic fields usually encase

Figure 2-7. No shielding.   Figure 2-8. Shielding.

their watches in soft iron, through which the magnetic field will not penetrate. The delicate watch movement is, therefore, protected from being adversely affected by the magnetic field.

2-5 TEMPORARY AND PERMANENT MAGNETS

Soft iron can be magnetized easily by placing it in a magnetic field. However, as soon as the iron is removed from the magnetic field, it loses its magnetism. Such a magnet is called a TEMPORARY MAGNET. Steel or hard iron, on the other hand, which is difficult to magnetize, retains its magnetism after it has been removed from the magnetic field. A magnet of this type is called a PERMANENT MAGNET. Permanent magnets are usually made in the shape of a bar or a horseshoe. The horseshoe type has the stronger magnetic field because the magnetic poles are closer to each other. Horseshoe magnets are used in the construction of headphones and loudspeakers.

2-6 RESIDUAL MAGNETISM

We stated above that a temporary magnet loses its magnetism when it is removed from a magnetic field. This is not entirely true because a small amount of magnetism does remain. This small amount is called the RESIDUAL MAGNETISM. Its importance will become apparent when we study the subject of generators.

2-7 ELECTROMAGNETISM

The same type of magnetic field that we have been discussing exists around all wires carrying current. This can be proven by placing a compass next to a current-carrying conductor. It will be found that the compass needle will turn until it is at right angles to the conductor. Since a compass needle lines up in the direction of the magnetic field, the field must exist in a plane at right angles to the conductor. Figure 2-9 illustrates a current-carrying conductor with its associated magnetic field; the current flows from left to right and the magnetic field is in a counter-clockwise direction. In Figure

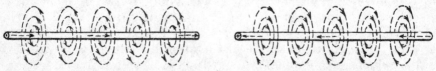

Figure 2-9. Current left to right.   Figure 2-10. Current right to left.

2-10, the current flows from right to left and the magnetic field is in a clockwise direction.

This magnetic field, of which only a number of cross-sections are shown, encircles the wire all along its length like a cylinder. Notice that the direction of the magnetic field, as indicated by the arrows, depends upon the direction of current flow in the wire.

2-8 THE COIL

If the same conductor is wound in the form of a coil, the total magnetic field about the coil will be greatly increased since the magnetic fields of each turn add up to make one resultant magnetic field. See Figure 2-11. The coil is called a SOLENOID or ELECTROMAGNET. The electromagnet has a North and South Pole, just like a permanent magnet. The rule for determining which end is the North Pole and which end is the South Pole states as follows: If we grasp the coil with the left hand so that the fingertips point in the direction of the current, the thumb will automatically point to the North Pole of the electromagnet. Thus, we see that the polarity of an electromagnet depends upon both the way in which the turns are wound and the direction of the current flow. If we reverse either the direction of the current flow or the direction of the windings, the North Pole will become the South Pole, and the South Pole will become the North Pole.

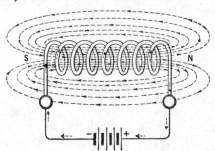

Figure 2-11. Magnetic field produced by current
flowing through coil of wire or solenoid.

A compass placed within a coil carrying an electric current, will point to the North Pole of the coil. The needle itself would be at right angles to the wire. The reason for this is that the compass needle lines itself up in the direction of the magnetic lines of force. You will recall that inside a magnet, the direction of the field is from the South Pole to the North Pole. This is also true in an electromagnet, as illustrated in Figure 2-11.

There are various factors which influence the strength of an electromagnet. They are:

(1) The number of turns. An increase in the number of turns in a coil increases the magnetic strength of the coil.

(2) The amount of current. If we increase the amount of current in a coil, the magnetic strength increases.

(3) Permeability of the core. The core of the coil is the ma-

terial within the coil. It may be air, glass, wood or metal. If we wind the coil on an iron core, we find that the strength of the electro-magnet is increased by several hundred times over what it is with an air core. The iron is said to have more permeability than air; PER-MEABILITY is the ability of a substance to conduct magnetic lines of force easily. Permeability is to a magnetic circuit as conductance is to an electrical circuit. If we have a core with a high permeability, we will have a large number of magnetic lines of force. This will result in a stronger magnetic field. Iron and permalloy are examples of materials having high permeability. Air is arbitrarily given a permeability of "one". The permeability of air is the basis for comparing the permeability of other materials. Iron and steel, for example, have a permeability of several hundred, depending upon the exact material.

Electromagnets are used in the manufacture of earphones, microphones, motors, etc.

2-9   RELUCTANCE

Magnetic reluctance is similar to electrical resistance. Magnetic reluctance is the opposition that a substance offers to magnetic lines of force. It is the property of a material that opposes the creation of a magnetic flux within itself. The unit of reluctance is the REL or the OERSTED.

2-10 MAGNETOMOTIVE FORCE

The magnetomotive force of a magnetic circuit is similar to the electromotive force of an electrical circuit. The magnetomotive force is the force which produces the magnetic lines of force or flux. The unit of magnetomotive force is the GILBERT. The number of gilberts in a circuit is equal to 1.26 x N x I, where N is the number of turns in the coil and I is the number of amperes. N x I, alone, is also known by the term AMPERE-TURNS. It is the number of turns multiplied by the number of amperes flowing in the circuit.

2-11 INDUCED VOLTAGE

If a coil of wire is made to cut a magnetic field, a voltage is induced in the coil of wire. The same reaction will occur if the magnetic field cuts the coil of wire. In other words, as long as there is relative motion between a conductor and a magnetic field, a voltage will be generated in the conductor. An induced voltage is sometimes called an induced EMF; EMF stands for electromotive force.

Figure 2-12A shows an iron bar magnet being thrust into a coil of wire. The dotted lines about the magnet represent magnetic lines of force. The relative movement between the coil and magnet will result in the turns of wire of the coil cutting the lines of force of the magnetic field. The net result of this action will be an induced voltage generated in the turns of the coil. This induced voltage will, in turn, cause a current to flow in the coil. A galvanometer (an instrument used to detect the presence of small currents) will deflect to the right indicating a current flow as a result of the induced EMF. Figure 2-12B shows the magnet being pulled out of the coil. The galvanometer needle will now deflect to the left indicating that the current is now in the opposite direction. Reversing the direction of the motion of the magnet in relation to the coil reverses the direction of the induced current as indicated by the position of the galvanometer needle and the polarity of the current flow.

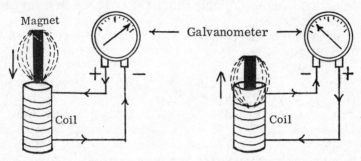

A. Magnet moving into coil.   B. Magnet moving out of coil.

Figure 2-12. Inducing a voltage in a coil of wire.

This method of electromagnetic induction is used in the generators which supply us with our electricity. If we wish to increase the strength of the induced EMF, we can do the following:
(1) Use a stronger magnet.
(2) Use more turns on the coil.
(3) Move the magnet or the coil back and forth at a faster rate.
(4) Have the coil cut the lines of force at right angles if it is not already doing so. In other words, the more lines of force cut per second, the stronger is the resultant, induced EMF.

In order to determine the direction in which the induced current will flow, we use LENZ'S LAW. Lenz's law states that when a moving magnetic field induces an EMF in a coil, a current will flow in such a direction as to form a magnetic field within the coil which will oppose the motion of the original magnetic field.

PRACTICE QUESTIONS - LESSON 2

(For answers, refer to Appendix 6)

2-1* The unit of magnetomotive force is:
   a. joule   b. gilbert   c. ohm   d. rel
2-2   Permeability is:
   a. another name for magnetomotive force
   b. the ability of a coil to induce a voltage into another coil
   c. the ability of a material to conduct magnetic lines of force
   d. the ability of a magnet to retain its magnetism

2-3　If we placed a compass inside a coil carrying direct current, the North Pole of the compass would:
a.　point to the South Pole of the coil
b.　point to the North Pole of the coil
c.　point to the center of the coil
d.　shift back and forth until the current was shut off

2-4　The opposition to the magnetic lines of force in a magnetic circuit is known as:
a.　ampere-turns　　　　　c.　resistance
b.　reluctance　　　　　　d.　reactance

2-5　The magnetism remaining in a material after the magnetizing force has been removed is known as:
a.　residual magnetism　　c.　conductance
b.　permeability　　　　　d.　residual permeability

2-6　Ampere-turns may be defined as:
a.　the square root of the number of turns multiplied by the current
b.　the number of turns multiplied by the square root of the current
c.　the number of turns multiplied by the current
d.　one-half the number of turns multiplied by the current

2-7　The unit of reluctance is the:
a.　mho　　　b.　gilbert　　　c.　ampere turns　　　d.　oersted

2-8　Inside of a bar magnet, the path of the lines of force is:
a.　from the North Pole to the South Pole
b.　from the South Pole to the North Pole
c.　either way, depending on the type of magnet
d.　there are no lines of force inside a magnet

2-9　Shielding is accomplished by:
a.　inserting the object to be shielded in a non-magnetic container
b.　inserting the object to be shielded in a lead container
c.　inserting the object to be shielded in a coil of wire
d.　inserting the object to be shielded in a soft iron container

2-10　The strength of an electromagnet will NOT be increased if we:
a.　increase the number of turns
b.　increase the permeability of the core
c.　change the iron core to an air core
d.　increase the current flow through the coil

SECTION I — LESSON 3
ALTERNATING CURRENT THEORY

3-1 INTRODUCTION

Up to this point, we have been studying DIRECT CURRENT which flows in one direction only. (The abbreviation for direct current is DC). We are now going to study a current which periodically reverses its direction of flow. This type is known as ALTERNATING CURRENT. A battery will generate a direct current, and an alternating current generator will generate an alternating current. The abbreviation for alternating current is AC. For a list of radio abbreviations, refer to Appendix I.

3-2 DEVELOPMENT OF THE ALTERNATING CURRENT WAVE

Figure 3-1 illustrates a loop of wire which can be rotated between the poles of a magnet. The magnetic field which exists in the

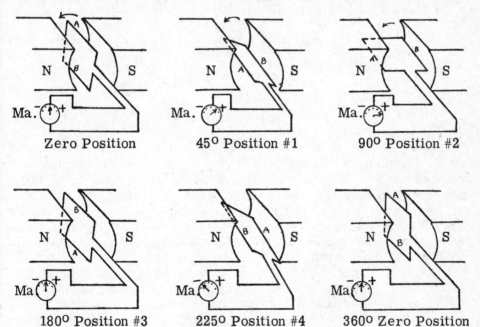

Figure 3-1. Generating the alternating current sine wave.

space between the North and South Pole is not shown in the diagram. If the loop of wire is rotated through the magnetic field, an EMF (electromotive force) will be induced in the wires of the loop. This EMF will cause a current to flow in the circuit of the loop of wire. The milliammeter in series with the loop will indicate the current

31

flow. From our previous study of magnetism (refer to Lesson 2, paragraph 11), we know that an EMF will be induced in a conductor when it cuts through a magnetic field. One of the factors influencing the strength of the induced EMF is the relative cutting position of the loop as compared to the direction of the magnetic field. When the conductors of the loop cut perpendicular to the magnetic field, a maximum induced voltage will be generated. When the conductors of the loop are moving parallel to the magnetic field, no lines of force will be cut and therefore, no voltage will be generated. If the loop is rotated at a constant speed in a counter-clockwise direction, a current will flow whose strength and direction will vary with different positions of the loop. The strength and direction of the current for different loop positions is indicated in Figure 3-1. The resulting curve obtained is illustrated in Figure 3-2. At zero degrees, the loop begins its rotation with the ammeter indicating zero current. (The

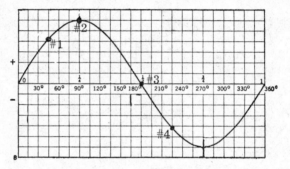

Figure 3-2. The sine wave.

conductors of the loop are moving parallel to the magnetic lines; therefore, no induced EMF will be generated). When the loop has reached position #1 (45 degrees), the current flow is indicated to be in a direction which we shall arbitrarily call positive; when the loop has reached position #2 (90 degrees), the current is at a maximum since the conductors are cutting into the magnetic field at right angles. The current flow is still in a positive direction. From position #2 to position #3, the current decreases in value and is still positive. At position #3 (180 degrees), the current is zero once again, as it was at the start. This is because the conductor is moving parallel with the magnetic field but is not actually cutting it. From position #3, through #4 and back to the starting position, the current goes through the same amplitude changes as it had gone through from starting position (zero degrees) to position #3 (180 degrees). However, from position #3 back to position zero, the direction of the current HAS REVERSED ITSELF and is now considered negative. The opposite to positive, or negative direction, is shown on the graph by drawing the curve below the horizontal line. The curve of Figure 3-2 representing the varying current through the loop, is a waveform known as an ALTERNATING CURRENT wave. The mathematical name for a fundamental alternating current wave is a SINE WAVE.

TO SUMMARIZE: Alternating current, as opposed to direct current, continuously varies in strength and periodically reverses its direction of flow.

3-3 CHARACTERISTICS OF THE SINE WAVE

A sine wave has the following important characteristics:

(1) The complete wave, as shown in Figure 3-3, is known as a CYCLE. The wave is generated in one complete revolution of the armature from 0 to 360 degrees.

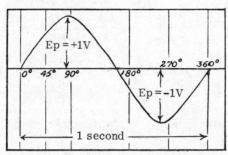

Figure 3-3. The sine wave.

(2) An alternation is one-half cycle, from 0° to 180°, or from 180° to 360°.

(3) The frequency of a sine wave is the number of complete cycles which appear in one second. In Figure 3-3, we have completed one cycle per second. If 60 such cycles were completed in one second, the frequency would be 60 cycles per second. The time taken for one cycle would be 1/60th of a second. This time in seconds is known as the PERIOD OF THE WAVE.

(4) The height of the wave at any point is known as its AMPLITUDE. The highest point of the wave is called the maximum or PEAK AMPLITUDE, which in our example is one volt. In a sine wave, the peaks always occur at 90 degrees and 270 degrees; the zero points always occur at 0, 180 and 360 degrees.

3-4 FREQUENCY

The unit of frequency is cycles per second or simply cycles. The abbreviation for cycles per second is CPS. The meter used to measure frequency is called a Frequency Meter.

The frequency of the AC power that is supplied to most homes in the United States is 60 cycles per second. This is known as the POWER FREQUENCY. Radio waves transmitted by radio stations have a frequency much higher than the 60 CPS power frequency. Their frequency is generally above 20,000 CPS. An electrical frequency higher than 20,000 CPS is known as a RADIO FREQUENCY. The abbreviation for radio frequency is "RF". Figure 3-4 illustrates a low frequency of 60 CPS and an RF frequency of 1,000,000 CPS.

Sound waves which can be heard by the human ear are called

33

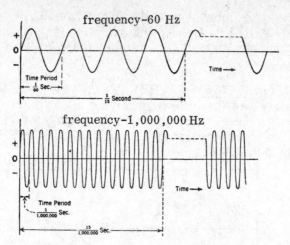

Figure 3-4. Low and high frequency wave.

audible sounds or audio sounds. The frequency of the audio sounds lie in the range from 16 to 16,000 CPS. When a sound wave frequency is converted into an electrical frequency, it is known as an audio frequency (AF). For example, when our voice is amplified by a public address system, the sound waves from our throats strike the microphone and are converted into electrical frequencies, or audio frequencies.

When a frequency is given as a large number of CPS, it can be converted into smaller units of kilocycles per second or megacycles per second, just as pennies can be converted into dollars. Example:

(a) 1000 cycles per second = 1 kilocycle. The abbreviation for kilocycle is "kc". (The prefix kilo always means 1000). Therefore, in order to convert cycles per second into kilocycles per second, we divide the number of cycles per second by 1000.

$$1,000,000 \text{ CPS} = \frac{1,000,000}{1000} = 1000 \text{ kc.}$$

(b) 1,000,000 CPS = 1 megacycle per second. The abbreviation for megacycle is "Mc". Therefore, in order to convert CPS into megacycles, we divide the number of CPS by 1,000,000.

$$1,000,000 \text{ CPS} = \frac{1,000,000}{1,000,000} = 1 \text{ Mc.}$$

Radio men very often shorten the term cycles per second to cycles. Instead of talking about a 5000 cycle per second wave, they talk about a 5000 cycle wave.

In recent years, the term "Hertz" (abbreviated Hz), has been used in place of "cycles per second". Therefore, "kiloHertz" (kHz) can be used for kilocycle and "MegaHertz" (MHz) can be used for "megacycles".

Throughout this book, we will use both cycles and Hertz as the unit of frequency.

34

3-5 THE MEANING OF PHASE RELATIONSHIP

Two alternating current generators are connected in parallel across a load. If their armatures are started rotating together from exactly the same point, two EMF's (electro-motive forces) will be produced in the wire connecting the generators to the load. Assume that the peak output of generator #1 is 7 volts, and the peak output of generator #2 is 5 volts. Since both armatures start from the same position, at the same time and at the same speed, they will both produce the maximum and minimum voltages at the same instant. This is illustrated in Figure 3-5. The outputs of these generators are then said to be IN PHASE WITH EACH OTHER.

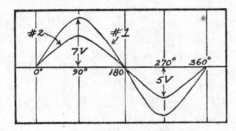

Figure 3-5. In phase.

If, on the other hand, armature #2 is started an eighth of a revolution (45 degrees) after armature #1 has started, the output of each generator will reach maximum and minimum points at different times. They will now be OUT OF PHASE, as shown in Figure 3-6. It should be observed that the same voltages are being considered here as in Figure 3-5, but that the 5 volt wave LAGS 45° behind

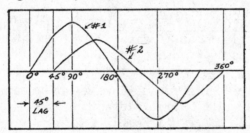

Figure 3-6. Out of phase.

the 7 volt wave. These waves are said to be out of phase by 45°. If the 5 volt wave had started 90° later than the other, the 5 volt wave would be lagging the 7 volt wave by 90°. The angle by which one wave leads or lags another wave is known as the PHASE ANGLE.

3-6 EFFECTIVE VALUE OF AN AC WAVE

Let us consider a DC voltage of 100 volts, and an AC wave whose peak is 100 volts (See Figure 3-7). We can see that the DC voltage is really peak voltage at all times; that is, it remains constant. The AC wave reaches its peak value only for a fraction of each cycle. If we connect a lamp first to the DC voltage and then to the

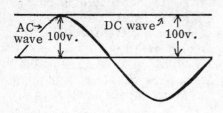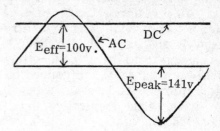

Fig. 3-7. DC wave equals   Fig. 3-8. Effective value
peak of AC wave.   of a sine wave.

AC, the lamp will light up more brilliantly when connected to the DC. This is because the DC voltage remains at 100 volts continuously, whereas the AC voltage reaches a 100 volt peak only at two points during the cycle. In order for the lamp to light with equal brilliance on AC as well as on DC, we must raise the AC voltage to 141 peak volts. Effectively then, 141 peak volts of AC will light up a lamp as brilliantly as does 100 volts of DC. The EFFECTIVE value of the 141 peak AC wave is, therefore, 100 volts. See Figure 3-8.

The effective value of an AC wave (either voltage or current), is 0.707 times as great as its peak value. For example, the effective value of the above AC wave is 0.707 x 141 volts or 100 volts, which is also the value of the DC wave. The magnitude of an AC wave is usually given by its effective value from which the peak value can be calculated to be 1.41 x the effective value. The effective voltage or current is frequently referred to as the RMS (root-mean-square) value.

3-7 CALCULATION OF PEAK AND EFFECTIVE VALUE

The peak value of an AC wave can be calculated from its effective value by using the following formula:

$$3\text{-}1)\quad E_{peak} = 1.41 \times E_{eff}$$

The effective value of an AC wave can be calculated from the peak value by using the following formula:

$$3\text{-}2)\quad E_{eff} = 0.707 \times E_{peak}$$

Formulas 3-1 and 3-2 apply for all sine waves, whether voltage or current. The value given to an AC wave will always be the effective value, unless stated otherwise. AC voltmeters and ammeters will always read the effective value of the AC wave, unless it is indicated otherwise.

3-8 INDUCTANCE

In Paragraph 2-8, we learned that a current-carrying coil of many turns behaves just like a magnet. The current will cause a magnetic field to surround the coil. If the current flowing through the coil is alternating, the magnetic field surrounding the coil will also be alternating. In Figure 3-9, we have a coil which has an alternating current flowing through it. This alternating current pro-

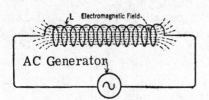

Fig. 3-9. Coil with AC
flowing through it.

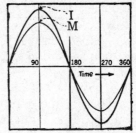

Fig. 3-10. Current wave and
magnetic field in phase.

duces an alternating magnetic field around the coil which expands and collapses in phase with the alternating current. When the current is zero, the magnetic field is zero; when the current reaches its peak at 90°, the magnetic field has reached its maximum value. This is shown in Figure 3-10. Evidently, since the field starts from zero and builds up to a maximum, it is an expanding field. This expanding field must cut through the conductors of the coil itself. According to Lenz's law, the cutting action induces an EMF in the coil which opposes the original current. The process wherein an induced EMF is generated in a coil which opposes the original current flow is called SELF-INDUCTION. The coil of wire is known as the INDUCTANCE. The unit of inductance is the HENRY, and the abbreviation of henry is h. The symbol for inductance is L. Smaller and more practical units of inductance are the millihenry (mh) and the microhenry (μh).

$$1 \text{ millihenry} = \frac{1}{1000} \text{ of a henry}$$

$$1 \text{ microhenry} = \frac{1}{1,000,000} \text{ of a henry}$$

The schematic symbol for inductance is:

$-\text{0000}-$ or mmm

Both types will be used throughout this course.

3-9   FACTORS AFFECTING INDUCTANCE OF A COIL

(1) Number of turns: The inductance of a coil varies as the square of the number of turns. For example, if we have two coils of the same length and diameter, and coil #1 has four turns while coil #2 has eight turns, the inductance of coil #2 will be four times the inductance of coil #1.

$$\frac{L_2}{L_1} = \left(\frac{8}{4}\right)^2 = \frac{64}{16} = \frac{4}{1} \; ; \; L_2 = 4 \times L_1$$

(2) Core material: The inductance of a coil varies with the core material. An iron-core coil will have a higher inductance than an air-core coil. Since the iron-core has a high permeability as compared to air, there will be a stronger magnetic field around the iron-core coil which results in a higher inductance.

37

(3) <u>Length of coil</u>: As the length of a coil increases, the number of turns remaining constant, the inductance of the coil decreases. This is because the resistance of the magnetic circuit increases due to the increased coil length, which results in a weakening of the magnetic field.

(4) Diameter of coil: The inductance of a coil varies directly as the square of the diameter. For example, if we double the diameter of a coil, the inductance will increase four times.

3-10 INDUCTANCE IN SERIES

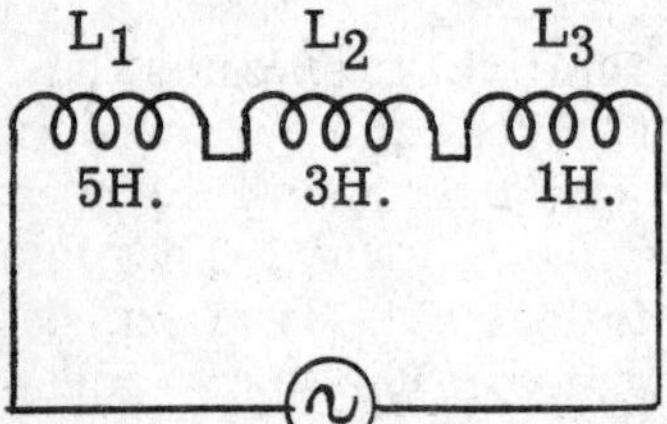

If two or more inductances are connected in series, as in Figure 3-11, the total inductance is equal to the sum of the individual inductors. We therefore use the following simple formula to find the total inductance of inductances connected in series:

$$L_T = L_1 + L_2 + L_3, \text{ etc.}$$

The total inductance in Figure 3-11 is 9H. The above formula assumes that the inductors are far enough apart so as not to affect one another. If the inductors are close enough so that they are in each other's magnetic field, we say that there is a "mutual inductance" present. The formula for the total inductance of a circuit where mutual inductance is present is somewhat more complex than the above formula.

Figure 3-11 Inductances in series.

L_1 5H. L_2 3H. L_3 1H.

3-11 INDUCTANCES IN PARALLEL

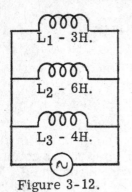

Figure 3-12.

If two or more inductances are connected in parallel, the total inductance can be found by using the following formula:

$$L_T = \cfrac{1}{\cfrac{1}{L_1} + \cfrac{1}{L_2} + \cfrac{1}{L_3} + \text{ etc.}}$$

Using the above formula, we can calculate the total inductance of Figure 3-12.

$$L_T = \cfrac{1}{\dfrac{1}{3} + \dfrac{1}{6} + \dfrac{1}{4}} = \cfrac{1}{\dfrac{4}{12} + \dfrac{2}{12} + \dfrac{3}{12}} = \cfrac{1}{\dfrac{9}{12}} = \cfrac{1}{\dfrac{3}{4}} = \dfrac{4}{3} \qquad L_T = 1\dfrac{1}{3} \text{ H.}$$

It can be seen from the formula and the problem that the total inductance goes down as we add more inductors in parallel.

If we are dealing with **ONLY TWO** inductors in parallel, we can find the total inductance by using the following simple formula:

38

$$L_T = \frac{L_1 \times L_2}{L_1 + L_2}$$

As with the formula for series inductance, the above formulas assume that there is no mutual inductance present.

3-12 INDUCTIVE REACTANCE

An inductance resists a change of current flow due to the counter-electromotive force of self-induction. This resistance or holding-back effect is measured in ohms. Instead of being called a resistance however, it is called a reactance; an INDUCTIVE REACTANCE. The abbreviation for inductive reactance is X_L.

The formula for computing inductive reactance is:

3-3) $X_L = 2\pi f L$ where: $\pi = 3.14$
f = frequency in Hz
L = inductance in henries

(If the inductance is given in mh or μh, it must first be converted into henries before it can be used in formula 3-3).

Problem: Find the inductive reactance of L1 and L2.

Find the voltage across each coil.

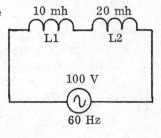

Solution: Convert mh to h and substitute the values in the above formula:

$X_{L1} = 2\pi f L = 2 \times 3.14 \times 60 \times .01 = 3.8$ ohms.

$X_{L2} = 2\pi f L = 2 \times 3.14 \times 60 \times .02 = 7.6$ ohms.

The total inductive reactance of two inductors in series is equal to the sum of the reactances. This is the same as resistors in series. The total X_L is, therefore, $3.8 + 7.6$ or 11.4 ohms.

Ohm's Law is the same for an AC circuit as for a DC circuit. We simply substitute X_L for R.

$$I = \frac{E}{X_L} = \frac{100}{11.4} = 8.77 \text{ A.}$$

We again use Ohm's Law to find the voltage across the inductors.

$$E_{L1} = I X_{L1} = 8.77 \times 3.8 = 33.3 \text{ V.}$$

$$E_{L2} = I X_{L2} = 8.77 \times 7.6 = 66.6 \text{ V.}$$

We can see from the answers to the problem that the source voltage divides itself across the inductors in proportion to their inductances or inductive reactances.

39

Inductive reactances in parallel behave the same as resistances or inductances in parallel. See Paragraph 3-11 above for the correct formula.

An inductance is sometimes called a "choke" because it opposes or "chokes" an alternating current flow. A filter choke is an inductance that is found in power supplies. Its purpose is to oppose the flow of AC power frequencies while allowing DC to pass through unopposed. An audio choke is an inductance that is found in audio circuits. Its purpose is to oppose the flow of audio frequencies while allowing DC to flow. A radio frequency choke is an inductance that is found in radio frequency (high frequency, AC) circuits. Its purpose is to oppose the flow of radio frequency currents while allowing the lower frequencies and direct current to flow.

3-13 SKIN EFFECT

When direct current flows through a wire, it flows through the entire cross-sectional area of the wire. This is also true of low frequency alternating current. However, as the frequency of the alternating current increases, we find that an inductive reactance or opposition to the current flow develops in the center of the wire. We can see from the formula for inductive reactance, that it increases with increasing frequency. The opposition at the center of the wire causes the high frequencies to flow at or near its surface. This phenomenon is known as skin effect.

The effects of skin effect can be reduced by using large diameter wires and by coating the surface with a low resistivity metal such as silver. Hollow copper tubing can be used for high frequency circuits since nothing flows through the conductor's center.

3-14 PHASE ANGLE IN AN INDUCTIVE CIRCUIT

A pure inductive circuit has no resistance. In a pure inductive circuit, the current lags the impressed voltage by 90° as shown in Figure 3-13. The waveform E starts 90° ahead of the waveform I as shown in the diagram of Figure 3-13. We say that the phase angle between the voltage and current is 90°. Since, in actual practice, a

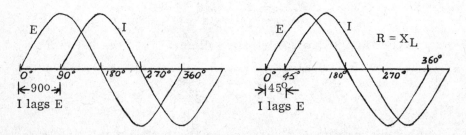

Fig. 3-13. Pure inductive circuit. Fig. 3-14. Inductive-resistive circuit.

40

coil or inductance will always have some resistance (the resistance of the wire), the phase angle between the impressed EMF and the current becomes less than 90°. The greater the proportion of resistance, the smaller will be the phase angle. Figure 3-14 illustrates the current lagging the impressed voltage by 45° in a circuit containing equal amounts of resistance and inductive reactance. When there is all resistance and no inductance, the phase angle becomes 0 degrees. The current and voltage are then in phase. This is to be expected since it is the counter EMF of the inductance which causes the current to lag.

3-15 IMPEDANCE OF AN INDUCTIVE CIRCUIT

In Figure 3-15A the total resistance which opposes the flow of current is $R_1 + R_2$. The total resistance to current flow in a series circuit is the sum total of the individual resistances. If the circuit consists of resistance and inductive reactance, as shown in Figure 3-15B, the total resistance to the flow of current is called the IMPEDANCE. The symbol for impedance is Z. The unit of impedance is the OHM. Unlike a resistive circuit, the impedance of an inductive circuit is NOT equal to the simple sum of the resistance and the inductive reactance.

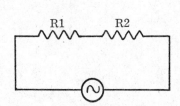
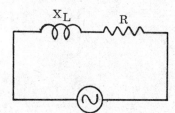

Fig. 3-15A. Resistive circuit.   Fig. 3-15B. Inductive-
resistive circuit.

The impedance of an inductive circuit can be calculated by using the following formula:

3-4) $Z = \sqrt{R^2 + X_L^2}$ ohms

where: Z is the total impedance in ohms

X_L is the inductive reactance in ohms

R is the series resistance in ohms

Problem: If a circuit contains a coil and resistor in series, and if the coil has a reactance of 12 ohms and the resistance is 5 ohms what is the (1) total impedance and (2) what is the current? The source voltage is 130 volts.

Solution: Note that the impedance IS NOT simply the sum of $R + X_L$ or 17 ohms. The impedance in an INDUCTIVE CIRCUIT must be calculated by using formula 3-4.

41

$$Z = \sqrt{R^2 + X_L^2} = \sqrt{5^2 + 12^2} = \sqrt{25 + 144} = \sqrt{169} = 13$$

$Z = 13$ ohms

The current in the circuit is simply the total voltage divided by the impedance according to Ohm's law.

$$I = \frac{E}{Z} = \frac{130}{13} = 10 \text{ amperes}$$

3-16 THE CAPACITOR

We have thus far studied two radio parts which exert a holding-back effect upon current: (1) resistors and (2) coils or inductors which exert a holding-back effect upon AC current only. We shall now investigate another holding-back device which has a tremendous application in radio; the CONDENSER or CAPACITOR.

A capacitor is a device having, in its simplest form, two conducting plates separated from each other by an insulating material called a DIELECTRIC. The dielectric may be air, mica, oil, paraffinned paper, etc. Figure 3-16 illustrates a two-plate capacitor connected across a battery. Figure 3-18 shows the symbol for a capacitor.

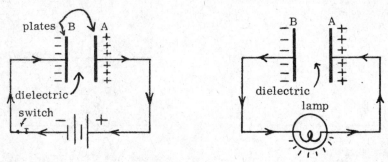

Fig. 3-16. Charging the capacitor.   Fig. 3-17. Capacitor discharge.

When the switch is closed, a certain number of free electrons on plate A will be attracted to the positive side of the battery. Plate A is left with a positive charge; at the same time, plate B will have the same number of electrons pushed on to it by the negative side of the battery. This electron flow continues until a charge is built up on the capacitor plates, which develops a voltage equal to the battery voltage. The plates of the capacitor are now said to be electrically charged. The charge on the capacitor plates depends upon the size of the plates (the capacity), and the force of the battery (the EMF). Notice that the accumulated electrons on plate B cannot cross to the other plate because of the insulator dielectric in between.

When the capacitor has become fully charged, the voltage across the capacitor is equal to the battery voltage. If we disconnect the battery from the capacitor, the capacitor will continue to hold its charge. If a lamp is now connected across the charged capacitor

42

(see Figure 3-17), the electrons on plate B will flow through the lamp and onto positive plate A where there is an attraction for them. During the brief duration of the electron flow, the lamp will light for an instant, indicating that a current has passed through it. The electrons will continue to flow until plate B no longer has a surplus of electrons. Plate B is then said to have a zero charge. Plate B is now neutral and, of course, plate A will have regained its electrons so that it is also neutral. The capacitor is now said to be DISCHARGED. A capacitor, then, is a device in which electricity may be stored for a period of time until it is ready for use.

A capacitor is a storage tank for electricity, just as a gallon jug, for example, is a storage place for water. If we force water into the jug under pressure, the amount of water that will go into the jug will be determined by the capacity of the jug and also, the pressure or force that the pump exerts on the water. Similarly, the amount of electricity that a capacitor will hold depends upon the same factors as apply to the water jug, namely, electrical pressure and capacity. The greater the capacity and the greater the pressure (voltage), the more electrons the capacitor will store up on its plates.

3-17 CAPACITANCE

The capacitance of a capacitor is determined by the size, shape, number and spacing of plates and the dielectric material. The symbol for capacitance is $\underline{C}$. The unit of capacitance is the FARAD; the abbreviation for farad is $\underline{fd}$. or $\underline{f}$. Since the farad is an extremely large unit of capacitance, it is very rarely used. The smaller and more common units of capacitance are the microfarad and the picofarad (formerly called the micromicrofarad). The symbol for microfarad is $\underline{\mu fd}$ or $\underline{\mu f}$ and the symbol for picofarad is $\underline{pfd}$ or $\underline{pf}$.

$$1 \text{ microfarad} = \frac{1}{1,000,000} \text{ of a farad}$$

$$1 \text{ picofarad} = \frac{1}{1,000,000,000,000} \text{ of a farad}$$

The range of capacitance used in electronics may vary all the way from 2 pf up to 300 μf. (Refer to Appendix I for a discussion of radio symbols).

3-18 THE DIELECTRIC

The dielectric is nothing more than the name for the insulating material between the plates of a capacitor. Examples of dielectrics used in capacitors are mica, ceramic, glass, oil, waxpaper, etc. Capacitors with different dielectric materials will have different capacities. For example, a capacitor with a mica dielectric will have a larger capacity than an air dielectric capacitor. The dielectric determines the ability of a capacitor to hold more or less charge.

3-19 THE VARIABLE CAPACITOR

Figure 3-19 shows the schematic symbol of a capacitor whose

capacity can be varied. This capacitor is known as a variable capacitor and is used wherever the capacitance in a circuit must be
continuously variable as, for example, tuning controls in radio receivers and transmitters.

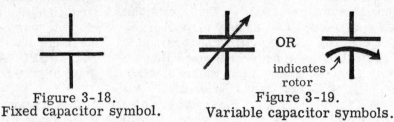

OR

indicates
rotor

Figure 3-18.　　　　　　　　　　Figure 3-19.
Fixed capacitor symbol.　　Variable capacitor symbols.

Most variable capacitors are of the air dielectric type. A single variable capacitor consists of two sets of metal plates insulated
from each other, and so arranged that one set of plates can be moved
in relation to the other set. The stationary plates are the stator; the
movable plates, the rotor. As the rotor is turned so that its plates
mesh with the stator plates, the capacity increases. If several variable capacitors are connected on a common shaft so that all may be
controlled at the same time, the result is known as a ganged **capacitor.** Figure 3-20 illustrates the rotor position of a variable capacitor for minimum, intermediate and maximum capacity.

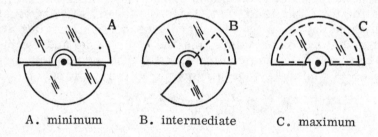

A. minimum　　B. intermediate　　C. maximum

Figure 3-20. Variable capacitor settings.

3-20 VOLTAGE RATING

Capacitors are rated, not only in capacity, but also in the maximum voltage they will stand before breaking down. If the voltage
across a capacitor is too high, the electrical pressure will force
electrons to jump from the negative plate to the positive plate. This
will puncture the dielectric and, in most cases, will ruin the capacitor. A typical capacitor would be rated as follows:

Capacity - 8 µfd　　DC working voltage - 450 V.

"DC working voltage" indicates that the capacitor may be used
in any circuit, as long as the DC voltage or the AC peak voltage across
it does not exceed 450 V.

3-21 CAPACITORS CONNECTED IN SERIES COMBINATION

When two or more capacitors are connected in series combination, the plate of one capacitor is connected to the plate of another capacitor, as shown in Figure 3-21.

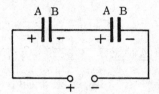

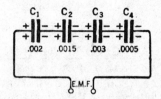

Figure 3-21. Capacitors in series.　　Figure 3-22. Problem.

Plate A of one capacitor is connected to B of another, and so on. The polarity at the plates of each respective capacitor is shown. It indicates that when one plate of one capacitor is charged negatively, the plate of an adjoining capacitor is charged positively. The EMF's or voltages impressed across the capacitors in a series circuit are not the same unless their capacities are equal. The voltage drop is inversely proportional to the capacity of individual capacitors. Therefore, although capacitors may be of similar voltage rating, a lower capacity in a series combination will be subject to a higher potential.

The effect of connecting capacitors in series is to decrease the total capacity of the circuit, just as the total resistance of a circuit is decreased when resistors are connected in parallel.

The total capacity of capacitors connected in series is equal to the reciprocal of the sum of the reciprocals of the capacities of the individual capacitors. The total capacity can be computed by using the following formula:

$$3\text{-}5)\ \ C_T = \frac{1}{\dfrac{1}{C_1} + \dfrac{1}{C_2} + \dfrac{1}{C_3}\,etc.}$$

This is similar to the formula for resistors in parallel.

Problem: If four capacitors with capacities as shown in Figure 3-22 are connected in series, what is the total capacity?

Solution: Substitute in formula 3-5 the capacity values of the four capacitors shown in Figure 3-22.

$$(1)\ \ C_T = \frac{1}{\dfrac{1}{.002} + \dfrac{1}{.0015} + \dfrac{1}{.003} + \dfrac{1}{.0005}}$$

(Dividing .002 into 1, we get 500, etc.)

$$(2)\ \ C_T = \frac{1}{500 + 667 + 333 + 2000}$$

$$(3)\ \ C_T = \frac{1}{3500} = .00029\ \mu fd$$

45

From the above example, it should be clear that in a series arrangement of capacitors, the total capacity of the series combination (bank) is always less than the capacity of any individual capacitor in the bank.

If two capacitors ONLY are in series, the total capacitance can be found by using the following formula:

$$C_T = \frac{C_1 \times C_2}{C_1 + C_2}$$

3-22 CAPACITORS CONNECTED IN PARALLEL COMBINATION

When two or more capacitors are connected in a parallel arrangement, as shown in Figure 3-23, the "A" plates are connected together and the "B" plates are connected together. Connecting capacitors in parallel has the effect of greatly increasing the effective plate area. Since the effective plate area is increased, the effective capacity is also increased, as shown in Figure 3-23.

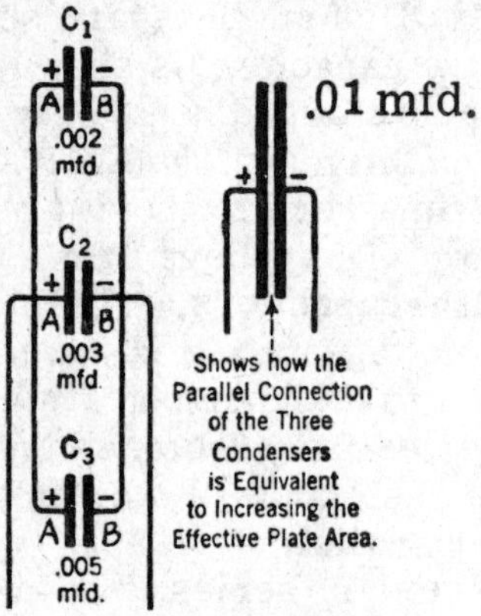

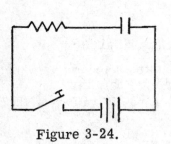

Figure 3-23.

When capacitors are connected in parallel, the resulting capacity is equal to the sum of the individual capacities. The total capacity can be computed by using the following formula.

3-6) $C_T = C_1 + C_2 + C_3$, etc.

Problem: If three capacitors of .002 µf., .003 µf and .005 µf, are connected in parallel, what is the total capacity?

Solution: Use formula 3-6.
1) $C_T = C_1 + C_2 + C_3$
2) $C_T = .002 + .003 + .005 = .01$ µf.

3-23 TIME CONSTANT

Figure 3-24.

Figure 3-24 shows a capacitor in series with a resistor. At the instant that the switch is closed, current starts to flow and the voltage across the capacitor begins to build up. After a while, the voltage across the capacitor will be the same as the battery voltage. The time that it takes for the voltage on the capacitor to reach the battery voltage depends upon the values of the capacitor and the resistor. The larger these two values are, the longer it will take for the full voltage to appear across the capacitor. This relationship is expressed by a factor called the "time constant". The time constant is equal to the time it takes for a capacitor to charge up to 63% of its final value. Its formula is: T = RC   Where: T is the Time Constant in seconds, R is the resistance in ohms and C is the capacity in farads.

The time constant also tells us the time it takes for the voltage to drop, or discharge to 37% of its initial value.

3-24 THE CAPACITOR IN AN ALTERNATING CURRENT CIRCUIT

If a capacitor is placed across an AC generator in series with an AC ammeter, the following action occurs: When the left side of

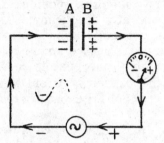
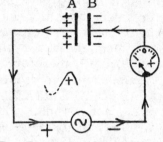

A. Negative alternation.   B. Positive alternation.

Figure 3-25. Capacitor across AC generator.

the generator is negative (Figure 3-25A), electrons flow from the negative terminal of the generator to capacitor plate A. At the same time, electrons flow off plate B and through the ammeter to the right side of the generator. When the polarity of the AC generator reverses, the electrons reverse in direction and flow from the left plate through the generator and ammeter onto the right plate (See Figure 3-25B). This reversal of current flow occurs many times in one second, depending upon the frequency of the generator. The ammeter registers a reversal of current flow since electrons flow through it, first in one direction and then in the other. In other words, although an electric current does not flow through the capacitor itself, it does flow in and out of the plates of the capacitor and therefore, flows back and forth through all the components connected in series with the capacitor. When it is said that AC current flows through a capacitor, what is actually meant is that the current is flowing in and out of the plates of the capacitor.

3-25 CAPACITIVE REACTANCE

Figure 3-25A shows a capacitor connected across an AC generator. At the instant shown (left side of generator is negative, right side is positive), electrons rush from the left side of the generator to the left plate of the capacitor. At first, only a few electrons will have reached the capacitor plate A. However, these few electrons will attempt to repel the electrons that are approaching this capacitor plate. This same action occurs on the B plate when the polarity of the generator reverses itself. (See Figure 3-25B). The first few electrons to reach the right plate of the capacitor will oppose the electrons that are approaching this plate. Every time the polarity of the generator reverses, the first few electrons that pile up on the capacitor will repel the remaining electrons. Thus we see that a capacitor offers a certain amount of opposition to alternating current. This opposition is actually a COUNTER EMF, since the original charge on the capacitor plates represents an opposition voltage to the generator voltage. This counter-EMF will vary inversely with the capacity of the capacitor and the frequency of the AC generator. The higher the frequency of the generator, the less time there will be for electrons to charge the capacitor. The capacitor counter-EMF, therefore, decreases with increases in generator frequency. As the capacity of the capacitor increases, the charge will be distributed over an effectively larger plate area, decreasing the counter-EMF. The counter EMF, therefore, decreases with an increase in capacity.

The opposition or resistance that the capacitor offers to AC is called CAPACITIVE REACTANCE. The symbol for capacitive reactance is X_c, and its unit is the OHM.

In order to compute the capacitive reactance of a capacitor in an AC circuit, the following formulas are used:

$$3\text{-}7) \ X_c = \frac{1}{2\pi fC} \text{ ohm} \qquad 3\text{-}8) \ X_c = \frac{1,000,000}{2\pi fc}$$

where: X_c = capacitive reactance in ohms

2π = 6.28

f = frequency of AC in cycles

c = capacity in farads in formula 3-7 and capacity in microfarads in formula 3-8.

Problem: Find the capacitive reactance of a 15 µf capacitor in an AC circuit where the frequency of the generator is 1 kilocycle. Solution: Use formula 3-8.

$$X_c = \frac{1,000,000}{2\pi fc} = \frac{1,000,000}{6.28 \times 1000 \times 15} = \frac{1,000,000}{94,200} = 10.6 \text{ ohms.}$$

In an AC circuit, a capacitor acts somewhat differently than an inductor. Whereas an inductance tends to PREVENT CURRENT CHANGES by means of a self-induced EMF, a capacitor tends to PREVENT VOLTAGE CHANGE by means of the counter-emf developed on its plates.

3-26 SERIES CAPACITORS IN AN AC CIRCUIT

Figure 3-26 shows two capacitors hooked up in series across

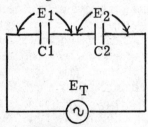

Figure 3-26.

an AC source. The voltage drop across each capacitor is the product of the current through each capacitor and the capacitive reactance of the capacitor (Ohm's law -- $E_{C1} = I_{C1} \times X_{C1}$). The current in each capacitor is the same because the two capacitors are in series. THE VOLTAGE ACROSS EACH CAPACITOR IN A SERIES CIRCUIT IS, THEREFORE, DIRECTLY PROPORTIONAL TO THE CAPACITIVE REACTANCES. The formula that expresses this is:

48

$$E_{C1} = \frac{X_{C1}}{X_T} \times E_T$$

Where: E_{C1} is the voltage across a particular capacitor, X_{C1} is the capacitive reactance of that capacitor, X_T is the total capacitive reactance and E_T is the total or source voltage.

An example will show how this formula is used: Assume that the AC source voltage of Figure 3-26 is 100 volts, X_{C1} is 2000 ohms and X_{C2} is 4000 ohms. What are the voltages across the capacitors?

$$E_{C1} = \frac{2000}{6000} \times 100 = \frac{1}{3} \times 100 = 33.3 \text{ volts}$$

$$E_{C2} = \frac{4000}{6000} \times 100 = \frac{2}{3} \times 100 = 66.6 \text{ volts}$$

The two voltages total 100 volts, a figure that checks with our source voltage.

An examination of the formula for capacitive reactance in the previous paragraph shows that the capacitance of a capacitor is inversely proportional to its reactance. We can, therefore, say that THE VOLTAGE ACROSS EACH CAPACITOR IN A SERIES CIRCUIT IS INVERSELY PROPORTIONAL TO ITS CAPACITANCE. The formula that explains this is:

$$E_{C1} = \frac{C_T}{C_1} \times E_T$$

Where: E_{C1} is the voltage across a particular capacitor, C_1 is the capacity of that capacitor, C_T is the total capacity of the series circuit and E_T is the total or source voltage.

An example will show how this formula is used. Let us assume that the source voltage is 100 volts, C_1 is 200 µf and C_2 is 600 µf. What are the voltages across the capacitors?

First, we must find the total capacitance:

$$C_T = \frac{C_1 \times C_2}{C_1 + C_2} = \frac{200 \times 600}{200 + 600} = \frac{120000}{800} = 150 \text{ µf.}$$

$$E_{C1} = \frac{150}{200} \times 100 = \frac{15000}{200} = 75 \text{ volts}$$

$$E_{C2} = \frac{150}{600} \times 100 = \frac{15000}{600} = 25 \text{ volts}$$

The two voltages total 100, which checks with the given source voltage.

The total reactance of two or more capacitive reactances in series is equal to the sum of the individual reactances. This is the same as resistances in series and inductive reactances in series.

Capacitive reactances in parallel behave the same as resistances in parallel. See Paragraph 1-15 of Lesson 1 for the formula for the total resistance of several resistances in parallel.

3-27 THE PHASE ANGLE

In an inductive circuit, we found that the current lags the impressed voltage. In a capacitive circuit, the opposite is true; THE CURRENT LEADS THE IMPRESSED VOLTAGE. This can be analyzed as follows: When a voltage or battery is first placed across a capacitor, there cannot be any back EMF across the capacitor because its plates are initially uncharged. A capacitor can only have a voltage across its plates provided there is a charge on its plates. If the charge is initially zero, then the voltage must be initially zero. Since the capacitor offers no initial back EMF, the initial current into it is a maximum. Therefore, the current is at a maximum when the voltage is still zero; or, the current leads the voltage. When the current falls to zero, the voltage just reaches its maximum value.

The current leads the source voltage by 90⁰ in a pure capacitive circuit (see Figure 3-27). If we introduce some resistance into the

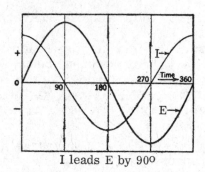

I leads E by 90⁰

Figure 3-27. Pure capacitive circuit.

circuit, the current will lead the voltage by less than 90⁰. When the resistance and capacitive reactance are equal, the current will lead the voltage by 45⁰. The greater the resistance in the circuit, the smaller the phase angle.

3-28 IMPEDANCE OF SERIES CIRCUITS

In paragraph 3-15, we discussed the impedance of a series circuit containing resistance and inductive reactance. We learned that the total impedance of the circuit was not the simple sum of the resistance and the inductive reactance. The same is true for the impedance of a circuit containing resistance and capacitive reactance (see Figure 3-28). To determine the impedance of a CAPACITIVE circuit, the formula becomes:

3-9) $Z = \sqrt{R^2 + X_c^2}$ ohms   Where: R = series resistance in ohms
X_c = capacitive reactance in ohms

Problem: If, in a resistive-capacitive circuit, X_c = 4 ohms and R = 3 ohms, what is the total impedance?

Solution: Use formula 3-9.

$$Z = \sqrt{R^2 + X_c^2} \qquad Z = \sqrt{3^2 + 4^2} \qquad Z = \sqrt{25} = 5 \text{ ohms}$$

50

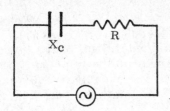
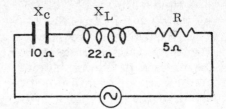

Figure 3-28. R-C circuit.   Figure 3-29. R-L-C circuit.

3-29 IMPEDANCE OF SERIES R-L-C CIRCUITS

Observe the series circuit of Figure 3-29. Notice that this circuit contains resistance, inductance and capacitance. What is the relationship of X_L to X_c, and how can we figure out the impedance of such a circuit? The effect of X_L and X_c on the current in a series AC circuit can be understood by considering the game "tug-of-war". The rope represents the current, and the men pulling on the rope in opposite directions represent the action of X_L and X_c on the current. X_L and X_c act in opposition on the current. If X_L and X_c are equal, they will have no effect on the current, since their effects will cancel. If X_L is larger than X_c, it will be the difference between X_L and X_c which will affect the current. Conversely, if X_c is larger than X_L, it will also be the difference between X_c and X_L which will affect the current. Before we can determine the impedance of the circuit, we must calculate the total reactance. The total reactance of the circuit is the difference between the two reactances, X_L and X_c. This difference is then added to the resistance in a manner similar to that of formula 3-9.

The following formula is used to find the impedance of a circuit containing resistance, inductance and capacitance:

3-10) $Z = \sqrt{R^2 + (X_L - X_c)^2}$ Where: Z is the impedance in ohms
R is the resistance in ohms
X_L is the inductive reactance in ohms
X_c is the capacitive reactance in ohms

Problem: Find the impedance of a circuit which contains a resistance of 5 ohms, an inductive reactance of 22 ohms and a capacitive reactance of 10 ohms (Figure 3-29).

Solution: Use formula 3-10.

1) $Z = \sqrt{R^2 + (X_L - X_c)^2} = \sqrt{5^2 + (22 - 10)^2}$

2) $Z = \sqrt{25 + (12)^2} = \sqrt{25 + 144} = \sqrt{169} = 13$ ohms

3-30 SERIES RESONANCE

In paragraph 3-29, we studied a series AC circuit containing resistance, inductance and capacitance. In order to find the impedance of such a circuit, we had to use formula 3-10.

Let us assume that the values of L and c, and the frequency of

51

the AC generator are so chosen that X_L and X_C are equal. In this case, the quantity $(X_L - X_C)$ in formula 3-10 would be equal to zero. The two reactances are equal and cancel each other. (Recall the analogy of the game of tug-of-war). The only opposition that remains in the circuit is the resistance, R. Therefore, the impedance in a circuit containing equal amounts of inductive and capacitive reactance is equal to the resistance in the circuit. At this point, the current flowing in the circuit reaches its maximum value, and the impedance of the circuit is at its minimum value. The condition where the inductive reactance is equal to the capacitive reactance in a circuit is known as RESONANCE. Since the components of this circuit are in series, the circuit is known as a SERIES RESONANT CIRCUIT. The frequency of the generator at resonance is called the RESONANT FREQUENCY.

If the frequency of the AC generator is increased, the inductive reactance will go up and the capacitive reactance will go down. The difference between the reactances is a number larger than zero. Our circuit is, therefore, no longer resonant. The impedance of the circuit has increased since the resistance is no longer the sole opposition to current flow. The impedance of the circuit is now determined by formula 3-10. Since the circuit impedance has increased, the current will now decrease below its resonance value.

If the generator frequency is decreased, the inductive reactance goes down and the capacitive reactance goes up. The reasoning in the preceding paragraph applies here as well. In this case, the current also decreases below its resonance value. Therefore, we can conclude that the current is maximum at resonance, and decreases on either side of the resonant frequency.

3-31 THE RESONANCE CURVE

If we were to draw a curve of the variations of current with changes in generator frequency, we would obtain a curve known as a RESONANCE CURVE, as illustrated in Figure 3-30. The vertical direction stands for the amount of current flowing in the circuit for different frequencies. The horizontal direction stands for the different generator frequencies. As the frequency of the generator is varied above and below the resonant frequency, the current will vary in the manner indicated. Notice that the current reaches a peak only at resonance, and decreases in value at either side of resonance.

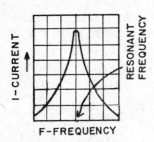

Figure 3-30.
The resonance curve.

3-32 RESONANT FREQUENCY OF A SERIES CIRCUIT

For every value of inductance and capacitance in a series circuit, there is ONE frequency at which the inductive reactance equals

52

the capacitive reactance. This frequency is referred to as the resonant frequency. The resonant frequency can be calculated by using the following formula:

Where:

f_R is the resonant frequency in Hertz

2π is 6.28

L is the inductance in henries in 3-11 and microhenries in 3-11A.

C is the capacitance in farads in 3-11 and microfarads in 3-11A.

$$3\text{-}11)\quad f_R = \frac{1}{2\pi\sqrt{LC}}$$

$$3\text{-}11A)\quad f_R = \frac{1,000,000}{2\pi\sqrt{LC}}$$

It is important to remember that the resonant frequency of a circuit goes up when either the inductance or capacitance goes down. This becomes apparent if we inspect the above formula. Examining the formula will also show that the frequency is inversely proportional to the square root of the inductance and the capacitance. Therefore, if we wish to double the resonant frequency of the circuit, we must reduce EITHER the capacity or the inductance to one quarter of its original value. By the same token, if we wish to cut the resonant frequency in half, we must increase EITHER the capacitance or the inductance by four times.

A shorted turn of a coil will cause the inductance of the coil to be reduced. This will, in turn, increase the resonant frequency.

3-33 PARALLEL RESONANCE

Figure 3-31 illustrates a coil and capacitor connected in parallel across an AC generator. Note that R_L represents the DC resistance of the coil. If the frequency of the generator is adjusted so that X_L is equal to X_C, we would have a condition of resonance known as PARALLEL RESONANCE. Notice that the conditions for resonance are the same here as in a series resonant circuit. The circuit in Figure 3-31 is called a PARALLEL RESONANT CIRCUIT. In a parallel resonant circuit, there are two different currents flowing; first there is the line current (I_{line}) which flows from the generator through the resonant circuit and back to the generator. At resonance, the line current is very low in value. The line current increases in value above and below resonance. At resonance, the line current supplies just enough energy to the parallel circuit to overcome the losses in the resistance of the coil. Secondly, there is the current which flows back and forth between the coil and capacitor. This current, I_c, is called the INTERNAL CIRCULATING CURRENT. At resonance, the internal circulating current is very high compared to the line current. Since the reactances of the coil and capacitor are equal and cancel each other, the only opposition to the internal circulating current at resonance is the resistance of the coil "R_L".

To understand the operation of the parallel resonant circuit more clearly, we can compare it to a water tank with a small leak in its bottom, as illustrated in Figure 3-32. The small leak represents the resistance of the coil. The tank represents the circuit of the coil

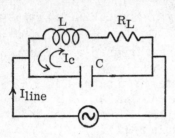

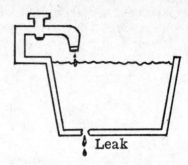

Figure 3-31.
Parallel resonance.

Figure 3-32. Water tank.

and capacitor in parallel. (The parallel combination of a coil and capacitor is actually given the name TANK CIRCUIT). The water in the tank represents the energy present in the tank circuit due to the internal circulating current flowing between the coil and capacitor. The faucet represents the generator, and the water flowing from the faucet into the tank represents the line current.

If there were no leak, the water tank would not lose any water and there would be no need to add water from the faucet. Similarly, if the electronic circuit had no resistance, no energy would be dissipated as the internal circulating current flows back and forth between the coil and capacitor. (Energy can only be dissipated in a resistor according to the I^2R factor). Therefore, the generator would not have to supply any energy since none would be lost in the circuit. Consequently, the line current will be zero. Practically speaking, there will always be some resistance present in the tank circuit. Energy will necessarily be dissipated in the tank circuit since the internal circulating current must flow through the resistance. In order to replenish this lost energy, the generator will have to supply energy by way of the line current flowing into the tank circuit.

3-34 IMPEDANCE OF A PARALLEL RESONANT CIRCUIT

The average tank circuit encountered in radio has a very low coil resistance. The energy dissipated will, therefore, be very low, and the line current will also be very low. Since the line current is small, the impedance (opposition to the line current) of a tank circuit at the resonant frequency must be very high. Compare this with the low impedance of a series resonant circuit. We will also find that the impedance of the tank circuit decreases as the frequency of the energy that is injected into the tank circuit varies above and below the resonant frequency. Thus, the impedance is a maximum at resonance.

3-35 Q OF A RESONANT CIRCUIT

The Q of a resonant circuit is the gain or figure of merit of the circuit at the resonant frequency. The formula for Q is:

$$Q = \frac{X}{R}$$

Where: X is equal to the reactance (inductive or capacitive since both are equal in a resonant circuit) and R is the AC resistance.

The Q of a tuned circuit determines its sharpness or selectivity. The higher the Q, the sharper the response curve or selectivity. The lower the Q, the broader is the response curve and the selectivity is poorer.

The Q of a resonant circuit is also the voltage gain of the resonant circuit. A voltage introduced into a resonant circuit gets multiplied Q times to give us a higher output voltage.

In addition to a circuit having a certain amount of Q, a coil, by itself, also has a certain amount of Q or figure of merit. The inductive reactance of a coil may be considered as a measure of its ability to store energy in a magnetic field, while the effective resistance of the coil is a measure of the energy lost in the coil. The ratio of these two factors is the Q or figure of merit of the coil.

$$Q \text{ of coil} = \frac{X_L}{R}$$

Most of the time, the Q of the coil is the Q of the circuit because the coil contains most of the circuit resistance.

3-36 SUMMARY OF CHARACTERISTICS OF RESONANT CIRCUITS
We will now summarize the characteristics of parallel and series resonant circuits. See the following Comparison Chart.

	Series Resonance	Parallel Resonance
Impedance	low	high
Current	high	line current - low internal circulating current - high
E across circuit	low	high
Formula for resonant frequency	$f_R = \dfrac{1}{2\pi\sqrt{LC}}$	$f_R = \dfrac{1}{2\pi\sqrt{LC}}$

3-37 AC POWER
In paragraph 1-18, we learned that the power loss in a DC circuit is determined by using the following formulas:

1) $P = EI$ 2) $P = I^2R$ 3) $P = \dfrac{E^2}{R}$

Where: R is the total resistance in the circuit.

This power is dissipated in the form of heat which, as far as electrical devices are concerned, is wasted energy.

The power loss in a pure resistive AC circuit is similarly determined by using the same formulas where E and I are in effective values.

3-12) $P = E_{eff.} \times I_{eff.}$ $\qquad$ $P = I^2_{eff.} \times R$ $\qquad$ $P = \dfrac{E^2_{eff.}}{R}$

In an AC circuit containing either inductance or capacitance, the voltage and current are out of phase. They are not acting together at the same instant. Therefore, the above formulas cannot all be used to determine the TRUE POWER loss in a reactive circuit. The product of E_{eff} and I_{eff} would, in this case, be known as the APPARENT POWER loss. This power is actually larger than the true power consumed in the circuit. The true power is the heat dissipated in the circuit. The electric company charges you for the true power consumed over a period of time. Power can only be dissipated or used up in a resistive element. Power cannot be dissipated in a pure capacitive or inductive circuit.

The apparent power can be determined from the readings of a voltmeter and ammeter placed in the circuit, as illustrated in Figure 3-33. The product of these readings, volts times amperes or VOLT-AMPERES, is the apparent power. The true power dissipated will always be indicated by an instrument called a wattmeter.

The one formula which can be used to determine the true power consumed in both DC and AC circuits is:

$P = I^2R$ $\qquad$ <u>Where:</u> I is either the DC current or the effective AC current, and R is the resistance in the circuit.

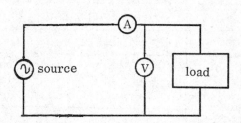

Figure 3-33. Determining apparent power.

3-38 THE TRANSFORMER
The voltage supplied to most communities in the United States is the standard 110 volts AC. Many home radios require a voltage higher than 110 volts AC in order to operate satisfactorily. To fill this need, a device is incorporated in those radios to step up the line voltage of 110 volts to a higher voltage. The device which can increase or decrease the value of an AC voltage is known as a TRANSFORMER.

3-39 PRINCIPLE OF THE TRANSFORMER
You will recall from our early discussion of AC voltage that an EMF will be induced in a loop of wire which cuts into a magnetic field.

56

As long as there is relative motion between the loop and the magnetic field, a voltage will be generated. If the loop is kept stationary and the magnetic field cuts across the loop of wire, the result obtained will be the same as if the loop were in motion instead of the magnetic field. In either case, a voltage will be induced in the conductors of the loop. The transformer operation is based upon a varying magnetic field inducing a voltage in a stationary coil of wire.

3-40 OPERATION OF THE TRANSFORMER

Every time current flows through a conductor, a magnetic field builds up around the conductor. The magnetic field is in phase with the current at all times. Therefore, if an alternating current flows through a coil of wire, an alternating magnetic field will exist about this coil. This alternating magnetic field expands outwardly away from the coil and collapses back into the coil periodically. If a second coil with a lamp across it is placed in the vicinity of coil #1, as illustrated in Figure 3-34, the alternating magnetic field will cut across coil #2 and induce an AC voltage in it; this will cause the lamp

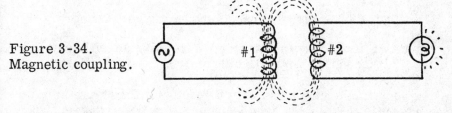

Figure 3-34.
Magnetic coupling.

to light. Notice that no electrical connection exists between the coils. Energy is transferred from coil #1 to coil #2 by means of the varying magnetic field. We say that the coils are MAGNETICALLY COUPLED. This method of transferring energy from one coil to another is known as TRANSFORMER ACTION. The entire device consisting of two coils magnetically coupled is known as a TRANSFORMER. Coil #1, which is connected to the voltage source, is called the PRIMARY

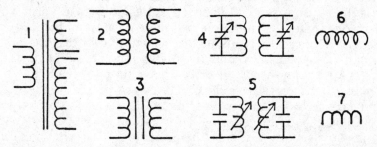

Fig. 3-35. Transformer symbols. #1 - power transformer. #2 - RF transformer. #3 - audio transformer. #4 & #5 - IF transformers. Note that either symbol #6 or #7 may be used to represent coils of a transformer or choke.

Coil #2, in which the induced voltage is developed, is called the SECONDARY.

Figure 3-35 shows the schematic symbols of typical transformers used in radio circuits.

3-41 THE POWER TRANSFORMER

The transformer in Figure 3-36B is known as an air-core transformer. Its use is confined to radio frequencies and it will be considered later on. A transformer which is used to transfer AC power at the power frequency of 60 cycles per second is known as a POWER TRANSFORMER.

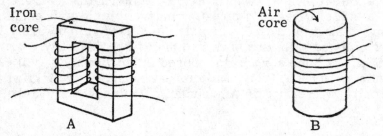

Iron core

Air core

A   B

Figure 3-36. Iron-core and Air-core transformers.

In order for a power transformer to operate efficiently, the primary and secondary are wound on an iron core, as illustrated in Figure 3-36A.

Power transformers can only be used on AC because an alternating magnetic field is required to induce an EMF in the secondary. It is dangerous to apply DC to the power transformer primary. The primary has a low DC resistance and therefore, a high DC current will flow through it. This high current will either blow a line fuse or damage the transformer beyond repair.

3-42 VOLTAGE AND TURNS RATIO

One of the most common uses of a transformer is to step up the 110 volts AC that is supplied to the average home. All AC radios and television sets require several hundred volts to operate. They must therefore incorporate a transformer which will step up the 110 volts. A fundamental principle of transformer action states that the voltage ratio between the secondary and the primary varies directly as the turns ratio. An example will clarify this point. If there are three times as many turns on the secondary as on the primary, the voltage of the secondary will be three times the voltage that is applied to the primary. Figure 3-37 illustrates a transformer whose secondary has three times as many turns as the primary. If the primary voltage is 110 volts, the secondary voltage which is applied to the load will be 330 volts. If there are ten times as many turns on the secondary as on the primary, the secondary voltage will be ten times as great as the primary voltage.

A transformer whose secondary voltage is greater than the primary voltage, is known as a STEP-UP TRANSFORMER.

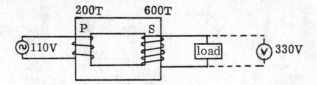

Figure 3-37. 1 to 3 step-up transformer.

Figure 3-38 shows a transformer where the turns on the secondary are less than the turns on the primary. In this case, the voltage will be stepped down from primary to secondary. This transformer is known as a STEP-DOWN TRANSFORMER.

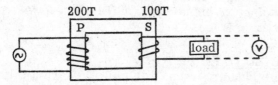

Figure 3-38. 2 to 1 step-down transformer.

3-43 TRANSFORMER LOSSES

There are three types of losses which are encountered in the operation of a transformer. They are:

1) EDDY CURRENTS
2) HYSTERESIS LOSSES
3) COPPER LOSSES

EDDY CURRENTS are wasted currents induced in the iron core of the transformer by the varying magnetic field. These currents take a circular path through the core material, as shown in Figure 3-39A. Since the resistance in their path in a solid core material is low, the eddy currents will be large. Eddy currents serve only to heat up the iron core and therefore, represent a power loss. Eddy current losses can be reduced by having the core made up of LAMINATIONS (thin insulated iron sheets) instead of solid iron. See Figure 3-39B. The laminations limit eddy currents by increasing the resistance in their path of flow.

HYSTERESIS LOSSES represent the energy that is used up in forcing the iron core to reverse the direction of its magnetic field every time the current reverses its direction. Hysteresis losses can be minimized by using cores made of special materials. Hysteresis losses, together with eddy current losses, are known as IRON-CORE LOSSES.

The third type of loss encountered in transformers is COPPER LOSSES. Copper losses are caused by the resistance of the wire

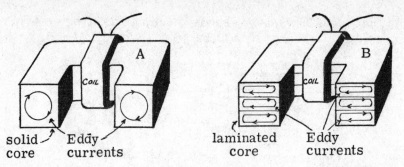

solid core / Eddy currents — laminated core / Eddy currents

Figure 3-39A. High Eddy-current flow in solid core.
Figure 3-39B. Low Eddy-current flow in laminated core.

which makes up the turns of the windings. Current flowing through the resistance of the winding develops an I^2R power loss in the form of wasteful heat. Copper losses can be minimized by using a heavier wire for the windings; a thicker wire will have a lower resistance and therefore, a lower I^2R loss.

3-44 THE TOROIDAL INDUCTOR

A toroidal inductor is a coil of wire wound in the shape of a doughnut (Figure 3-40). The core can be air, powdered iron, permalloy, or other similar ferrite-type material. Powdered iron and ferrite type cores are preferred over air cores because of their higher permeability.

The shape of the toroidal coil confines the magnetic field to the core itself. This gives us a higher inductance and practically no stray magnetic field outside of the windings. Because of the higher inductance, fewer, heavier turns of wire are required, resulting in lower losses.

All the above factors add up to give the toroidal inductor an extremely high Q for a small size coil. The toroidal coil is therefore ideal for circuits where high selectivity is required.

The fact that the toroid coil has a closed magnetic loop means that the toroid form can be used in a transformer with a high degree of coupling between the primary and secondary. This results in a highly efficient transformer, and also one that may be used in wide band applications.

The closed magnetic loop also makes the coil self-shielding. It can be used in small areas (miniature circuits) near other components, without the danger of undesirable coupling.

Figure 3-40.
A toroidal inductor.

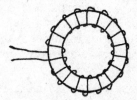

3-45 MAXIMUM POWER TRANSFER

In order that there be a maximum transfer of energy from a generator to a load, the impedance of the load should equal the internal impedance of the generator. This law applies to all circuits in radio and electricity. For instance, in Figure 1-10 of Lesson 1, the maximum power will be transferred from the battery to the load when the resistance of the load is equal to the internal resistance of the battery. The battery is considered to be the "generator" in this application.

Sometimes a load such as a speaker voice coil may have a very low impedance as compared to the very high internal impedance of the vacuum tube which is to energize the speaker. In order that there be maximum energy transfer between the vacuum tube (generator) and the speaker (load), a matching transformer (output transformer) is interposed between the two. The transformer steps up the impedance. We say that the transformer MATCHES the load to the generator, effecting maximum power transfer.

PRACTICE QUESTIONS - LESSON 3

(For answers, refer to Appendix 6)

3-1* Alternating current:
  a. flows only in one direction
  b. reverses its direction of flow periodically
  c. flows more in one direction than in the other
  d. none of the above

3-2* The frequency of a sine wave is:
  a. the time in seconds for one cycle
  b. the amplitude of the wave
  c. the number of cycles per second
  d. the angle of rotation

3-3 The peak amplitude of a sine wave occurs at:
  a. 45° b. 270° c. 360° d. 180°

3-4 One complete cycle has:
  a. one positive alternation
  b. one negative alternation
  c. two negative alternations
  d. a positive and negative alternation

3-5 One kiloHertz equals:
  a. $\frac{1}{1000}$ of a Hertz   c. 1000 Hertz
  b. 25 Hertz   d. 1 Hertz

3-6 The phase angle is:
  a. always large
  b. the angle by which current leads resistance
  c. the angle by which one wave leads or lags another
  d. the angle between 0° and 90°

3-7 If the effective value of the wave is 100 volts, the peak value is:
  a. 78 volts   c. 141 volts
  b. 70.7 volts   d. 250 volts

3-8 If the peak value is 155 volts, the effective value is:
  a. 185   b. 220   c. 155   d. 110

3-9 The inductance of a coil varies:
  a. inversely with the number of turns
  b. directly as the square of the number of turns

c. directly with the number of turns
d. directly as the square-root of the number of turns

3-10* Inductive reactance is:
    a. the opposition a coil offers to AC current flow
    b. the AC current flowing through the coil
    c. the DC resistance of the coil
    d. the coil inductance

3-11 In an inductive circuit:
    a. the current leads the voltage
    b. the current lags the voltage
    c. the voltage lags the current
    d. the current and voltage are in phase

3-12 A capacitor is:
    a. two conducting plates connected by a wire
    b. a resistance
    c. two insulator plates separated by air
    d. two conducting plates separated by a dielectric

3-13 A capacitor is:
    a. a short-circuit for DC
    b. an open-circuit for DC
    c. offers little opposition to DC current flow
    d. a DC generator

3-14* A toroidal coil has the shape of a:
    a. doughnut
    b. horseshoe
    c. bar
    d. ball

3-15* The reactance of a capacitor:
    a. remains constant
    b. increases with increase in frequency
    c. decreases with an increase in frequency
    d. is very high

3-16 Capacitors in series:
    a. add like resistors in series
    b. add like resistors in parallel
    c. are equal to the smaller capacitor
    d. are equal to the larger capacitor

3-17 At resonance:
    a. the resistance is equal to the voltage
    b. the current is zero

c. $X_L = X_C$
d. the voltage varies

3-18* In a series resonant circuit
    a. the impedance is a minimum
    b. the impedance is a maximum
    c. the current lags the voltage
    d. the current leads the voltage

3-19* In a parallel resonant circuit:
    a. the line current equals the circulating current
    b. the line current is much smaller than the circulating current
    c. the line current is larger than the circulating current
    d. the line current is constant

3-20 In a power transformer, DC should not be applied to the primary because:
    a. a counter EMF will be developed
    b. no load will be present
    c. a high DC current will flow
    d. the efficiency will be poor

3-21* In a transformer, the secondary voltage:
    a. always equals the primary voltage
    b. is less than the primary voltage
    c. equals the primary voltage times the turns ratio
    d. is high

3-22 Short-circuiting a turn of a coil in a tuned circuit will:
    a. increase the resonant frequency
    b. have no effect on the resonant frequency
    c. decrease the resonant frequency
    d. increase the "Q"

3-23* A toroidal coil is known for its:
    a. low distributed capacity   c. high permeability
    b. high Q   d. narrow band application

3-24* Which of the following does not increase a tuned circuit's Q?
    a. reduce resistive losses   b. increase length of coil
    c. increase wire thickness of coil
    d. increase permeability of coil form

3-25* The total of two inductive reactances in series is equal to:
    a. the sum of the reactances
    b. the difference of the reactances
    c. the sum of the reactances divided by the difference
    d. the product of the reactances divided by their sum

STUDY GUIDE – SECTION I

Your Amateur Communications Course has been written with two purposes in mind:

1. To aid you to successfully pass the written part of the Federal Communications Commission examinations for the Amateur Licenses.

2. To give you, the prospective radio amateur, a complete understanding of radio theory so that you can properly operate a radio amateur receiving and transmitting station.

At the present time, the government is issuing six types of Amateur licenses. They are for the Novice Class, the Technician Class, the General Class, the Conditional Class, the Advanced Class and the Amateur Extra Class.

In order to qualify for any of these licenses, you must pass a written test, as well as an examination in the sending and receiving of International Morse Code. The written test for the Novice Class license consists of twenty questions. The written tests for all the other classes of amateur licenses have fifty questions. All of the questions are of the multiple choice type.

Before the prospective amateur can take the written examination, he must pass the code test. The code speed for the Novice Class and Technician Class licenses is 5 words per minute. It is 13 words per minute for the General, Conditional and Advanced Class licenses. The Amateur Extra Class license requires 20 words per minute.

If your code speed is not up to the FCC requirements, write to the AMECO PUBLISHING CORP. for information regarding code courses that prepare one for the FCC code examinations.

This Radio Theory Course consists of three sections. Each section contains a number of lessons and a study guide such as this one. The study guide assists you by calling special attention to the material that you will be questioned about on the FCC examinations. At the end of each lesson, you will find a series of questions that will review the important information in the lesson. The questions with an asterisk are similar to questions that are asked on the government examination. Know them thoroughly! The answers to the study questions at the end of each lesson will be found in Appendix 6.

After you have thoroughly studied the lessons and practice questions in a section, you will be ready to take an "FCC-type" examination that tests your knowledge of the most important material contained in the section. This examination is found at the back of each study guide. Bear in mind that these questions are not the actual questions that are asked in the government license examination. They are, however, similar. Also, the practice questions contain the same information that you will be responsible for on the examination given by the FCC. For example, our practice question may ask for the third harmonic of a given fundamental frequency. The government examination question may state the third harmonic and ask for the fundamental frequency. Thus you can see where an understanding of the practice questions will enable you to correctly answer the actual FCC question.

When taking a practice FCC-type examination, do not refer back to the test material to obtain the correct answers. You will not be allowed to use any reference material when taking the actual license examination. Answer all the questions as best as you can. When you are finished with all the questions of a particular test, check them against the correct answers. If you have wrong answers, look up the material in the text to learn why your answer is incorrect. Make sure that you know and understand the correct answer before you go on.

The multiple choice question consists of a statement and four answers labeled a, b, c and d. Only one of these answers correctly finishes the statement.

For example: 1. The United States is a:

a. democracy   b. kingdom   c. colony   d. dictatorship

The only correct answer to the question is "a".

The same question can be worded in a negative way.

For example: 2. The United States is not a:

a. democracy   c. kingdom
b. union of states   d. land of many religions

The only correct answer to the question is "c".

The first three lessons of Section 1 are:

(1) DC Theory   (2) Magnetism   (3) AC Theory

These three lessons are extremely important because they contain fundamental material that is basic to an understanding of the lessons that follow. Therefore, you should study Section 1 thoroughly and completely.

This study guide, as well as the other two study guides, do not differentiate between material to be studied for the Novice examination and material to be studied for the General examination. Appendix 5 lists the material to be studied for the Novice Class license. The entire course must be studied for the General Class examination.

The following outline is a guide to the material in Section 1 that you will most likely be questioned about on the FCC license examinations.

LESSON #1.   DIRECT CURRENT THEORY

1. You must know the meanings and basic units of electrical resistance, current, electromotive force, power, energy and electrical quantity. (Refer to practice questions 1, 4 and 16).

2. You must know the names of the instruments used to measure current, potential difference, power, resistance and energy. (Refer to practice questions 2 and 17).

3. You should be thoroughly familiar with the application of Ohm's law. (Refer to practice questions 8, 12, 14 and 15).

4. You should know the formulas for finding the power in a circuit. (Refer to practice question 11).

5. You should be familiar with the internal resistance of a battery. (See paragraph 1-14 and practice question 18).

6. You must know the difference between a conductor and an insulator.

7. You must know how to calculate the total resistance of circuits containing resistors in series and/or in parallel.

8. You must know how voltage divides itself in a circuit containing resistors in series.

LESSON #2. MAGNETISM

1. You must know the unit of magnetomotive force. (Refer to practice question 1).

LESSON #3. AC THEORY

1. You must know the unit of frequency. (Refer to question 2).

2. You should know that the instrument used to measure frequency is called a frequency-meter.

3. You should be familiar with the theory of tuned circuits. (Refer to questions 17 through 19).

4. You must be able to understand the theory of the transformer, and be able to work out problems on transformer action. (Refer to questions 20 and 21).

5. You should know how to calculate inductive reactance. You should also know how to add inductances and inductive reactances in a circuit. See question 25.

6. You should know how voltage divides itself across the various components in an AC circuit.

7. You should be familiar with the Q of a tuned circuit.

8. You should be familiar with the transfer of power between a source and its load.

9. You should be familiar with the toroidal inductor.

10. You should know the difference between AC and DC. You should know the meaning of "RF".

11. You should understand inductance and capacitance and know their units.

12. You should know how to calculate capacitive reactance. You should also know how to add capacitors and capacitive reactances in a circuit.

13. You should be familiar with series and parallel resonance.

"FCC-TYPE" EXAMINATION — SECTION I

1.* The unit of electrical resistance is:
   a. ampere   b. volt   c. ohm   d. joule

2.* The unit of electrical current is:
   a. ampere   b. volt   c. watt   d. farad

3.* The unit of electromotive force or potential difference is:
   a. ampere   b. volt   c. watt   d. coulomb

4.* The unit of power is:
   a. ampere   b. volt   c. watt   d. coulomb

5.* The unit of energy is:
   a. watt   b. ampere   c. joule   d. henry

6. The unit of electrical quantity is:
   a. ampere   b. volt   c. coulomb   d. watt

7.* The instrument used to measure electric current is:
   a. wattmeter   b. ammeter   c. voltmeter   d. ohmmeter

8.* The instrument used to measure potential difference is:
   a. wattmeter   b. ammeter   c. voltmeter   d. ohmmeter

9.* The instrument used to measure power is:
   a. wattmeter   b. ammeter   c. voltmeter   d. ohmmeter

10.* The instrument used to measure resistance is:
   a. wattmeter   b. ammeter   c. voltmeter   d. ohmmeter

11. The unit of magnetomotive force is:
   a. henry   b. coulomb   c. farad   d. gilbert

12.* The unit of capacitance is:
   a. henry   b. coulomb   c. farad   d. gilbert

13.* The unit of inductance is:
   a. henry   b. coulomb   c. farad   d. gilbert

14.* The line current in a parallel circuit is equal to:
   a. the sum of the branch currents divided by two
   b. the source voltage divided by the smallest resistor
   c. the sum of the individual branch currents
   d. a very small value

15.* Ohm's law states that the:
    a. current is equal to the voltage times the resistance
    b. resistance is equal to the voltage divided by the current
    c. voltage is equal to the current divided by the resistance
    d. current is equal to the resistance divided by the voltage

16.* The voltage drop in a 300 ohm resistor through which 5 ma. flow is:
    a. 1500 volts   b. 60 volts   c. .017 volts   d. 1.5 volts

17.* The voltage drop in a resistor is 13 volts when 4 ma. flow through it. The resistor is:
    a. 3250 ohms   b. 52 ohms   c. 3.25 ohms   d. 308 ohms

18.* If the primary of a 60 cycle power transformer were connected directly to the mains carrying DC current:
    a. the primary winding would burn out due to an excessive current flow
    b. nothing would happen
    c. the secondary winding would burn up due to an excessive current flow
    d. the primary winding impedance would rise

19.* The unit of frequency is:
    a. kilometers per second   c. cycles per second
    b. meters per second   d. degrees per second

20.* The instrument used to measure frequency is:
    a. wattmeter   c. wavemeter
    b. frequency meter   d. ohmmeter

21. The peak value of an AC wave is:
    a. $0.707 \times E_{eff}$ c. $\dfrac{E_{eff}}{1.41}$
    b. $\dfrac{E_{eff}}{1,410}$ d. $E_{eff} \times 1.41$

22.* The inductive reactance of a coil is:
    a. the resistance to DC current flow
    b. the induced voltage in volts
    c. the opposition in ohms that a coil builds up to AC current flow
    d. always constant

23. In a pure capacitive circuit:
    a. the voltage leads the current by 45°
    b. the current leads the voltage by 45°
    c. the voltage leads the current by 90°
    d. the current leads the voltage by 90°

24.* Capacitive reactance is:
    a. the opposition in ohms that a capacitor builds up to AC current flow
    b. the voltage charge on a capacitor
    c. the resistance to DC current flow
    d. always constant

25. In a circuit containing equal amounts of resistance and inductive reactance:
    a. the voltage leads the current by 45º
    b. the current leads the voltage by 90º
    c. the voltage lags the current by 45º
    d. the current is in phase with the voltage

26. If the two plates of a capacitor touch, the capacitor is said to be:
    a. open   c. shorted
    b. good   d. a variable capacitor

27. A capacitor is used to:
    a. pass DC and block AC   c. pass AC and block DC
    b. pass DC only   d. generate an AC voltage

28.* In a power transformer, the secondary to primary turns ratio is 6 to 1. If 110 volts are applied to the primary, a voltmeter across the secondary will measure:
    a. 660 volts   c. 18.5 volts
    b. 330 volts   d. 9000 volts

29.* In a series resonant circuit:
    a. the current is a minimum and the impedance is a minimum
    b. the current is a maximum and the impedance is a minimum
    c. the current is a maximum and the impedance is a maximum
    d. the current is a minimum and the impedance is a maximum

30.* In a parallel resonant circuit:
    a. the current is a minimum and the impedance is a minimum
    b. the current is a maximum and the impedance is a minimum
    c. the current is a maximum and the impedance is a maximum
    d. the current is a minimum and the impedance is a maximum

31.* An advantage of a toroidal inductor is:
    a. low cost
    b. the same core is efficient over a wide range of frequencies
    c. high efficiency at extremely high frequencies
    d. very high Q

SECTION II — LESSON 4
THE VACUUM TUBE

4-1 THE DEVELOPMENT OF THE VACUUM TUBE

Thomas A. Edison was one of the great pioneers in the development of the vacuum tube. Edison invented the incandescent light bulb whose basic principles were later put to use by men such as Fleming and DeForest, in the development of the modern vacuum tube.

Edison's incandescent electric lamp, which was the forerunner of the modern electric bulb, consisted of a resistance wire called a filament, enclosed within a glass envelope. The air within the glass envelope had been removed to create a vacuum. The ends of the resistance wire protruded through the glass, as illustrated in Figure 4-1. If a current passes through the resistance wire, it will heat up and glow. We can then say that the filament wire has been heated to INCANDESCENCE. While working with his electric light, Edison discovered that the incandescent wire emitted, or boiled off, electrons. These electrons remained around the wire in the form of an electron cloud or SPACE CHARGE. This phenomenon of electron emission is known as the EDISON EFFECT, and is the basis of operation of all vacuum tubes.

4-2 ELECTRON EMISSION

Many metallic substances will emit electrons when heated to incandescence. In the previous paragraph, it was shown that the resistance wire in a light bulb emits electrons. These emitted electrons are wasted since they serve no useful purpose.

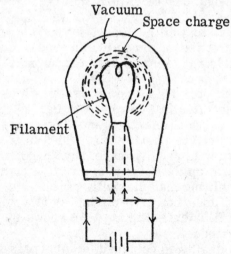

Figure 4-1. The electric lamp.

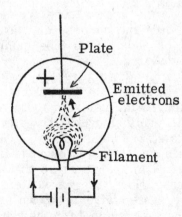

Figure 4-2. Positive plate attracting electrons.

The vacuum tube is similar to the light bulb in that it also contains a resistance wire which emits electrons when heated. The vacuum tube, however, is designed to make use of the emitted electrons. In addition to the resistance wire, the vacuum tube has a positively charged collector of electrons called THE PLATE. The positive plate attracts the emitted electrons, as illustrated in Figure 4-2.

The purpose of the battery in Figure 4-2 is to force current through the filament, thereby heating it.

4-3   THE CATHODE

The element in the vacuum tube which supplies the electrons for the tube operation is known as the CATHODE. The cathode, as does the resistance wire, emits or boils off electrons when energy in the form of heat is supplied to it. There are two different types of cathodes used in vacuum tubes. They are the directly heated and the indirectly heated types. We will now discuss these two types in detail.

1. The directly heated cathode. This type is also known by the name FILAMENT-CATHODE. An example of a filament-cathode is illustrated in Fig. 4-3. The heating current is passed directly through the cathode wire, which is made of tungsten. The current heats up the cathode wire, which then emits electrons from its surface. Directly heated filament-cathodes usually require very little heating power. They are, therefore, used in tubes designed for portable battery operation because it is necessary to impose as small a drain as possible on these batteries. Examples of battery-operated filament-cathode tubes are the 1A7, the 1R5 and the 1U4.

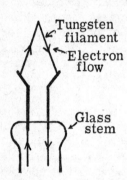

Figure 4-3. Directly heated cathode.

All vacuum tubes are classified by tube numbers. If you desire to know the purpose and characteristics of a particular tube, you simply look up its tube number in any tube manual for the information wanted.

2. The indirectly-heated cathode. This type is also known as the HEATER-CATHODE and is illustrated in Figure 4-4A. Part A is a thin metal sleeve or cylinder coated with electron-emitting material. This sleeve is the cathode. Part B is a heater wire which is insulated from the sleeve. The heater is usually made of a tungsten material. Its sole purpose is to heat up the cathode sleeve to a high enough temperature so that the emitting material will boil off electrons. Note that the heater itself does not give off the electrons. The heater wire is known as the filament. Figure 4-4B shows the schematic symbol for the heater-cathode.

Almost all present day receiving tubes designed for AC operation are of the indirectly-heated cathode type. We will always refer

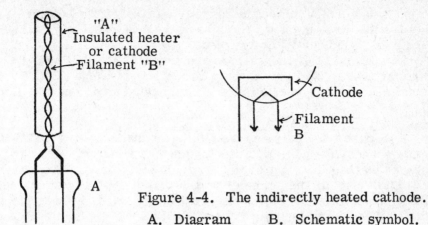

Figure 4-4. The indirectly heated cathode.

A. Diagram   B. Schematic symbol.

to the electron emitting surface as the CATHODE and the heater as the FILAMENT.

4-4   FILAMENT OPERATING VOLTAGE

The first number in a tube designation usually indicates the proper filament operating voltage. For example, a 6H6 tube should have its filament operated at 6.3 volts. All filaments should be operated at their designated operating voltages, which are determined by the manufacturer. If the filament is operated above its rated voltage, the excessive current will shorten the filament life. Operating the filament below its rated voltage will decrease electron emission and lower the tube operating efficiency.

4-5   THE DIODE

Let us see how electrons emitted from the cathode can be collected and made to do useful work. Electrons are negatively charged and will be attracted by a positively charged object. Therefore, if a positively charged object called a PLATE is put into the vacuum tube, it will serve as a collector of electrons. A vacuum tube which con-

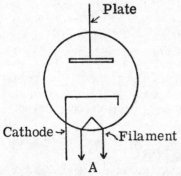

Figure 4-5A. Indirectly heated.

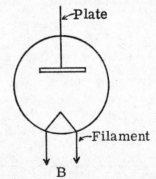

Figure 4-5B. Directly heated.

tains a plate and a cathode is known as a DIODE. The schematic symbol for the diode is shown in Figure 4-5. B is a directly-heated diode and A is an indirectly-heated diode.

The plate and the cathode are known as the ELEMENTS of the vacuum tube. The diode is, therefore, a two-element tube. The heater of the indirectly-heated tube is not counted as a separate element.

4-6   THE DIODE AS A CONDUCTOR

Figure 4-6 illustrates a simplified schematic of a diode with the plate connected to the positive terminal of a battery; the cathode is connected through a switch to the negative terminal. The instant the switch is closed, the ammeter in the circuit will register a current flow, indicating that electrons are flowing from the cathode to the plate. The diode is said to be CONDUCTING. The diode conducts because the plate is positive with respect to the cathode. Therefore, the plate attracts to it the negatively charged electrons emitted by the cathode. The electrons flow from the plate to the positive terminal of the battery. They then flow through the battery and back to the cathode, where they once more can be emitted to the plate. If the battery voltage is increased, the plate will become more positive and will, therefore, attract more electrons. Consequently, the ammeter will register a larger current flow. Conversely, if the battery voltage is decreased, the plate will attract less electrons and the ammeter will register a smaller current flow.

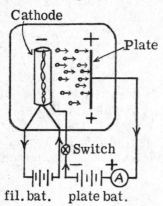

Figure 4-6. Electron flow
when plate is positive.

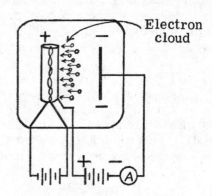

Figure 4-7. Diode action
when plate is negative.

When the diode conducts, it presents a very low resistance path between the cathode and plate. For all practical purposes, we can consider a conducting diode as a closed switch (short circuit) between the cathode and plate.

4-7   THE DIODE AS A NON-CONDUCTOR

If we reverse the battery connections, as shown in Figure 4-7, the plate becomes negative and the cathode positive. Since the negative plate will not attract electrons, the diode will NOT CONDUCT.

74

The diode, therefore, acts like an open switch (open-circuit) and permits no current flow. The ammeter will consequently read zero amperes. The emitted negatively-charged electrons are repelled by the negative plate and remain close to the cathode where they form an ELECTRON CLOUD. The cloud of electrons around the cathode is known as a SPACE CHARGE. The space charge, by virtue of its large negative charge, prevents the plate from receiving any more electrons. When the plate becomes positive once again, the space charge is rapidly dispelled since it is attracted to the plate. The cathode is free once again to emit electrons.

Let us now summarize the operation of the diode:

1) electrons flow in one direction only - from cathode to plate.

2) electron flow to the plate will take place only when the plate is positive with respect to the cathode.

3) the current flow will vary with the plate to cathode voltage.

4) the diode acts as a conductor (short circuit) when the plate is positive.

5) the diode acts as a non-conductor (open circuit) when the plate is negative.

4-8   THE DIODE CHARACTERISTIC CURVE

Figure 4-8 illustrates a diode connected to a source of variable voltage. The heater circuit has been omitted for the purpose of simplicity. "A" is a milliammeter connected in series with the tube. The voltage applied to the plate of the diode can be varied by changing the position of the plate tap from position #1 to position #8. As the tap is moved from position #1 to position #8, the plate to cathode voltage increases. For every value of plate voltage, there will be a different value of diode plate current as measured by the milliammeter. The

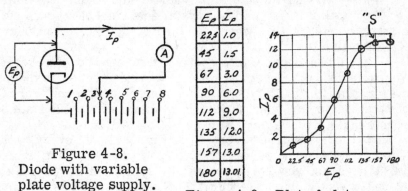

E_p	I_p
22.5	1.0
45	1.5
67	3.0
90	6.0
112	9.0
135	12.0
157	13.0
180	13.01

Figure 4-8.
Diode with variable
plate voltage supply.

Figure 4-9. Plot of plate current
against plate voltage.

table in Figure 4-9 is a tabulation of plate current readings for various values of plate voltage. If we plot these readings on the graph in Figure 4-9 and then draw a line through the different points, we obtain a curve known as the DIODE CHARACTERISTIC CURVE. I_p is

75

the electronic symbol for plate current; E_p is the electronic symbol for plate to cathode voltage, or simply plate voltage. The plate current, plate-voltage curve shows the amount of current that a particular diode will conduct for a given plate voltage. The curve indicates that the plate current increases as the plate voltage increases up to point "S". Beyond point "S", the curve becomes practically horizontal. In other words, as the plate voltage increases beyond point "S", the plate current remains essentially constant. This point "S" is known as the saturation point. It is the point at which the plate is collecting all of the electrons that the cathode is capable of emitting.

The characteristic curve is important because it tells us at a glance what the plate current will be for any particular plate voltage. This information is useful if we are designing a diode circuit for a certain application. Characteristic curves for diodes, as well as all other tubes, may be found in tube manuals.

4-9 SUMMARY OF FILAMENTS AND DIODE TUBES

1. The emission of electrons from a filament is the principle upon which all electron tubes are based.

2. Electrons are negatively charged particles which are attracted to a positively charged object, such as a plate.

3. A diode consists of an emitting surface called the cathode (whether it is directly or indirectly heated) and a receiver of electrons called the plate. These elements are placed within an evacuated (vacuum) glass or metal bulb to prevent the hot filament from burning up, and to provide a clear path from the cathode to the plate for the fast-moving electrons.

4-10 SEMICONDUCTOR DIODES

In the early days of radio, a receiver known as a "crystal set" was very popular. The original crystal sets used earphones because the amplifier tubes that were required to operate a speaker were quite expensive.

When tubes became less costly and demand for speaker-operated receivers became strong, the crystal set began to disappear. However, the "crystal" itself, in a somewhat different form, has made a strong comeback. Today, it is known as a solid-state semiconductor.

The diode semiconductor is used in just about every radio and television set. Its popularity is based on the fact that, unlike the tube, it does not require a socket; it is light in weight and can be soldered directly into a circuit. Furthermore, it has no filament and so its operation is instantaneous. The semiconductor diode works both as a rectifier and a detector. Let us see how this type of diode functions, why it works and also, how it differs from a vacuum tube.

4-11 INSULATORS

Certain substances and certain elements are good conductors;

others are good insulators. Copper wire is a good conductor, while glass is a good insulator. The element iron is put in the conductor class, while other elements, such as pure germanium, selenium or pure silicon, are insulators.

We can modify the characteristic of any element by mixing in other elements. For example, we can add boron, antimony or arsenic to pure germanium or pure silicon and change these elements from non-conductors to conductors.

4-12 DOPING

The addition of antimony to either germanium or silicon, is known as doping. Since the germanium or silicon, at the start, is as pure as it can be made, the added element is referred to as an impurity. It takes a very small amount of impurity to modify the germanium or silicon so that they are no longer insulators.

All elements are made up of atoms and each atom contains a nucleus surrounded by one or more rings of electrons. By diffusing certain elements, such as antimony, into pure germanium or silicon, we change the total number of electrons in the germanium or silicon. These "doped" elements now have more electrons than they originally had. Since electrons are negatively charged, we refer to them as negative germanium or negative silicon. We abbreviate negative germanium as n-germanium or n-type germanium. The antimony, diffused into the pure germanium or silicon is referred to as a "doner" element since it has, in effect, donated or contributed electrons.

We can diffuse substances that have a deficiency of electrons into germanium or silicon. An element, such as boron, for example, likes to borrow electrons and so, when mixed with germanium or silicon, will take electrons from these substances. For this reason, we call boron an acceptor element - it accepts or takes away electrons.

When a substance or an element loses electrons, it is no longer neutral. It has become less negative or, stated in another way, has become more positive. We can also refer to an atom that has lost an electron as a "hole". The "hole" is the positive charge around the atom due to the removal of one of its electrons by the acceptor. Germanium or silicon, doped with boron, is referred to as positive germanium or positive silicon. We abbreviate this as p-germanium or p-silicon or p-type. We can represent n-type or p-type pictorially, as shown in Figure 4-10. The minus signs indicate an excess of negative charges; the plus signs tell us that we have a shortage of electrons or an excess of positive "holes".

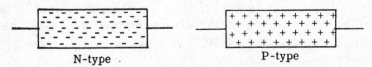

Figure 4-10. N-type and P-type germanium or silicon.

4-13 THE SEMICONDUCTOR DIODE

If we take a block of p-type germanium and a block of n-type germanium (or silicon) and put them together, we will have a semiconductor diode. The semiconductor diode is referred to as a solid-state device.

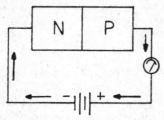   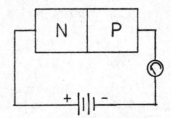

Fig. 4-11A. Forward biasing.   Fig. 4-11B. Reverse biasing.

In Figure 4-11, we have a battery connected across our two blocks of doped germanium or silicon. In drawing A, the negative terminal of the battery is connected to the n-type material, while the positive terminal is connected to the p-type material. Connecting a voltage in this manner is known as biasing. Electrons will now flow from the battery, through the n-type material, into the p-type material and back to the battery. The reason for the current flow is that the battery urges or forces electrons into the n-type block, which already has more electrons than normal. The electrons migrate over to the p-type block since this region is more positive and attracts them. However, as electrons leave the p-type block to the battery, more electrons from the n-type block cross the junction between the two blocks, and so the process is a continuous one. The current that flows is referred to as a forward current. The voltage producing this current is then called a forward voltage or forward bias.

Now examine drawing B. The only difference is that we have reversed the polarity of the battery. As a result, very little current flows. The small current that does flow, moves in an opposite direction to the way it previously moved. We, therefore, call it a reverse current and the battery voltage is referred to as a reverse voltage or reverse bias.

Aside from the fact that the semiconductor diode in Figure 4-11 does have a small amount of reverse current, its basic action is very much like the vacuum tube diode described earlier in this lesson. Note that there is no filament or cathode to be heated and so, unlike the tube, the semiconductor diode does not get warm or hot when operating. Therefore, since we do not need to wait for the filament or cathode to get hot enough to emit electrons, the semiconductor diode acts at once.

Figure 4-12 illustrates two symbols that are commonly used to illustrate a solid state diode.

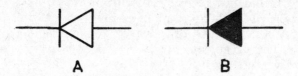

Figure 4-12. Solid state diode symbols.

PRACTICE QUESTIONS - LESSON 4

(For answers, refer to Appendix 6)

4-1* The diode tube has:
a. one element   c. three elements
b. two elements   d. four elements

4-2 Electron emission:
a. is undesirable in vacuum tubes
b. is necessary for the operation of a light bulb
c. can only take place when the filament is cold
d. is the giving off of electrons by a metal when heated to incandescence.

4-3 The plate is:
a. a positively charged collector of electrons
b. a positively charged emitter of electrons
c. not necessary for the operation of a diode
d. connected directly to the cathode

4-4 The cathode:
a. is not necessary for the operation of a diode
b. is a positively charged collector of electrons
c. repels electrons
d. emits electrons for tube operation

4-5 The directly-heated cathode type tube:
a. has the heating current pass directly through the cathode
b. has a separate filament and cathode
c. does not require heater current
d. is the same as the indirectly-heated cathode type tube

4-6 The diode acts as an open-circuit:
a. when the tube conducts
b. when the plate is negative with respect to the cathode
c. when the plate emits electrons
d. when the cathode is negative with respect to the plate

4-7 A diode tube allows current to flow:
    a. only from cathode to plate
    b. only from cathode to heaters
    c. in either direction
    d. straight up

4-8 The indirectly-heated cathode type tube:
    a. has the heating current pass directly through the cathode
    b. has a separate filament and cathode
    c. does not require heater current
    d. has no cathode

4-9 When the plate of a diode is positive, relative to the cathode:
    a. current will flow from plate to cathode
    b. the cathode stops emitting
    c. the tube conducts
    d. an electron cloud forms

4-10 When the plate of a diode is negative, relative to the cathode:
    a. the cathode stops emitting
    b. the tube conducts
    c. current will flow from cathode to plate
    d. the tube acts as an open-circuit

4-11* What are the majority carriers in N-type material?
    a. holes   c. protons
    b. electrons   d. neutrons

4-12* Which of the following creates N-type material when diffused into germanium?
    a. antimony   c. selenium
    b. boron   d. copper oxide

4-13* In semiconductor conduction, a "flow of holes" refers to:
    a. a flow of positive carriers
    b. a flow of electrons
    c. a flow of protons
    d. a flow of neutrons

SECTION II – LESSON 5
RECTIFICATION, FILTERING

5-1 RECTIFICATION

Vacuum tubes in receivers and transmitters will only operate when connected to a direct current source of power. Portable radios, for example, are energized by batteries which are in themselves a source of direct current. As previously noted, the electrical power that is delivered to most homes throughout the country today is alternating current. If we were to connect the tubes in our radios directly to the AC wall outlet, the radio would not operate because a radio tube needs a source of DC power. We all know that our radios DO operate when we plug them into the AC socket. Obviously, there must be something in the radio which converts the alternating current into direct current. The device in a radio which converts the alternating current into direct current is known as a RECTIFIER. The process of conversion is known as RECTIFICATION.

5-2 THE DIODE AS A HALF-WAVE RECTIFIER

The ability of the diode to pass current in only one direction makes it possible to convert alternating current into direct current. Let us see how this takes place. Figure 5-1 illustrates a simple diode rectifier circuit.

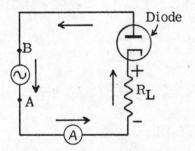

Figure 5-1. Diode used as half-wave rectifier.

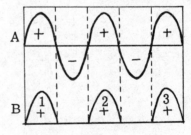

Figure 5-2. Half-wave rectifier wave-forms.

When terminal "B" of the AC generator is positive with respect to terminal "A", the diode plate becomes positive with respect to its cathode. The diode, therefore, conducts current in the direction indicated by the arrow. The DC milliammeter will deflect to the value of the current flow.

On the next half of the alternating current cycle, the polarity of the generator will be reversed, making the plate negative with respect to the cathode. The diode becomes a non-conductor, and the current will stop flowing. On the next cycle, the polarity of "A" and "B" will again reverse itself. The diode will conduct and once again, current will flow. Examination of Figure 5-2 shows what is really happening. Figure 5-2A is the sine wave which is generated across the terminals of the AC generator. Figure 5-2B is the wave which is obtained across the load resistor R. Alternations 1, 2 and 3 are the positive halves of the cycle when the plate of the diode is positive with respect to the cathode. At that time, the diode conducts and acts as a short circuit. The positive voltage alternations are therefore impressed directly across the resistor R. During the negative half of each AC cycle, the tube does not conduct and is an open circuit. During these times, there is no voltage developed across the resistor since there is no current flow. The current through the resistor is therefore a pulsating direct current, and the voltage across the resistor is a pulsating direct voltage. Even though the current flows in spurts or pulses through the resistor, the current is DC because it flows only in ONE direction. This action of the diode in passing only one-half of the AC input wave to the load resistor is known as HALF-WAVE RECTIFICATION.

The ends of the load resistance have been marked with a polarity because electrons are entering and emerging from this resistance. The end they enter becomes more negative than the end from which they emerge. The pulsating direct-voltage, if properly filtered, can be utilized to operate a radio receiver.

A transformer can be considered as an AC generator. We can, therefore, replace the AC generator of Figure 5-1 with a transformer as shown in Figure 5-3, without altering the operation of the circuit.

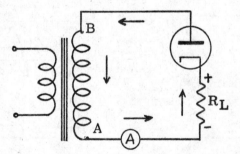

Figure 5-3. Diode used as half-wave rectifier.

5-3 THE DIODE AS A FULL-WAVE RECTIFIER

In half-wave rectification, only the positive half of the AC input is used. The negative alternations are completely cut off and wasted. If we could somehow utilize the negative as well as the positive alternation, we would be operating our rectifying system more efficiently. This is accomplished in full-wave rectification.

We can modify the half-wave rectifier circuit of Figure 5-3 by adding another diode and center-tapping the transformer secondary. The resulting circuit is illustrated in Figure 5-4. The cathodes of the diodes are connected together, and the circuit is known as a FULL-

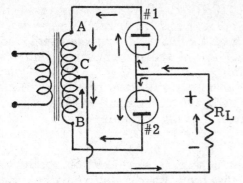

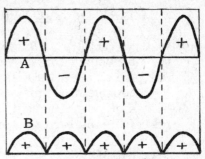

A. input wave-form.
B. output wave-form.

Figure 5-4. Full-wave rectifier.

Figure 5-5. Full-wave rectifier wave-forms.

WAVE RECTIFIER.

The operation of a full-wave rectifier is as follows: When an AC voltage is impressed across the primary of the transformer, an AC voltage will be induced across the secondary. When point "A" is positive with respect to point "B", the plate of diode #1 is positive and the tube conducts. The electrons flow through the transformer, from A to C, out of C into the load resistance R_L, and back to the cathode of diode #1. During all this time, the plate of diode #2 is negative and does not conduct. On the next half of the AC cycle, the bottom of the transformer, point "B", goes positive while the top, point "A", goes negative. The plate of diode #2 is now positive and the plate of diode #1 is negative. Now, diode #2 conducts and diode #1 does not. The electrons flow through the transformer from B to C, into the load resistor R_L, and back to the cathode of diode #2. Notice that the current flows through the load resistor in the same direction as it did previously. Notice, also, that the current flows through the resistor in the same direction during both the positive and negative halves of the input cycle. We have very definitely used both halves of the AC input cycle, and have accomplished full-wave rectification. Figure 5-5A shows the AC across the transformer secondary. Figure 5-5B shows the pulsating DC flowing through the load. Compare this output with the rectified wave picture of Figure 5-2B.

5-4   VOLTAGE OF HALF-WAVE AND FULL-WAVE RECTIFIERS

In the half-wave rectifier, the entire transformer secondary delivers voltage to the tube and load. In the full-wave rectifier, only one-half of the transformer secondary delivers voltage to a conducting tube and load at any one time. A full-wave rectifier delivers one half of the total transformer secondary voltage to the load, as compared to a half-wave rectifier (provided the same transformer is used for both rectifiers).

For example: If the full transformer secondary voltage (A to B) is 400 volts (see Figure 5-3 and 5-4), the full 400 volts will appear across the load of the half-wave rectifier; whereas only 200 volts will appear across the load in the full-wave rectifier.

5-5 SUMMARY OF RECTIFICATION

(1) A single diode may be used as a half-wave rectifier for converting AC to DC. Only half of the input AC wave is used, and the full voltage of the secondary of the power transformer is obtained as useful DC output.

(2) A double diode may be used as a full-wave rectifier. Both halves of the AC wave are used, and the output voltage is only half of the total transformer secondary voltage.

5-6 FILTERING

Figure 5-6 illustrates the output voltage waveform of a battery. Notice that the voltage output remains constant. It does not vary with time. The output voltage of the battery is pure DC. Remember, this is the type of voltage that the vacuum tubes of a radio require in order to operate properly. Now, look back to Figures 5-2 and 5-5 which show the output wave shapes of a half-wave and full-wave rectifier system. Compare these wave shapes to that of the battery output wave shape.

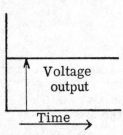

Figure 5-6. Pure DC.

It is evident that the output of the rectifier systems is far from being pure DC. The output is actually a pulsating DC, or a DC with a superimposed AC wave called a ripple. If we could somehow remove or filter out the AC component from the pulsating DC, we would end up with a straight line or pure DC. Since we are striving to get a pure DC output from our rectifier systems, it is obvious that we are going to have to remove the ripple from the output waveform. The method of removing the ripple from the DC output is known as FILTERING. The device which does the filtering is called a FILTER.

The output waveform of the rectifier is actually a combination of DC plus a ripple. The DC and the ripple are called the COMPONENTS of the pulsating wave shape. The ripple is known as the AC component.

5-7 RIPPLE FREQUENCY

The ripple has a very definite fundamental frequency. Examination of Figure 5-2 should indicate to you that the ripple frequency for a half-wave rectifier is the same as the line frequency or 60 cycles per second. Recall the definition of frequency, which is the number of times a wave shape repeats itself in one second. Examination of Figure 5-5 should also indicate to you that the ripple frequency for a full-wave rectifier is twice the line frequency or 120 cycles per second.

5-8 THE FILTERING SYSTEM

Filtering out the ripple component is accomplished by connecting a filter system to the output of the rectifier tube. A filter system is a circuit consisting of capacitors and inductors. The capacitors are known as filter capacitors, and the inductors are known as filter chokes. A rectifier system in combination with a filter system which provides a source of pure DC voltage, is known as a POWER SUPPLY.

5-9 CAPACITOR INPUT FILTER

Figure 5-7 shows a capacitor input filter system connected to the output of a full-wave rectifier. The filter is enclosed within the dotted line. The filter is recognized as a capacitor input filter because the filter component nearest to the rectifier is a capacitor, C_1. The complete filter is given the name π filter. π is a Greek letter pronounced pi. The π filter is the one most commonly found in radio receivers today. Notice that the filaments of the rectifier tubes are heated by means of a low voltage (usually 5 or 6 volts) filament winding on the transformer secondary.

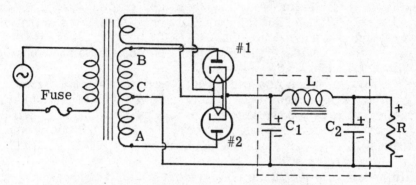

Figure 5-7. Full-wave rectifier circuit.

The filter operates to remove the AC component in the following manner: Point B in Figure 5-8 illustrates the rectified wave shape at the input to the filter. Remember that

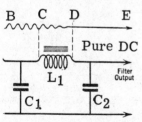

Figure 5-8. Filtering.

this wave is a combination of a DC voltage and an AC ripple component. Now, C_1 is a very high capacitance capacitor of about 20 µf. A 20 µf capacitor has a very low reactance to a 120 cps. ripple component. It will, therefore, short-circuit or by-pass most of the ripple component. The DC voltage, on the other hand, is not affected by the presence of capacitor C_1. Remember that a capacitor acts like an open-circuit to a DC voltage. We say that a capacitor blocks DC. Point C shows the resulting wave shape after it is acted upon by capacitor C_1. Notice that some of the ripple still remains superimposed on the DC wave. The choke, L_1, has a very low DC resistance. The DC will, therefore, pass right through L_1 without any opposition. The choke will, however, generate a very strong counter EMF to oppose the AC ripple. The result is that practically all of the remaining ripple will be prevented from

85

passing through the choke. The wave shape appearing on the other side of the choke is shown at point D. The wave shape is practically pure DC with just a very slight ripple remaining. Capacitor C_2 acts in exactly the same manner as C_1. It will short circuit the remaining ripple, leaving just the pure DC as illustrated at point E. The pure DC voltage can now be satisfactorily applied to the vacuum tubes for their proper operation. The DC voltage which is applied to the vacuum tubes is known as the B+ VOLTAGE.

5-10 VOLTAGE REGULATION

The load current is the current that is drawn from the power supply by the vacuum tubes of the receiver or transmitter. If the load current varies, the B+ voltage will also vary. The B+ voltage is at a maximum when the load current is zero. As the load on the power supply increases, the B+ voltage drops. At full load current, the B+ voltage is at a minimum. A good power supply is one whose B+ voltage varies very little under varying load conditions. We say that such a power supply has good VOLTAGE REGULATION. A power supply with poor voltage regulation is one whose B+ voltage varies considerably with changes in load conditions.

The vacuum tubes in a radio receiver draw a constant load current from the power supply. A receiver power supply is, therefore, not required to have good voltage regulation characteristics. A transmitter, on the other hand, presents a varying load to the power supply. The transmitter power supply should, therefore, have good voltage regulation characteristics.

In order to improve the voltage regulation of a power supply, a resistor is often bridged across the output capacitor C_2, as shown in Figure 5-7. This resistor is known as a BLEEDER RESISTOR. A bleeder resistor improves the voltage regulation by acting as a minimum load for the power supply. It also serves to discharge the filter capacitors when the power is turned off.

The bleeder resistor may also be used as a voltage divider to supply different voltages for use in the receiver or transmitter.

5-11 ADVANTAGES OF FULL-WAVE OVER HALF-WAVE RECTIFICATION

A filter system will do a better job of filtering for a full-wave rectifier system than for a half-wave rectifier. Capacitors C_1 and C2 in the π filter are more effective for filtering if their reactances are as low as possible. Recall the formula for capacitive reactance:

$$X_c = \frac{1}{2 \pi fc}, \text{ as given in Section 3-25.}$$

From this formula, we see that the higher the frequency, the lower the capacitor reactance. The ripple frequency for a full-wave rectifier of 120 cps. is twice that of a half-wave rectifier of 60 cps. The reactances of C_1 and C_2 will be one-half as much at 120 cps. as compared to what they would be at 60 cps. X_{C1} and X_{C2} will, therefore, more effectively by-pass a 120 cps. ripple than a 60 cps. ripple.

Also note that the counter EMF, or opposition of the choke, will be twice as great at 120 cps. as compared to its opposition at 60 cps. This is because the reactance of an inductance is directly proportional to the frequency: $(X_L = 2\pi fL)$.

5-12 THE BRIDGE CONNECTED, FULL-WAVE RECTIFIER

The main disadvantage of full-wave rectification as compared to half-wave rectification, is that only half of the transformer secondary voltage is converted into useful DC voltage.

For example: If a center-tapped transformer has a full secondary voltage of 500 volts, the output voltage of a half-wave rectifier connected across the entire transformer would be 500 volts; whereas the output of a full-wave rectifier would be only 250 volts. We would like to be able to use the full-wave rectifier principle and still be able to convert the full transformer secondary voltage into useful DC output. How then can we modify the full-wave rectifier circuit in Figure 5-7 to accomplish this? Figure 5-9 shows how this can be done. The circuit is known as a BRIDGE CONNECTED FULL-WAVE RECTIFIER.

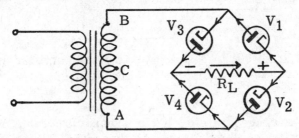

Figure 5-9. Bridge connected full-wave rectifier.

The system uses four rectifier tubes. The plate of V_1 and the cathode of V_3 are connected to the top of the transformer secondary (point B). The plate of V_2 and the cathode of V_4 are connected to the bottom of the transformer secondary (point A). Notice that the center-tap connection, point C, is NOT used.

The bridge type of rectification operates as follows: When the top of the transformer secondary is positive, the plate of V_1 and the cathode of V_3 are positive; whereas, the plate of V_2 and the cathode of V_4 are negative. V_3 and V_2 will be cut off and V_1 and V_4 will conduct. The current flows from the bottom of the transformer, through V_4, into the load resistor R_L through V_1, and back to the top of the transformer. Thus the full secondary voltage is impressed across the load resistor. When the polarity of the AC voltage reverses, the bottom of the transformer now becomes positive. V_1 and V_4 are now cut off and V_3 and V_2 conduct. The current flows from the top of the transformer through V_3, into the load resistor R_L, through V_2 and back to the bottom of the transformer. Again the full secondary voltage is impressed across the load. Notice that the current flows in the same direction through the load resistor during both halves of the

AC cycle.

A bridge type full-wave rectifier combines the advantages of a full-wave and a half-wave rectifier as indicated below:

1) the ripple frequency is 120 cps. and, therefore, is easy to filter out.

2) the DC output voltage is the same as the output of a half-wave rectifier (assuming we use the same transformer).

Therefore, if a full-wave rectifier is converted to a bridge rectifier (using the same transformer), filter capacitors of twice the working voltage rating would be required.

Figure 5-10 illustrates the bridge-connected full-wave rectifier of Figure 5-9, using solid state diodes instead of vacuum tubes.

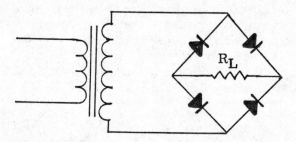

Figure 5-10. A bridge-connected rectifier circuit
using solid state diodes.

5-13 THE ELECTROLYTIC CAPACITOR

The average value of a filter capacitor for a receiver lies in the range between 4 and 50 µf. At these high values of capacity, the ordinary paper or mica capacitor would be too large for practical use. A special type of capacitor, called an ELECTROLYTIC CAPACITOR, was designed to have a large value of capacity in a small size container. The electrolytic capacitor depends on a chemical action to produce a very thin film of oxide which forms the dielectric.

All electrolytic capacitors are polarized; that is, they have a positive and negative terminal. The positive terminal must always be connected to the positive DC voltage point in the circuit, and the negative must similarly be connected to a negative DC point. If these rules are not observed, the capacitor will short-circuit under operation and will have to be replaced. The short-circuit may also damage the rectifier tube.

The principle disadvantage of the electrolytic capacitor is its comparatively short life and its high leakage current. A capacitor is said to have leakage when a small value of DC current flows through its dielectric. In other words, the dielectric is not an absolutely perfect insulator. A good electrolytic capacitor will have a low value of leakage current never exceeding 3 or 4 ma. at its rated working voltage. Electrolytic capacitors are used chiefly in power supplies where leakage current is not important.

The working voltage of an electrolytic capacitor should never be exceeded under actual operation as the capacitor may break down and short-circuit.

5-14 THE FILTER CAPACITOR IN A TRANSMITTER POWER SUPPLY

The filter capacitors in a transmitter power supply require a higher working voltage than those used in a receiver power supply. For example, a 1000 volt transmitter power supply requires a filter capacitor with a working voltage higher than 1000 volts. It is impractical to design an electrolytic capacitor with a working voltage much above 600 volts. Therefore, the only capacitor that can be used in the above example would have to be either of a paper, oil-filled or pyranol dielectric type. Filter capacitors used in transmitter power supplies are generally between 2 and 4 µf.

5-15 FILTER CAPACITORS CONNECTED IN SERIES

Filter capacitors are often connected in series to double their total voltage rating. For example, Figure 5-11 illustrates a half-wave power supply with two 400 volt filter capacitors in series. The two capacitors in series can stand a total voltage of 800 volts. Since the two capacitors are in series, their total capacity is 2 µf. (see Section 3-21). The resistors which are connected across the capacitors are called balancing or EQUALIZING resistors. Their purpose is to equalize the DC voltage drop across the different capacitors. If the equalizing resistors are removed, unequal voltage drops may result across the series capacitors, due to either unequal capacities or unequal leakage resistances. This may result in too great a voltage stress across one of the series capacitors, causing it to break down. For example, if the equalizing resistors are removed, capacitor C_1 may have 500 volts across its plates and therefore, capacitor C_2 will have 300 volts across its plates. Since 500 volts exceeds the working voltage of capacitor C_1, it will break down. Inserting equalizing resistors into the circuit will insure that only 400 volts will build up across each capacitor. The equalizing resistors also serve to discharge the filter capacitors when power is removed from the set.

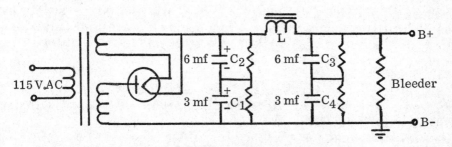

Figure 5-11. Half-wave rectifier.

5-16 THE SHORT-CIRCUITED FILTER CAPACITOR

If capacitor C_1 of Figure 5-7 shorts, the rectifier tube will conduct excessive current. As a result, the safety fuse, in series with the primary of the power transformer, will blow. The fuse acts as a protective device for the components in the rectifier circuit against damage due to the large current flow. If there is no fuse, the plates of the vacuum type rectifier tube will become red hot due to the bombardment of the plate by the large electron flow. The tube will become damaged and will have to be replaced. The primary or secondary windings of the transformer may also burn out due to the excessive current.

If capacitor C_2 in Figure 5-7 were to short, the rectifier tube will conduct very heavily through the choke coil. The choke coil may therefore burn out, in addition to the above-mentioned components.

If either C_1 or C_2 shorts, there obviously will be no B+ voltage and the radio or transmitter will not function.

5-17 THE FILTER CHOKE

Filter chokes in a receiver power supply run from 10 to 30 henries. Chokes are designed to have as low a DC resistance as possible. As a consequence, the DC voltage drop across the choke will be low; and, therefore, the remaining B+ voltage will be as high as possible.

5-18 THE SWINGING CHOKE

The ordinary filter choke, just described, is suitable for receiver power supplies which supply a constant load current. Transmitter power supplies, however, supply a varying load current to the transmitter tubes. If an ordinary choke is used in a transmitter power supply, the B+ voltage will be found to vary as the load current varies. This results in poor voltage regulation, which is highly undesirable. We must use a special choke which will operate to improve the voltage regulation of the transmitter power supply. This special choke is called a SWINGING CHOKE. A swinging choke has a very small air gap cut into the core material. The air gap causes the inductance of the choke to vary with the load current. As the load current increases, the inductance decreases; and, as the load current decreases, the inductance increases. This variable inductance characteristic improves the voltage regulation of the power supply by keeping the B+ voltage constant. Swinging chokes are used only where large load current changes take place - such as in transmitters.

5-19 THE CHOKE INPUT FILTER

Figure 5-12A illustrates a filter using a choke (L_1) as its first component after the rectifier tube. This type of filter is called a CHOKE INPUT FILTER.

A choke input filter (Figure 5-12A) has the following characteristics as compared to a capacitor input filter (Figure 5-12B).

1. The output voltage is less than that of the capacitor input

90

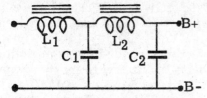

Figure 5-12A. Choke input.

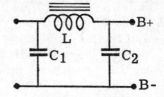

Figure 5-12B. Capacitor input.

filter system.

2. The voltage regulation is superior to that of a capacitor input filter. The input filter choke (L_1) of a well regulated transmitter power supply should be a swinging choke. The second choke (L_2) can be of the ordinary type.

5-20 SUMMARY OF FILTERING ACTION

1. Filtering smooths out the ripple in a rectified DC wave.

2. A capacitor input filter is used when a high output voltage is desired, and where regulation is not too important. Receiver power supplies almost always use capacitor input filters.

3. A choke input filter is used where regulation is of first importance - as in a transmitter power supply.

4. Improvement in regulation can be obtained by connecting a resistor across the filter output terminals. (See Figure 5-7). This resistor is known as a bleeder because it discharges or "bleeds" the charged filter capacitors after the power is shut off. The bleeder may also be used as a voltage divider to obtain various voltages for different applications in the receiver.

5. The output ripple frequency of a half-wave system is equal to the line frequency of 60 cps. The ripple frequency for the full-wave rectifier is double the line frequency, or 120 cps. For equal filtering action, the filter capacitors in a half-wave power supply should have a higher capacity than the filter capacitors in a full-wave power supply.

5-21 THE MERCURY VAPOR RECTIFIER

In previous discussions (Lesson 4, Paragraph 6), the rectifier tube was considered a short circuit when conducting. Actually, this is not the case. When a high vacuum rectifier tube conducts, it has a fairly constant internal resistance of 100 ohms or so. This internal resistance remains constant; it does not change with fluctuations in load current. The voltage drop across the tube, however, does change. As the load current increases, the voltage drop across the tube increases. As the load current decreases, the voltage drop across the tube decreases. This varying tube voltage drop will, in turn, cause the B+ voltage to vary. The result is that a high vacuum rectifier system under varying load conditions will have poor regulation. It is, therefore, desirable to use a rectifier tube with a constant voltage drop, regardless of fluctuations in load current. A

MERCURY VAPOR RECTIFIER TUBE fulfills this requirement. It differs from a high vacuum rectifier tube in that it has mercury gas enclosed in the glass envelope.

The theory of conduction in a mercury vapor tube is as follows: The space between the cathode and plate is filled with mercury vapor atoms. An electron traveling at high speed from the cathode to the positive plate, will hit a mercury atom with great force. The tremendous impact will cause an electron to be knocked out of the structure of the mercury atom. This electron will be attracted to the positive plate, just as if it had been emitted by the cathode. The result is that for every emitted electron that crashes into a mercury atom, two electrons will end up at the plate. As the load current increases, the cathode current of the mercury vapor tube increases. The increased cathode current will produce many more electrons by atom bombardment of the mercury gas. The resulting large increase in the number of electrons flowing to the plate causes the internal resistance of the tube to drop. We say that the CONDUCTIVITY of the tube has increased. The final result is that as the load current increases, the internal resistance of the tube decreases. The product of an increasing current and a decreasing resistance is a constant voltage drop across the tube. This will produce a constant B+ voltage, regardless of load current changes. The voltage drop across most mercury vapor tubes is a constant 15 volts. This constant voltage characteristic of the mercury vapor rectifier tube greatly improves the regulation of the rectifier system.

When a mercury atom loses an electron by bombardment, it becomes IONIZED. The atom is now called a POSITIVE ION. IONIZATION is caused by the bombardment of mercury atoms by high velocity electrons. Ionization is accompanied by a characteristic bright blue glow of the mercury vapor gas.

The filaments of a mercury vapor tube must be heated for at least one minute before the plate voltage is turned on. This allows any liquid mercury that may have condensed on the walls and on the filaments to vaporize. If the filament and plate voltages are turned on at the same time, the heavy positive mercury ions will bombard and possibly ruin the cathode. If the filament is turned on before the plate voltage, there will be a sufficient number of electrons to neutralize the ions and eliminate the possibility of damage to the cathode by ion bombardment.

It is important to maintain proper filament operating temperature. A high filament voltage increases ionization and reduces tube life, while a low voltage produces overloading. The mercury vapor tube is used in transmitter power supplies because of its high current load capabilities and excellent voltage regulation.

5-22 INVERSE PEAK VOLTAGE

A rectifier does not conduct during one-half of the input AC cycle. The plate is then negative with respect to the cathode. During this non-conducting time, there will be a high negative voltage on the plate. Figure 5-13 illustrates a half-wave capacitor input rectifier during the half cycle when it is not conducting. The voltage across

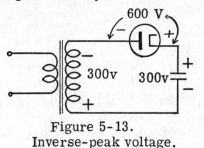

Figure 5-13.
Inverse-peak voltage.

the transformer secondary is 300 volts peak, and the input capacitor is charged up to 300 volts. Notice that the two voltages are in series and in phase across the rectifier tube. The maximum voltage between the plate and cathode during non-conduction is 600 volts. This voltage is called the INVERSE PEAK VOLTAGE. If this inverse voltage exceeds the rating given by the manufacturer, there is a great danger of an arc-back occurring between the two elements. A tube can be ruined in this fashion. High vacuum tubes have a higher peak inverse voltage rating than mercury vapor types. This is an advantage which allows them to be used at higher relative voltages, as compared to the mercury vapor type. Due to the low peak inverse voltage rating for mercury vapor tubes, choke input filter systems are necessary. The input choke clips the peak of the AC wave and thus prevents the inverse peak voltage from rising too high. The input choke also limits the initial current surge, thus preventing damage to the filaments.

5-23 RADIO FREQUENCY INTERFERENCE

Gaseous rectifier tubes tend to produce radio frequency interference. This radio frequency interference is called HASH. Hash can be minimized by enclosing the rectifier tube in a grounded shield can and connecting a radio frequency choke in series with the rectifier plate lead at the tube socket. Hash capacitors can also be connected across the transformer secondary. Their purpose is to bypass the RF interference to ground.

5-24 COMPARISON OF MERCURY VAPOR TUBE AND HIGH VACUUM RECTIFIER TUBE

Listed below is a comparison of the characteristics of the mercury vapor and high vacuum rectifiers:

HIGH VACUUM: (1) Poor regulation. (2) Filament and plate voltage can be turned on at the same time. (3) A high peak inverse voltage rating.
MERCURY VAPOR: (1) Excellent regulation. (2) Filaments must be turned on at least 60 seconds before the plate voltage. (3) A lower peak inverse voltage rating.

5-1* A rectifier is used to:
   a. change DC to AC
   b. change AC to DC
   c. increase the ripple frequency
   d. improve voltage regulation

5-2 A swinging choke:
   a. is used in a power supply which supplies a fixed load
   b. is used mostly in receiver power supplies
   c. tends to keep the output voltage constant with varying load
   d. has a high capacity

5-3 The ripple frequency of a full-wave rectifier system is:
   a. the same as that of a half-wave rectifier system
   b. twice that of a half-wave rectifier system
   c. one-half that of a half-wave rectifier system
   d. 60 cycles per second

5-4 A mercury vapor rectifier has:
   a. a constant internal voltage drop
   b. a very high internal voltage drop
   c. a higher internal voltage drop than a high vacuum rectifier
   d. no internal voltage drop

5-5 A mercury vapor rectifier has a:
   a. constant current rating
   b. high internal voltage drop
   c. high inverse peak voltage rating
   d. relatively high current rating

5-6 A mercury vapor rectifier:
   a. is always connected to a capacitor input filter
   b. should be connected to a choke input filter
   c. does not require a filter
   d. none of the above

5-7 The purpose of a filter in a plate power supply system is to:
   a. provide AC voltage
   b. filter out the DC component
   c. smooth out the AC ripple component in the output
   d. limit the peak inverse voltage

5-8 A shorted filter capacitor in an unfused power supply would:
   a. increase the DC voltage
   b. half the ripple frequency
   c. increase the output current
   d. probably burn out the rectifier tube

94

5-9 A bleeder resistor:
   a. improves voltage regulation
   b. improves ripple frequency
   c. should be replaced
   d. is very critical

5-10 If the primary of a 60 cycle power transformer were connected to DC mains:
   a. the output would be pure DC
   b. the primary winding would most probably burn out
   c. the DC output would decrease
   d. the ripple frequency would increase

5-11 A choke input filter, compared to a capacitor input filter, will:
   a. provide a higher output voltage
   b. limit the DC voltage
   c. cause a higher ripple frequency
   d. provide the best voltage regulation

5-12 The purpose of equalizing resistors is to:
   a. improve the voltage regulation
   b. equalize the DC drop across the different filter capacitors connected in series
   c. limit the ripple voltage
   d. prevent an arc-back

5-13 In a mercury vapor rectifier system:
   a. the filament and plate voltages may be applied simultaneously
   b. the plate voltage must always be turned on first
   c. the filament voltage must always be turned on first
   d. the filament voltage is turned on 10 seconds after the plate voltage

5-14 A filter choke with a low DC resistance is desirable in a power supply because:
   a. the ripple frequency is decreased
   b. the voltage regulation is made worse
   c. the output voltage is increased
   d. the peak inverse voltage is increased

5-15 The visible operating characteristic of mercury vapor rectifiers is:
   a. a bluish-green glow   c. green cathode
   b. red plates   d. hot anode

5-16* Which of the following capacitor types has the largest capacity in a small physical area?
   a. mica   c. electrolytic
   b. paper   d. equalizing

SECTION II – LESSON 6
TRIODE, TETRODE, PENTODE
AND TRANSISTORS

6-1 INTRODUCTION

Lessons 4 and 5 covered the construction and purpose of a diode vacuum tube. We studied the action of the diode vacuum tube as a rectifier in changing alternating current to direct current. We will now go into the details of the operation of the vacuum tube when used as an amplifier. An amplifier makes larger, or amplifies, the small voltages that are present in the radio receiver. The vacuum tubes that are used for amplification purposes are three, four and five element tubes. The three element tube is called a TRIODE; four and five element tubes are called TETRODES and PENTODES respectively. We shall now proceed to study each one of these tubes in detail.

6-2 THE TRIODE

The TRIODE is different from the diode in that it contains one more element. This new element is called the CONTROL GRID. The control grid is a thin piece of wire wound in the form of a spiral mesh which surrounds the cathode. Electrons emitted by the cathode can pass easily through the grid structure and onto the plate. Figure 6-1A shows the actual physical arrangement of the cathode, grid and plate structure in a typical triode. Notice that the grid is placed much closer to the cathode than to the plate.

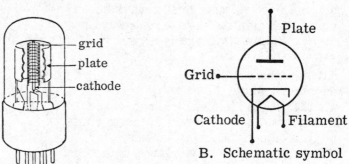

grid
plate
cathode

Plate

Grid

Cathode   Filament

B. Schematic symbol

A. Cut away section of a triode

Figure 6-1. The triode.

Figure 6-1B illustrates the schematic representation of the triode. The grid is shown by means of a dotted line between the cathode and plate.

6-3 OPERATION OF A TRIODE

Figure 6-2 shows a triode circuit which is used to study the effect of grid voltage variations upon the plate current. The symbol for the plate voltage is E_p. The plate voltage is measured between the plate and cathode. The symbol for plate current is I_p. Plate current is measured by placing an ammeter in series with the plate circuit. E_g is the symbol for control grid voltage, measured between the control grid and the cathode. All tube voltage measurements are taken with the cathode as a reference point.

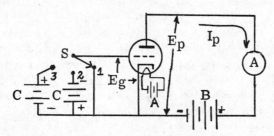

Figure 6-2. Effect of grid voltage on plate current flow.

Note the letters A, B and C that are near the battery symbols in the diagram (Figure 6-2). These letters indicate the voltages applied to the different elements in the tube. The "A" voltage is applied to the heater or filament. The "B" voltage is applied to the plate; the "C" voltage is applied to the grid. "S" is a three-position switch in the control grid circuit. With the switch in position #1, the control grid is connected directly to the cathode. With the switch in position #2, the control grid is connected to the negative terminal of the battery. With the switch in position #3, the control grid is connected to the positive terminal of a battery. Let us see how changes in the control grid voltage affect the operation of the triode. With the switch in position #1 and the plate positive, electrons will flow from the cathode through the grid structure to the plate. Since the grid is connected directly to the cathode, it will not affect the flow of plate current. Therefore, all the emitted electrons will pass through the grid and onto the plate.

If the switch is thrown to position #2, the grid becomes negative with respect to the cathode. The negatively charged grid will repel

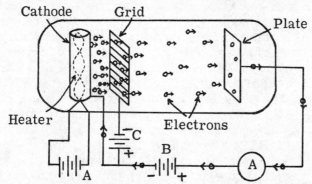

Figure 6-3. Effect of negative grid on plate current flow.

many of the negatively charged electrons back into the area surrounding the cathode. Hence, the number of electrons which are able to reach the plate is reduced. This effect is illustrated in Figure 6-3. The milliammeter in the plate circuit will show a reduction in plate current when the grid voltage is changed from a zero voltage to a negative voltage.

If the switch is thrown to position #3, the grid becomes positive with respect to the cathode. The plate current will increase since the positive control grid attracts the negative electrons and allows many more electrons to be drawn to the plate than it did in switch position #1 and #2. A positive grid actually pulls electrons from the cathode to the plate. Thus, we see how the control grid acts as a control valve for plate current flow. As we vary the voltage on the grid, the plate current varies. The control grid, therefore, controls the flow of electrons to the plate.

6-4   PLATE CURRENT - GRID VOLTAGE CURVE

In order to further study the relationship between the plate current and the grid voltage, let us take measurements to see exactly how the plate current varies with changes in the grid voltage. Figure 6-4 illustrates a schematic of a triode whose grid voltage can be varied by means of a potentiometer placed across the "C" battery. Let us plot on a graph the milliammeter plate current readings for different values of grid voltage. Figure 6-5 illustrates the resulting graph. The horizontal line represents the grid voltage in volts, and the vertical line represents the plate current in milliamperes. The plate current measurements are taken with the plate voltage kept constant at 150 volts. If we draw a line through the points that represent the various plate current readings, we obtain a curve known as the E_g-I_p characteristic curve. Notice that if the grid is made sufficiently negative (minus 10 volts), the plate current drops to zero. At this point, the highly negative grid repels all electrons back to the cathode area. As the grid voltage is made less negative, the electrons begin to flow to the plate. If we continue to make the grid voltage less negative (more positive), the plate current will continue to increase. When we make the grid voltage positive, the plate current keeps on increasing. As the grid voltage is made more positive, the plate current continues to rise. A point is soon reached where the plate current can no longer increase, regardless of further increases in positive grid voltage. This point is called the SATURATION POINT. The voltage that is applied to the grid is called GRID BIAS VOLTAGE, or simply BIAS. The BIAS that cuts the plate current to zero is called the CUT-OFF BIAS. In Figure 6-5, the cut-off bias is -10 volts. Whenever the voltage on the grid prevents current from flowing, we say that we have a BLOCKED GRID.

The curve of Figure 6-5 was obtained with the plate voltage held constant. Suppose we take data of grid voltage and plate current readings for different values of plate voltage. The result of plotting all

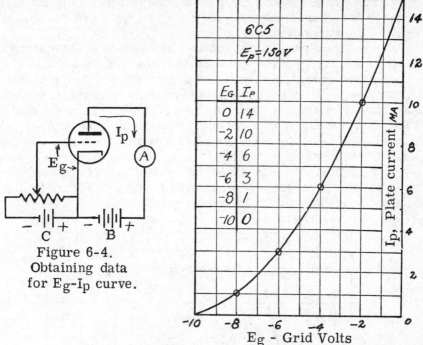

E_G	I_P
0	14
-2	10
-4	6
-6	3
-8	1
-10	0

6C5
$E_p = 150V$

E_g - Grid Volts

Figure 6-5. Grid voltage, plate current curve.

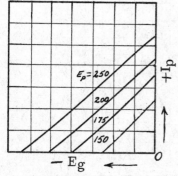

Figure 6-4.
Obtaining data
for E_g-I_p curve.

Figure 6-6. Family of E_g-I_p curves.

these points is a series of curves called a FAMILY OF CURVES. This is illustrated in Figure 6-6. Each curve is plotted with the grid voltage varied, while the plate voltage is kept constant. Notice that for a given grid voltage, the plate current increases with increases in plate voltage. This is to be expected since an increase in plate voltage should result in an increase in plate current.

6-5   THE E_p-I_p CHARACTERISTIC CURVE FOR THE TRIODE

In Figure 6-5, the plate voltage was kept constant and plate current readings were plotted as we varied the grid voltage. Another popular characteristic curve is the E_p-I_p curves of Figure 6-7. Here, the grid voltage is kept constant and plate current readings are plotted as we vary the plate voltage. Notice that the plate current rises as the plate voltage increases. The E_p-I_p curves are the ones that are usually illustrated in tube manuals.

6-6   THE TRIODE AS AN AMPLIFIER

In Paragraph 6-1, it was stated that multi-element tubes are used to amplify weak signals. We will now proceed to study the exact manner in which a triode tube amplifies a signal voltage that is applied to its control grid.

The control grid is physically much closer to the cathode than the plate is. The grid voltage will, therefore, have a greater effect on the plate current than will the plate voltage. A small change in grid voltage will cause a large change in plate current; whereas, a small change in plate voltage causes a small change in current. Let us see, graphically, how a changing voltage such as an AC signal on the grid of a triode, causes the plate current to vary. Figure 6-8 illustrates a triode whose plate is connected to a fixed B+ voltage. The grid is in series with an AC generator and a fixed bias voltage. The total voltage between the grid and cathode will always be the sum of the signal voltage and the bias voltage.

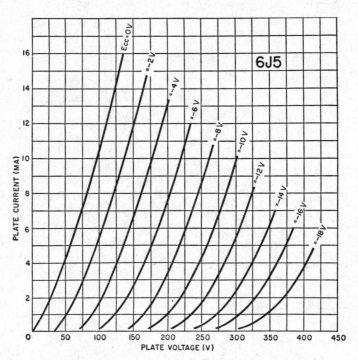

Figure 6-7. Family of Ep-Ip curves.

Let us see what happens on the positive half-cycle of the AC signal. Since the signal voltage of +1 volt and the -3 volts of bias are in series, the resultant voltage between grid and cathode will be -2 volts. (The sum of +1 and -3 = -2). On the negative half of the AC cycle, -4 volts will be applied between the grid and cathode of the tube. (The sum of -1 volt and -3 volts = -4 volts). From the I_p-E_g curve of Figure 6-9, it can be seen that when there is no AC signal applied to the grid, the plate current will be fixed at 8 milliamperes because of the three volts of bias supplied by the bias battery. The

100

value of 8 milliamperes is obtained from the curve by working vertically from the -3 volt point on the grid voltage line until the curve is reached. From this point we go straight across until we hit the vertical plate current line. In this case, we reach the vertical line at 8 milliamperes. On the peak of the positive half of the AC signal (when there are -2 volts on the grid), the plate current rises to 10 milliamperes. On the negative half of the incoming signal (when there are -4 volts on the grid), the plate current decreases to 6 milliamperes. Note that the waveform of the plate current variation is an exact reproduction of the AC signal applied to the grid of the tube. A 2 milliampere variation is caused in the plate current by applying a one volt signal to the grid.

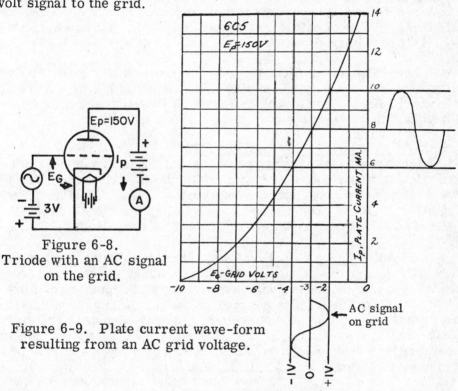

Figure 6-8.
Triode with an AC signal
on the grid.

Figure 6-9. Plate current wave-form
resulting from an AC grid voltage.

Thus far, we have converted grid voltage variations into plate current variations. In order to make use of these plate current variations, some device must be placed in the plate circuit to act as a load across which the varying plate current will develop a varying voltage. The plate load may be a resistor, an inductor or a tuned circuit. Figure 6-10 shows a resistor used as a plate load in a triode amplifier circuit. Except for the plate load resistor, this circuit is the same as that in Figure 6-8. As we explained before, the 1 volt signal will cause a total plate current variation of 4 milliamperes (from 6 to 10 ma.). This 4 ma. variation will cause a total voltage variation of 40 volts to be produced across the 10,000 ohm resistor. This can easily be proven by Ohm's law. One form of Ohm's law

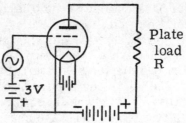

Figure 6-10.   Triode using a resistor as a plate load.

states that: E = IxR   E = .004 x 10, 000   E = 40V.
Thus it can be seen that a 2 volt AC signal (2 volts peak to peak) can produce a 40 volt variation in the plate circuit. In other words, the original signal or variation that was applied to the grid has been AMPLIFIED twenty times. $(\frac{40}{2} = 20)$

From Figure 6-9 it can be seen that the voltage variation in the plate circuit is not only an amplified, but also a faithful reproduction of the grid signal. The circuit in Figure 6-10 is, therefore, the basis for all amplification circuits in radio and television.

6-7   VACUUM TUBE CHARACTERISTICS

Since many different types of vacuum tubes are used in radio and television circuits, it is important to classify tubes according to the performance which may be expected of them. The three most important factors by which tubes are classified are the AMPLIFICATION FACTOR, the TRANSCONDUCTANCE and the PLATE RESISTANCE.

1. AMPLIFICATION FACTOR. The amplification factor of a tube is the maximum voltage amplification which can be expected from the tube. It is a theoretical value never reached in actual circuit use. Stated mathematically, it is the ratio of the change in plate voltage to the change in grid voltage; both voltages to cause the same change in plate current. For example, let us assume that a certain tube is operating with a plate voltage of 250 volts, a grid voltage of -10 volts and a plate current of 18 ma. If we should change the plate voltage to 280 volts and leave the grid voltage constant, the plate current would go up to 23 ma. This means that a plate voltage change of 30 volts results in a plate current change of 5 ma. Suppose that a grid voltage change from -10 volts to -13 volts returns the plate current from 23 ma. back to 18 ma. We can say that a grid voltage change of 3 volts has the same effect on the plate current as a plate voltage change of 30 volts. The amplification factor would, therefore, be the plate voltage change (30 volts) divided by the grid voltage change (3 volts) or 10.

The amplification factor is commonly designated by the Greek letter μ. The formula for the μ, or mu, of a tube is:

6-1) Amplification factor $(\mu) = \dfrac{\Delta E_p}{\Delta E_g}$

102

The terms ΔE_p and ΔE_g mean a small change in plate voltage and a small change in grid voltage, respectively.

2. <u>TRANSCONDUCTANCE</u>. The transconductance, or mutual conductance of a tube is what is known as the figure of merit of the tube. It tells us how much of a plate current variation we can get for a certain amount of grid voltage variation. Transconductance is defined as the ratio of a small change in plate current to the change in grid voltage that produced it. The formula for transconductance is:

6-2) Transconductance $(G_m) = \dfrac{\Delta I_p}{\Delta E_g}$

Where: ΔI_p is a change in plate current
ΔE_g is the change in grid voltage that caused ΔI_p
G_m is the symbol for transconductance.

The basic unit of the transconductance of a tube is the MHO. The mho was previously mentioned in Lesson 1, Paragraph 7, as the unit of conductance. Since the transconductance of a tube is equal to current divided by voltage, (see Formula 6-2) which is the opposite or reciprocal of resistance, then the mho is the unit to be used for the G_m of a tube. The transconductance is the most desirable tube factor in the choice of a vacuum tube to be used as a voltage amplifier.

3. <u>PLATE RESISTANCE</u>. The plate resistance of a tube is the internal resistance between the cathode and plate to the flow of varying plate current. Mathematically speaking, it is the ratio of a small change in plate voltage to the change in plate current that this voltage change produces. Expressed as an equation:

6-3) Plate Resistance $(R_p) = \dfrac{\Delta E_p}{\Delta I_p}$

A tube may be considered to be a variable resistor in its operation as an amplifier. If the grid is made positive, the current flow from cathode to plate is increased. This means that the resistance from the cathode to the plate has gone down. On the other hand, if the grid is made more negative, the plate current will go down. This means, of course, that the plate resistance has gone up.

6-8 EFFICIENCY OF VACUUM TUBES

We often use the term EFFICIENCY when we speak about the performance of a certain device or machine. Efficiency refers to how much power can be gotten out of a device, as compared to how much power is put into it. For instance, if 100 watts of electrical power are used up in a light bulb and only 2 watts of equivalent light power are produced, we can say that the electric bulb is a low efficiency device. The bulb generates into light only 2% of the power that is put into it. (The other 98 watts are dissipated inside the bulb in the form of heat). On the other hand, an electric motor may draw 100 watts of electric power and produce 75 watts of equivalent mechanical power. We can say that the motor is a high efficiency device. The motor produces, in the form of useful work, 75% of the power put into it.

In radio, we classify vacuum tubes according to their efficiency in delivering useful power to a load.

The plate efficiency of a vacuum tube is defined as the ratio of the AC plate power output to the DC plate power input. It is given in a percentage, and its mathematical formula is:

$$6\text{-}4) \quad \text{Plate efficiency} = \frac{\text{AC output power}}{\text{DC input power}} \times 100$$

For example, if the AC power output of a vacuum tube is 150 watts, and the DC power input is 200 watts, the efficiency is 150 divided by 200 or 75%.

The AC power output of a tube is the power in watts that the tube delivers to its load. The load may be the loudspeaker or the grid of a following tube. The DC power input, on the other hand, is the product of the DC plate voltage applied to the stage and the DC plate current. For instance, if the plate voltage is 750 volts and the plate current is 150 milliamperes, then the power input is 112.5 watts. The power input is derived in the following manner:

Power input in watts = E_p x I_p = 750 x .15 = 112.5 watts.

Note that the 150 milliamperes were changed to amperes by moving the decimal three places to the left.

6-9 MAXIMUM PLATE DISSIPATION

In the above problem concerning the plate efficiency of a vacuum tube, it is apparent that only a certain percentage of the applied power (input power) appears as output power. What happened to the remainder of the input power? The remainder of the input power is wasted in the form of heat within the tube, exactly as in a light bulb. Remember that the tube represents a resistance between the cathode and plate. Power loss applied to the resistance of a tube, as well as any ordinary resistor. The plate current, in flowing through the plate resistance, dissipated heat. The power dissipated on the plate in the form of heat is equal to $I_p^2 R_p$. Where I_p is the plate current and R_p is the plate resistance.

There is a limit to the amount of power in watts that a tube can dissipate in the form of heat in its plate without damaging the tube. This limit is known as the MAXIMUM PLATE DISSIPATION. This can be found in any tube manual for a particular tube.

6-10 LIMITATIONS OF A TRIODE

In the early days of radio, triodes were used exclusively in radio receivers and transmitters. Later on the tetrodes and pentodes made their appearance and replaced the triode in many applications. The reason for this change was that the triode had certain characteristics which limited its application in radio work. Before we discuss the tetrode and pentode, we shall first examine in detail the limitations of the triode.

In Lesson 3, Paragraph 16, we learned that two conducting surfaces separated by an insulator form a capacitor. Since the plate and grid of a tube are two conducting surfaces separated by a vacuum dielectric, there exists a capacitance between the plate and grid. By the same reasoning, a capacitor is formed between the grid and cathode, and between the plate and cathode. These internal tube capacitances are called INTERELECTRODE CAPACITANCES. The interelectrode capacitance between the plate and the grid exerts a detrimental effect upon the action of a triode amplifier. This capacitance gives rise to a condition known as OSCILLATION, which is extremely undesirable. Oscillations come about in the following manner: A varying grid voltage causes a varying plate voltage, which is then passed on to the next stage. However, because of the undesirable grid to plate capacitance, the voltage variations from the plate circuit are FED BACK to the grid circuit and are reamplified until oscillations or howling takes place. This is especially true at radio frequencies. Later on, we will discuss this condition of oscillation in greater detail.

Another defect of the triode results from the fact that the plate current depends not only upon the grid voltage, but also upon the plate voltage. Because of this, the gain of a triode, used as an amplifier, is kept down. For example, a positive grid signal will cause the plate current to go up; the increasing I_p will increase the voltage across the load resistor. The voltage across the load resistor and the voltage between plate and cathode are in series and, therefore, must always add up to the fixed B+ voltage value. If the voltage across the load resistor goes up, the plate voltage must go down. The decreased plate voltage, in turn, will cause the plate current to decrease somewhat, counteracting the effect of the signal on the plate current. Thus the amplification is kept down. The way to circumvent this defect would be to make the plate current independent of the plate voltage. Variations in plate voltage would then have no effect on the plate current. This is achieved in the tetrode and pentode.

6-11 THE TETRODE

In an effort to reduce the grid-plate capacitance within the tube, a fourth element was added to the conventional triode. This fourth element is called a SCREEN GRID; the screen grid is placed between

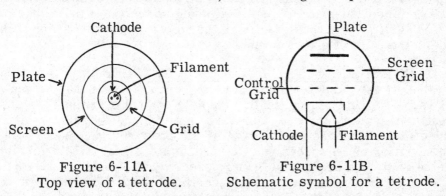

Figure 6-11A.
Top view of a tetrode.

Figure 6-11B.
Schematic symbol for a tetrode.

the control grid and the plate. The top view of a tetrode is shown in Figure 6-11A; the schematic symbol of a tetrode is shown in Figure 6-11B. The screen is wound in the form of a spiral grid, similar to the control grid. The screen grid shields the control grid from the plate and thereby reduces the grid-plate capacitance.

In order for the screen grid to act as an effective shield, it must be grounded for AC. But, as we shall soon see, the screen grid must, at the same time, be kept at a high positive DC potential. Refer to the schematic circuit of a tetrode in Figure 6-12. The screen is grounded for AC through capacitor C. Thus, we can use a tetrode as an RF amplifier without incurring oscillations.

A typical screen grid or tetrode (four elements) tube connected in a circuit is shown in Figure 6-12. The screen grid is operated at a DC potential somewhat lower than that of the plate. The positive screen grid acts like the plate of a triode in attracting electrons emitted by the cathode. A few of the electrons will hit the screen grid, resulting in screen current flow. The screen current flows through resistor R_1. R_1 is called the screen-dropping resistor. The screen current, in flowing through R_1, causes a voltage drop across it. The screen grid voltage is, therefore, the B+ voltage minus the voltage drop across the resistor R_1. The screen voltage is measured from the screen grid to the cathode.

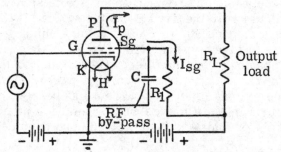

Figure 6-12. Tetrode amplifier circuit.

Since the screen grid is similar to the control grid in construction, most of the electrons will pass through the screen and reach the plate. Since the plate is a solid element and more positive than the screen grid, it will receive most of the electrons emitted by the cathode in the form of plate current.

6-12 INCREASED AMPLIFICATION OF TETRODE

Because the screen grid is closer to the cathode than the plate, the screen grid has practically complete control over the plate current. The plate current is, therefore, not influenced by plate voltage variations. Since the screen is at AC ground potential, there will be no variation in the screen voltage when an AC signal is being applied to the grid. The screen grid, therefore, exerts a constant pull on the electrons that make up the plate current. The only element in the tetrode that causes the plate current to vary is the control grid. The

106

control grid, however, no longer shares its control over the plate current with the plate, as it did in the triode. Small variations of voltage on the control grid will cause the plate current to vary without any interference from a varying plate voltage. The plate resistance and the amplification factor of the tetrode are, as a result, greatly increased.

6-13 THE PENTODE

The introduction of the screen grid in the tetrode successfully reduced the plate-grid capacitance and increased the amplification factor. The tetrode, however, suffers from one important defect. This defect is known as SECONDARY EMISSION. The pentode (five element tube) was developed to overcome the bad effects of secondary emission.

Secondary emission is a condition which arises when high velocity electrons strike a metal object, such as a plate. The force of the impact will cause additional electrons to be knocked out of the atomic structure of the plate. For every electron that strikes the plate, two or three electrons will be knocked out of the plate. In a triode, these secondary emission electrons normally find their way back to the highly positive plate and cause no ill-effect in the operation of the tube. In the tetrode, as long as the plate is more positive than the screen, the secondary emission electrons fall back to the plate and tube operation will be normal. However, if the screen is operated at a high voltage, and a large signal voltage is applied to the control grid, the plate voltage may drop below the screen voltage at the positive peak of the input signal. The result of this lowered plate voltage is to cause the secondary emission electrons to flow to the positive screen grid instead of returning to the plate. Thus, the number of electrons reaching the plate drops, while at the same time, the screen current is increased. This results in a reduction in the amplification of the tube and distortion in its output.

In the pentode, a third grid is placed between the screen grid and the plate. (See Figure 6-13). The third grid is similar in physical construction to the screen grid and the control grid. This third grid is connected to the cathode so that it will be highly negative with respect to the plate and will force the secondary emission electrons

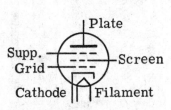

Figure 6-13.
Schematic symbol for pentode.

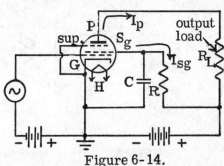

Figure 6-14.
Pentode amplifier circuit.

back to the plate. Because it suppresses secondary emission, the third grid is called the SUPPRESSOR GRID. The negative suppressor grid will not interfere with the flow of electrons from the cathode to the plate, even though it does suppress the secondary electrons coming from the plate. The reason for this is that the electrons from the cathode are traveling at such a high velocity when they reach the vicinity of the suppressor grid, that they go right on through to the highly positive plate. On the other hand, the secondary electrons coming from the plate are moving at a rather low velocity and are easily pushed back to the plate. Figure 6-14 illustrates a pentode hooked up as an amplifier. Note that the only difference between this circuit and the tetrode amplifier circuit of Figure 6-12 is the addition of the suppressor grid.

6-14 THE BEAM POWER TUBE

A beam power tube is a pentode with special construction features. A beam power tube has greater power handling ability than the ordinary tetrode or pentode. With very small grid voltages, a beam power tube can develop large amounts of power in its plate circuit. The tube is, therefore, said to have high power sensitivity.

The beam power tube is constructed so that the individual wire turns of the control grid and the screen grid line up with each other

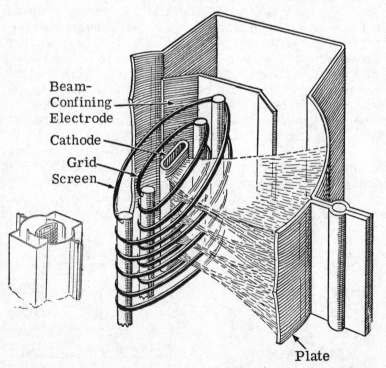

Figure 6-15. The beam power tube. (Courtesy RCA)

108

horizontally. This means that every turn of the screen grid mesh is directly behind a turn of the control grid mesh. Thus, electrons flowing from the cathode travel through the control grid and onto the plate without striking the screen grid. The screen grid current is, therefore, very low and, since the plate gets the electrons which normally would have gone to the screen grid, the plate power output is increased. Because of the physical alignment of the control grid and the screen grid, the electrons flow to the plate in sheets or beams. Figure 6-15 illustrates this condition. To further concentrate and form the heavy beams of plate current, deflecting plates are incorporated into the tube structure. These deflecting plates are placed between the screen grid and the plate, and extend partway around the tube, as shown in Figure 6-15. These beam forming deflecting plates are internally connected to the cathode and therefore, acquire a negative charge with respect to the plate. As a result, the deflecting plates repel the electrons into concentrated, heavy beams of plate current. No actual suppressor grid is necessary because secondary emission from the plate is suppressed by the space charge which forms between the plate and screen grid. The space charge has been indicated by the dashes in Figure 6-15. The space charge of the electron beam is caused by the slowing up of electrons in the area between the screen grid and the plate. By operating the plate of the beam power tube at a lower potential than the screen grid, the plate is made negative with respect to the screen. The electrons are, therefore, slowed down when they pass through the screen on their way to the plate. Stray secondary emission electrons cannot return to the screen grid outside of the beam area because of the beam forming plates. Some beam power tubes use an actual suppressor grid in place of the space charge effect.

The beam power tube has: (1) high power sensitivity (2) high power output, and (3) high plate efficiency.

6-15 THYRATRONS

A THYRATRON is a gas-filled triode or tetrode tube. The thyratron is used to control large amounts of power flow by means of control grid action. When the grid of a thyratron is sufficiently negative, no plate current flows. However, if the bias is lowered to the point where plate current begins, the gas in the tube immediately ionizes and a heavy plate current flows. At this point, the control grid loses control over the plate current. Varying the bias voltage after plate current starts will have no effect on the plate current. The only way to stop the flow of plate current is to remove the plate voltage, or lower it below the ionization potential of the gas. The thyratron grid, therefore, acts as a trigger to turn on relatively large currents in the plate circuit. Thyratrons also function as high voltage rectifiers, such as the 884 and 885 triodes, or the 2D21 tetrode.

6-16 GAS IN A VACUUM TUBE

The thyratron and the mercury vapor rectifier are special type tubes with gas-filled envelopes. The ordinary vacuum type tube is supposed to be free of any gas or air. If a vacuum tube does contain gas which was not excluded during the manufacturing process, it is known as a SOFT tube. The visible indication of a soft tube is a blue or purple haze, sometimes accompanied by a reddened plate. The plate current of a soft tube is excessively high. A soft tube is often erratic in its operation and should be replaced.

Most vacuum tubes contain a GETTER. A getter is a small piece of metal made of barium or some similar chemical. This chemical removes or destroys stray gases that remain in the vacuum tube after the evacuation process.

6-17 THE TRANSISTOR

From what we have learned about tubes in the previous lesson, we know that we can make a diode into a triode by adding a new element called the control grid. This single, added electrode makes a tremendous difference, for the triode tube can amplify, whereas the diode cannot. Thus, it was the triode that advanced receivers from the headphone state to speaker operation.

In a similar manner, semiconductor triodes that amplify can be made from the semiconductor diodes previously described. Figure 6-16 illustrates a pair of P-N diodes placed back to back. The drawing shows that the two diodes have been pushed together.

Combining the two diodes of Figure 6-16 gives us the unit shown in Figure 6-17. We still have our pair of semiconductor diodes because we can divide the combined center or N section into two parts. Figure 6-17 is known as a transistor. The transistor of Figure 6-17 is called a P-N-P type. However, if we go back to our two diodes of Figure 6-16 and turn them around, we can have the two N-sections on the outside and the two P-sections joining each other. In this case, the transistor would be an N-P-N type. Figure 6-18 shows the N-P-N type.

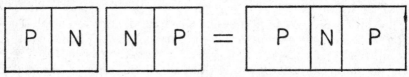

Figure 6-16. Figure 6-17. A P-N-P
Two diodes - A P-N and an N-P. transistor from two diodes.

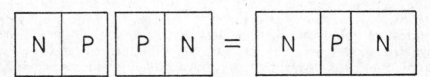

Figure 6-18.
An N-P-N transistor from two diodes.

110

6-18 BIASING THE TRANSISTOR

The DC voltages applied to the transistor are known as bias voltages. Figure 6-19 shows the bias voltages on a P-N-P transistor. Note that we have named the three parts of the transistor -- Emitter, Base and Collector. Their vacuum tube equivalents are Cathode, Control Grid and Plate, respectively.

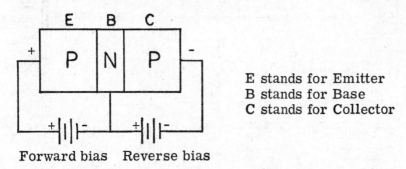

E stands for Emitter
B stands for Base
C stands for Collector

Forward bias   Reverse bias

Figure 6-19. Method of biasing a P-N-P transistor.

Let us consider the voltage on the left hand side P-N section. We have a positive voltage on the emitter and a negative voltage on the base. We have learned in lesson 4 that this is forward biased and a current will flow through this section. From our previous discussion in lesson 4, we can see that the right hand side N-P section is reverse biased and very little current flows in this section.

6-19 THE TRANSISTOR CIRCUIT

Figure 6-20 illustrates the electron flow in a basic N-P-N transistor circuit. Section EB is forward biased, while section BC is reverse biased. Electrons from the negative terminal of battery Ee flow into the emitter. From the emitter it would normally be expected that all the electrons leaving Ee would drift into the P section (the base) and return to the positive terminal of Ee. This does not happen. Very few electrons return to Ee through the base. The reason for this is that the base is actually made up of a very thin slice of P-type material. Therefore, we have very few positive "holes" present. This being the case, there are very few "holes" to combine with the electrons and propel them to the positive terminal of Ee. On the other hand, batteries Ee and Ec are series aiding and they give us a high voltage that forces the electrons from the emitter, through the base (P), into the collector and on to the positive terminal of Ec. The approximate electron distribution is shown in percentages in Figure 6-20.

It is important to note that while very little current goes into the base to return to Ee, the voltage across EB (Ee) is a large factor in determining the total current flow in the circuit. This is analagous to the vacuum tube where very little current enters the grid circuit, but where the control grid voltage is a large factor in determining

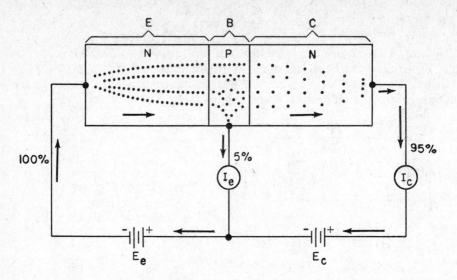

Figure 6-20. Electron flow in a transistor.

or controlling the plate current.

Let us see how a transistor is able to amplify. Figure 6-21 is the same as Figure 6-20, except that an AC signal voltage has been inserted and resistors have been added. The AC signal voltage is now in series with Ee and the signal will alternately add and subtract from the battery voltage. As noted above, this changing voltage will cause the current flowing through the transistor to change.

In Figure 6-21, 5.2 ma. enters the emitter. Of this amount, 0.2 ma. returns to Ee via the base and 5.0 ma. travel to the collector and back to Ee. This current will increase and decrease as the signal varies. Let us assume that the signal is one volt, peak to peak, and let us further assume that the AC signal causes the collector current to vary from 4.0 ma. to 6.0 ma. This 2.0 ma. variation causes a 10 volt variation across the 5,000 ohm resistor. ($E = IR$, $E = .002$ A. x $5,000 = 10$ volts). Thus, we can see how the transistor amplifier stage took a 1.0 volt signal and amplified it ten

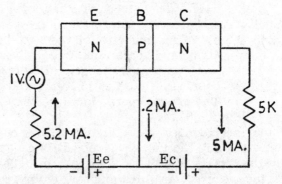

Figure 6-21. Electron flow in a transistor.

times to a 10 volt signal. This is similar to the explanation of a vacuum tube amplifier described in Page 101.

We could get the same results using a P-N-P transistor. However, the batteries being used for bias would have to be reversed. The current in an N-P-N circuit flows in an opposite direction to that of a P-N-P circuit, but other than this, both circuits work in exactly the same manner.

6-20 TRANSISTOR SYMBOLS

Figure 6-22 shows the same circuit as that of Figure 6-21. However, the transistor pictorial has been replaced with the transistor symbol. There are two transistor symbols; one for P-N-P types and the other for N-P-N. The symbol in Figure 6-22 is that of an N-P-N transistor. The P-N-P symbol is exactly the same, except that the arrow for the emitter points inward. The letters E, B and C represent the emitter, base and collector, respectively.

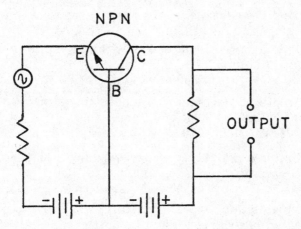

Figure 6-22. A basic transistor amplifier circuit.

PRACTICE QUESTIONS - LESSON 6
(For answers, refer to Appendix 6)

6-1 Increasing the negative voltage on the control grid will:
a. decrease the plate voltage   b. increase the plate current
c. decrease the plate current
d. have no effect on the plate current

6-2 The grid voltage of an indirectly heated tube is the voltage between the:
a. grid and cathode   c. grid and filament
b. grid and plate   d. grid and B+

6-3 A tube is said to have a blocked grid when:
   a. the grid is negative enough to cut off plate current
   b. the grid is positive enough to saturate the plate
   c. the grid cuts off grid current
   d. the grid cuts off filament current

6-4 The tube that cannot amplify is the:
   a. pentode   b. tetrode   c. triode   d. diode

6-5 The amplification factor of a tube is the change in:
   a. plate current over the change in grid voltage that causes the plate current change
   b. plate voltage over the change in grid voltage, both of which cause the same change in plate current
   c. the plate resistance over the change in plate current
   d. plate voltage over the change in plate current, caused by the change in plate voltage

6-6 An increase in positive grid voltage causes the plate:
   a. current to decrease   c. resistance to increase
   b. resistance to decrease   d. voltage to increase

6-7* The DC plate power input to a tube having a plate voltage of 800 volts and a plate current of 85 ma. is:
   a. 6,800 W.   b. 68,000 W.   c. 680 W.   d. 68 W.

6-8* The DC plate power input to a tube having a plate voltage of 550 volts and a plate current of 120 ma. is:
   a. 66,000 W.   b. 670 W.   c. 66 W.   d. 660 W.

6-9* The DC plate power input to a tube having a plate voltage of 750 volts and a plate current of 150 ma. is:
   a. 112.5 W.   b. 10 W.   c. 100 W.   d. 112,500 W.

6-10* The DC plate power input to a tube having a plate voltage of 650 volts and a plate current of 110 ma. is:
   a. 40 W.   b. 71,500 W.   c. 3,000 W.   d. 71.5 W.

6-11 The screen grid:
   a. reduces plate-grid capacity b. increases plate-grid capacity
   c. increases the space charge surrounding the cathode
   d. shields the filament from the cathode.

6-12* The schematic of a PNP transistor is recognized by:
   a. its vertical base   b. its input resistor
   c. the inward pointing arrow on the emitter
   d. the outward pointing arrow on the plate

6-13* An important advantage of a tetrode over a triode is:
   a. reduced possibility of oscillation in a tetrode RF amplifier
   b. repulsion of secondary emission electrons
   c. increased cathode emission   d. reduced rectification

6-14 A soft tube is one with:
   a. high voltages on its elements   c. a shield around its plate
   b. low voltages on its elements   d. unwanted gas in it

114

6-15* A triode has:
    a. no grids   c. two grids
    b. one grid   d. three grids

6-16* A pentode has:
    a. no grids   c. two grids
    b. one grid   d. three grids

6-17 The maximum safe heat radiation capability of the plate of a tube is indicated by the following rating:
    a. transconductance expressed in mhos
    b. maximum plate dissipation expressed in watts
    c. plate resistance expressed in ohms
    d. grid bias expressed in volts

6-18* A tetrode RF amplifier will not oscillate because:
    a. there are no space charges in a tetrode
    b. the plate of a tetrode is larger than the plates of other tubes
    c. it is impossible for any RF amplifier to oscillate
    d. the screen grid reduces the plate-grid capacitance

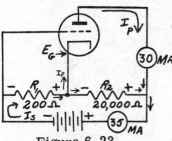

Figure 6-23.

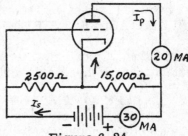

Figure 6-24.

      See Study Guide, Page 140, for hints in answering the next two questions.

6-19* Answer the following questions concerning Figure 6-23:
    a. what is the DC grid bias?
    b. what is the DC plate voltage?
    c. what is the B supply voltage?

6-20* Answer the above questions for Figure 6-24.

6-21* What is the element in a transistor that is equivalent to the control grid in a tube?
    a. base   c. collector
    b. emitter   d. N-P junction

SECTION II – LESSON 7
AUDIO AMPLIFIERS

7-1 INTRODUCTION

At this point, we understand that when a small amplitude signal is applied to the grid of a triode or pentode, it will be amplified and will appear many times larger in the plate circuit. This property of grid-controlled vacuum tubes makes possible their use as AMPLIFIERS. An amplifier may be defined as a device which transforms a small input signal into a large output signal.

7-2 AMPLIFIER APPLICATION

Amplifiers find many practical applications. For example, the signal that is developed in the crystal pickup of a record player is much too weak to be applied directly to a loud-speaker. This weak signal must first be amplified (made larger) before it can properly drive a loud-speaker. A lecturer addressing an audience in a large auditorium must have his voice amplified in order for him to be heard by everyone in the hall. The amplifier that accomplishes this is called a PUBLIC ADDRESS SYSTEM. Amplifiers are also extensively used in fields such as motion pictures, electrical recording and photo-electronics. Since amplifiers find such a wide application, it is important that we thoroughly understand their operation.

7-3 A TYPICAL AMPLIFIER

Figure 7-1 illustrates a simple resistance-coupled amplifier. This amplifier consists of the following basic components:

1. a vacuum tube, such as a triode or pentode.
2. a power source for the filament of the vacuum tube, which is called an "A" supply.
3. a source of DC power (B+) for the plate circuit of the vacuum tube, which is called a "B" supply.
4. a bias voltage supply called a "C" supply.
5. a means of coupling the signal to be amplified to the grid circuit of the amplifier.
6. a means of coupling the amplified signal from the plate circuit to the load. In Figure 7-1, the transformer couples the signal from the plate to the speaker.

When an amplifier consists of one vacuum tube, it is called a one-stage amplifier. If additional amplification of the signal is required, a second vacuum tube is connected in series with the first tube. The amplifier is then a two-stage amplifier; the vacuum tubes are said to be connected in CASCADE.

7-4 AMPLIFIERS USED IN RADIO RECEIVERS

The modern radio receiver uses two types of amplifiers in its operation. They are:

116

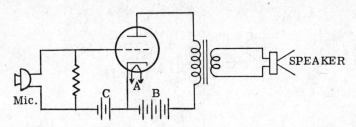

Figure 7-1. Simple one-stage amplifier circuit.

1. The Radio-Frequency (RF) Amplifier: This amplifier amplifies the weak radio-frequency signals picked up by the antenna of the receiver. A radio frequency signal is a high frequency radio wave (usually above 30 kiloHertz (kHz) which is sent out into space by the radio transmitter.

2. The Audio-Frequency (AF) Amplifier: This amplifier amplifies the sound frequencies or audio frequencies which are applied to the loud-speaker. Audio frequencies are in the range between 16 and 16,000 Hz.

7-5 CLASSIFICATION OF AMPLIFIERS

Amplifiers are classified according to the work they are intended to perform and the manner in which they are operated. The classification is determined by the grid bias of the amplifier which, in turn, determines the portion of the cycle during which plate current flows. Amplifiers are classified into three general categories: Class A, Class B and Class C. The audio amplifier is invariably operated either Class A or Class B. (We will discuss RF amplifiers in a later lesson).

7-6 CHARACTERISTICS OF A CLASS A AMPLIFIER

Characteristics of a Class A amplifier are as follows:

1. Plate current flows for the entire cycle of the input signal. In other words, the tube conducts current continuously. The average plate current, as measured by a DC milliammeter, remains constant with or without the application of a signal on the grid.

2. The grid is never driven so far negative that the tube is cut off.

3. The signal never drives the grid positive with respect to the cathode. A positive grid would result in grid current flow, which would cause the amplified signal to become distorted.

4. A Class A amplifier operates with poor efficiency because plate dissipation occurs throughout the entire cycle of the input signal. Poor efficiency results in low power output from medium-sized tubes. The efficiency of a Class A amplifier is in the order of 15 to 25%.

7-7 LINEAR AMPLIFICATION

A Class A amplifier reproduces a signal almost exactly. In

117

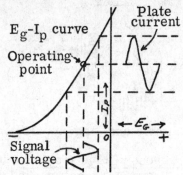

Figure 7-2. Class A operation.

other words, the amplified output signal is an exact reproduction of
the input signal. Linear Class A operation is illustrated in Figure
7-2. This figure shows the plate current-grid voltage (E_g-I_p) characteristic curve of a Class A amplifier. For Class A operation, the
bias voltage or operating point is chosen to be at the mid-point of the
"linear", or straight line portion of the characteristic curve. The
grid signal swings the grid voltage over the linear portion of the
curve. The plate current variation is, therefore, an exact reproduction of the grid signal.

7-8   THE BIAS VOLTAGE SUPPLY

All amplifiers operate with a certain bias voltage whose value
depends upon the class of operation. The two methods of obtaining
bias voltage for an AF amplifier are:

(1) fixed bias and (2) self-bias or cathode bias.

Figure 7-1 illustrates an amplifier with fixed bias. The fixed
bias can be obtained from a source called a "C" battery whose terminals are connected as shown in this diagram. The fixed bias voltage can also be obtained from a negative DC voltage point in the power
supply. The bias voltage is of constant value and cannot be changed.
The only way to change the bias is to insert another "C" battery of
different voltage. The disadvantage to fixed bias operation is that an
external means of biasing is required.

Figure 7-3 illustrates an amplifier with cathode bias.   The
biasing circuit consists of a resistor, R, and capacitor, C, connected from cathode to ground. The bias voltage is developed by the DC
plate current flowing from ground through
the resistor to the cathode. Since the current flows into the resistor from ground,
this side of the resistor is negative with
respect to the cathode side. The purpose
of the capacitor C, is to by-pass the AC
component of plate current around the resistor. If the AC component of current
were allowed to flow through the biasing
resistor, a varying bias voltage would be

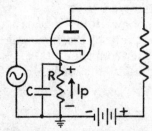

Fig. 7-3. Cathode bias.

118

developed. Under normal amplifier operation, this is not desirable. The AC component of plate current, therefore, flows through the by-pass capacitor C, while the DC component of plate current flows through the biasing resistor R, establishing a source of fixed bias voltage. The advantage of cathode bias is that it eliminates the need for a separate source of bias voltage. Most receiver circuits use this self-biasing principle.

It may sometimes be necessary to compute the value of the biasing resistor R. For example, suppose we wish to operate a certain tube as a Class A amplifier. The tube manual states that for Class A operation, the bias for that tube is -3 volts and the plate current will be 10 ma. (.01A). Since we know the voltage across the resistor and the current through it, we can easily find the value of the resistor by using Ohm's law: $R_k = \dfrac{E}{I} = \dfrac{3}{.01} = 300$ ohms

7-9   COUPLING SYSTEMS IN AMPLIFIERS

Audio amplifiers are usually classified according to the method of coupling the signal from one stage to another. There are two common types of AF coupling used in receivers and transmitters. One type is transformer coupling and the other is resistance-capacitance coupling.

7-10   TRANSFORMER COUPLED AMPLIFIER

A simple transformer coupled audio-amplifier is shown in Figure 7-4. V_1 and V_2 are the voltage amplifiers. T_1 is a special type of matching transformer (refer to Lesson 3, Paragraph 38), known as an audio interstage transformer. For maximum power transfer from the plate of V_1 to the grid of V_2, the transformer is so designed that its primary impedance approximately matches the plate circuit impedance, and its secondary impedance matches the grid circuit impedance. The turns ratio for this type of transformer is usually 1 to 3 step up from plate to grid. The secondary, therefore, has about three times as many turns as the primary.

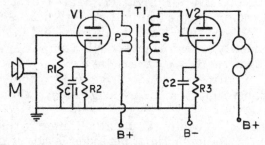

Figure 7-4.   Two-stage transformer-coupled amplifier.

The coupling operates as follows: The signal is coupled from the plate of the first stage to the grid of the second stage by means of the audio interstage transformer, T_1. The varying plate current of V_1 generates a varying magnetic field about the primary of transformer T_1. This varying magnetic field, in turn, induces a voltage in the secondary of T_1 which is applied as a signal voltage to the grid of V_2. This signal is then amplified by V_2 and applied to the headphones.

Let us now discuss the functions of the parts indicated on the diagram: "M" is the microphone which supplies the input signal to the grid of V_1. "R_1" is the grid load resistor which serves two purposes:

(a) Microphone current flowing through the resistor establishes a necessary alternating current voltage drop between the grid and cathode. This voltage drop is the signal which is to be amplified.

(b) Electrons which collect on the grid can leak off to ground through the resistor. These electrons might otherwise accumulate sufficiently on the grid to cause the tube to cut-off. This condition is known as a blocked grid. "R2" is the cathode resistor chosen to provide the correct tube bias for Class A operation. "C1" is the cathode by-pass capacitor. It provides a low-impedance path around the bias resistor for the audio currents. "T1" is the interstage audio transformer. "R3" is the bias resistor. "C2" is the by-pass capacitor.

7-11 ADVANTAGES OF TRANSFORMER COUPLING
The advantages of transformer coupling are:
1. High gain due to step-up ratio of transformer.
2. The B+ voltage need not be as high as in resistance coupling. This is because the low DC resistance of the primary causes a low voltage drop across itself. Thus, a greater percentage of the supply voltage appears at the plate than in resistance coupling.

7-12 DISADVANTAGES OF TRANSFORMER COUPLING
The disadvantages of transformer coupling are:
1. Distortion of the signal due to the transformer characteristics. An amplifier which reproduces faithfully and amplifies equally the band of audio frequencies which is applied to its input, is said to have low distortion or HIGH FIDELITY. The average transformers used in a transformer-coupled amplifier introduce some distortion into the signal. As a result, the amplifier is said to have POOR FIDELITY. High fidelity transformer-coupled amplifiers are very difficult to design and, therefore, are quite expensive.
2. The transformers are too large and expensive.
3. The transformers must be magnetically shielded to prevent pick-up of hum.
4. Transformer coupling is usually limited to triode amplifiers with the result that the high gain of pentodes is not realized.

7-13 RESISTANCE-CAPACITANCE COUPLED AMPLIFIER
The disadvantages of the transformer-coupled amplifier are overcome in the design of a resistance-capacitance coupled amplifier. The major difference between the two amplifiers is that the interstage

coupling transformer is replaced with a resistance-capacity coupling network in the RC amplifier. The elimination of the transformer allows for the use of pentode amplifiers with a consequent increase in the overall gain of the amplifier. The elimination of the audio-coupling transformer also does away with the distortion associated with its use. Generally speaking, the RC amplifier is the superior of the two amplifiers considered because of its simplicity, compactness, cheaper cost and higher fidelity output.

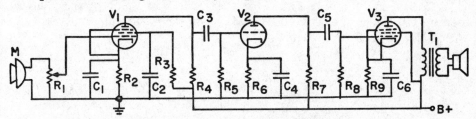

Figure 7-5. Three-stage resistance-coupled amplifier.

Figure 7-5 illustrates a three-stage, resistance-coupled (RC) amplifier. V_1 and V_2 are voltage amplifiers. V_3 is a pentode power amplifier with an output coupling transformer. The coupling network between the plate of V_1 and the grid of V_2 consists of a resistance-capacity network. The capacitor "C_3" is known as a COUPLING or BLOCKING capacitor. Its function is to pass the audio current from the plate of V_1 to the grid of V_2 while, at the same time, to block the positive plate voltage of V_1 from being applied to the grid of V_2. If the coupling capacitor becomes shorted, the DC plate voltage of V_1 would be applied directly to the grid of V_2. The positive voltage on the grid of V_2 would result in excessive grid and plate current flow, and would cause the audio signal to become distorted. The capacity of C_3 is determined by the reactance it should have for the lowest audio frequency that it is to pass on to the grid of V_2. This reactance should be very low for the lowest audio frequency that is to be passed on. The AC signal for the grid of V_2 is developed across the resistance, R_5, by the audio currents which flow through the coupling capacitor, through R_5 to ground, and back to the cathode of V_1.

The following is a summary of the functions of the components in Figure 7-5:

PARTS		FUNCTION
R_1	.....	Volume control, grid load resistor
C_1, C_4, C_6	.....	Cathode by-pass capacitor
R_2, R_6, R_9	.....	Cathode bias resistor
R_3	.....	Screen dropping resistor
C_2	.....	Screen by-pass capacitor
R_4, R_7	.....	Plate load; High impedance for audio
C_3, C_5	.. ...	Coupling and blocking capacitor; transfers the audio voltage to grid of V_2; does not allow the DC voltage from the plate of V_1 to reach the grid of V_2.

121

| R_5, R_8 | ..... | Grid resistor. Connects grid to DC ground potential, but does not by-pass audio to ground. |
| T_1 | ..... | Output matching transformer (step-down) matches the high plate impedance of V_3 to the low voice coil impedance of the speaker. |

7-14 POWER OUTPUT MEASUREMENTS

You may sometimes want to determine how much power you are feeding into your speaker voice coil. The procedure is quite simple and is illustrated in Figure 7-6.

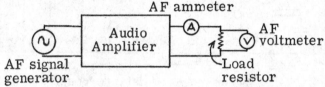

Figure 7-6. Power output measurements.

Disconnect the speaker voice coil and replace it with an equivalent resistance of the proper power rating. Then connect an audio frequency signal generator to the input of the amplifier, and an AC ammeter and voltmeter to the output, as indicated. An audio-frequency signal generator is an electronic device which can generate audio-frequency voltages. With the amplifier volume control set at maximum, adjust the output of the signal generator at 5,000 Hz. for maximum power output. The point of maximum power output can be determined by observing the output waveform by means of an oscilloscope. Maximum distortionless power output is the point just before distortion is observed in the waveform. At this point, take readings of the voltmeter and ammeter. The product of the voltmeter and ammeter readings will be equal to the electrical power output of the amplifier in watts.

7-15 FREQUENCY RESPONSE

An amplifier is said to have a FLAT FREQUENCY RESPONSE when it amplifies equally all frequencies applied to the input grid. A frequency response curve is a graph which plots the amplifier voltage output in either volts or decibels over a frequency range. Figure 7-7 illustrates the response curve for a typical transformer-coupled amplifier and a resistance-coupled amplifier. The RC amplifier has the flatter curve and has, therefore, a flatter frequency response. A flatter response means better fidelity.

7-16 DISTORTION IN CLASS A AMPLIFIER

Figure 7-8A illustrates a pure sine wave of a certain frequency. A pure sine wave is an AC wave which is free of distortion. The ideal audio amplifier is one which will amplify a sine wave, not changing its waveshape or distorting it. The amplified plate signal must,

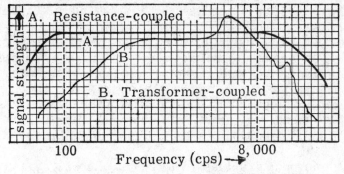

Figure 7-7. Frequency response curve.

therefore, be an exact duplicate of the grid signal. Figure 7-8B illustrates an amplified version of the sine wave of Figure 7-8A. Figure 7-8B has the same waveshape as Figure 7-8A and therefore, is still considered a pure sine wave (undistorted) even though it is amplified. Figure 7-8C is no longer a pure sine wave. It is a distorted sine wave.

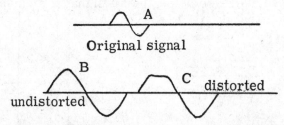

Figure 7-8. Distortion in Class A amplifier.

7-17 CAUSES OF DISTORTION IN CLASS A AMPLIFIERS

Figure 7-9 illustrates the E_g-I_p curve for a properly operated Class A amplifier. The bias point "A" is at the mid-point of the linear portion of the curve. The input signal is of the correct amplitude so that the plate signal is an amplified and undistorted version of the input signal. A DC ammeter in the plate circuit will indicate the same

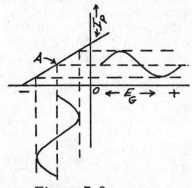

Figure 7-9.
Proper Class A operation.

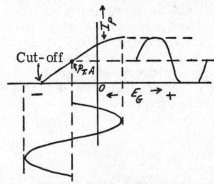

Figure 7-10. Distortion due to excessive signal voltage.

123

plate current reading when the signal is applied to the grid and when it is removed. This is because the average plate current remains the same.

The causes of distortion in a Class A amplifier are as follows:

1. <u>Too strong a signal on the grid</u> (signal overloading): Excessive excitation voltage will drive the grid positive with respect to the cathode on the positive peaks of the signal. A positive grid draws grid current, which results in distortion of the signal. The negative peaks of the signal may drive the grid so negative that the tube will cut-off. Cut-off condition results in distortion to the signal, as shown in Figure 7-10.

2. <u>Improper grid bias</u>: The result of operating the amplifier with too little grid bias is shown in Figure 7-11. The positive peaks of the signal voltage drive the grid into the positive grid voltage region of grid current. The resulting distortion is a flattening or clipping of the positive peaks of the plate current output signal. The DC ammeter will now read a decreased plate current when a signal is applied, as compared to a no-signal reading. The clipping of the positive peaks of the plate current signal causes the average value of plate current to decrease below the no-signal level (See Figure 7-11).

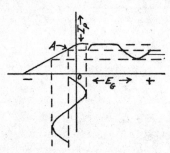 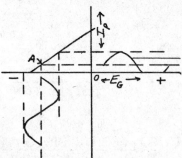

Figure 7-11. Distortion in Class A operation caused by too little bias.   Figure 7-12. Distortion in Class A operation caused by excessive bias.

The result of operating the amplifier with an excessive negative grid bias is shown in Figure 7-12. The negative peaks of the signal drive the tube into cut-off. The resulting distortion is a clipping of the negative peak of the plate current output signal. The DC ammeter will read an increase in plate current when a signal is applied, as compared to a no-signal reading. The clipping of the negative peaks of the plate current signal causes the average value of the plate current to increase.

PRACTICE QUESTIONS - LESSON 7
(For answers, refer to Appendix 6)

7-1* Draw a diagram of a two stage, resistance-coupled amplifier.

7-2* In a Class A amplifier, the grid bias is adjusted for operation over:
   a. the non-linear portion of the E_g-I_p curve
   b. the bottom of the E_g-I_p curve
   c. all over the E_g-I_p curve
   d. the linear portion of the E_g-I_p curve

7-3* In a Class A amplifier, the output signal is:
   a. similar to a sine wave
   b. a faithful reproduction of the input signal
   c. smaller than the input signal
   d. twice the frequency of the input signal

7-4* In a Class A amplifier:
   a. plate current flows continuously
   b. plate current is cut-off during the negative half of the input signal
   c. plate current is cut-off during the positive half of the input signal
   d. the tube is always cut-off

7-5* In a Class A amplifier:
   a. the grid is driven positive during the positive peaks of the input signal
   b. the grid draws current during the positive peaks of the input signal
   c. the signal never drives the grid positive with respect to the cathode
   d. the grid bias is below cut-off

7-6* In a Class A amplifier, the average plate current:
   a. decreases with application of a signal
   b. increases with application of a signal
   c. remains constant with application of a signal
   d. varies with application of a signal

7-7* In a Class A amplifier:
   a. the grid is never driven into cut-off
   b. the grid is driven into cut-off during the negative signal swing
   c. the grid is driven into cut-off during the positive signal swing
   d. the grid bias is at cut-off

7-8* The plate efficiency of a Class A amplifier is:
   a. quite high
   b. relatively low
   c. the best of all the amplifiers
   d. 100%

7-9 Draw a schematic diagram of a pentode audio power amplifier stage with an output coupling transformer and load resistor, showing suitable instruments connected in the secondary for measurement of the audio-frequency voltage and current; and name each component part.

7-10* If R_2 of Figure 7-5 is 1500 ohms, and the plate current of V_1 is 15 ma., the bias voltage for V_1 is:
   a. 2.25 V   c. 30 V
   b. 0.35 V   d. 22.5 V

7-11 An upward fluctuation of Class A amplifier current when signal voltage is applied to the grid indicates:
   a. insufficient negative grid bias
   b. excessive negative grid bias
   c. positive grid bias
   d. proper operation

7-12 A downward fluctuation of the Class A amplifier plate current when signal voltage is applied to the grid, indicates:
   a. insufficient negative grid bias
   b. excessive negative grid bias
   c. positive grid bias
   d. proper operation

7-13* Improper Class A bias results in:
   a. distortion of the output waveform
   b. decrease in amplification
   c. phase distortion
   d. improved operation

7-14* A typical efficiency of a Class A amplifier would be:
   a. 25%   b. 50%   c. 70%   d. 90%

SECTION II – LESSON 8
MICROPHONES, REPRODUCERS, POWER AMPLIFIERS

8-1 SOUND

A Class A audio amplifier is used to amplify the small signal output of a microphone. The action of a microphone depends upon certain characteristics of a sound wave. We have, therefore, reached a point in our discussion of amplifiers where a brief resume of the nature of sound becomes necessary.

SOUND is defined as a disturbance in a material medium caused by the vibration of any body at a certain definite frequency. A sound wave travels through a material medium, such as air or steel, in the form of a compressional wave. This compressional wave travels out from a region of disturbance in exactly the same manner as ripples do when a pebble is dropped into a pool of water. Vibrating objects, such as your vocal cords, cause regions of compressed air, followed by rarefied air, to move outward and away from them in the form of concentric spheres. These vibrations or disturbances reach the ear and cause the eardrum to move inward and outward, according to the pressure exerted by compressions and rarefactions. The human ear is capable of hearing such disturbances only if they occur within the range from 16 to 16,000 cycles per second. The FREQUENCY RESPONSE of the ear is, therefore, said to be from 16 to 16,000 Hz. This range of frequencies is designated by the term AUDIO FREQUENCIES. Although a frequency vibration of 30,000 Hz will cause the diaphragm in the ear to vibrate, the nerves in the ear are incapable of detecting the vibration.

Most of the sound frequencies caused by SPEECH lie between 200 and 3,000 Hertz. Therefore, sound equipment that is used only for voice communication need not be capable of handling audio frequencies beyond this range.

8-1A DECIBELS

The decibel (db) is a unit used to express a ratio between two power, current, or voltage levels in sound and electrical work. The decibel, as shown by the formula, is a logarithmic unit. This is because our impression of loudness is proportional to the logarithm of the increase in sound energy and not to the energy itself. For example, if a sound were increased in energy to 1,000 times its original value, it would only appear to the ear to be 30 times as loud. In other words, the decibel is a comparison of power levels with respect to our hearing. The formulas for determining power or voltage gains or losses are as follows:

$$db = 10 \log \frac{P_2}{P_1}, \quad db = 20 \log \frac{E_2}{E_1}, \quad db = 20 \log \frac{I_2}{I_1}$$

where: P_2, E_2 and I_2 represent the larger power, voltage and current, respectively, and P_1, E_1 and I_1 represent the smaller power, voltage and current, respectively.

When the ratio that is expressed in decibels is for an increase in level or gain, it is considered positive. When it is for a decrease in level, or loss, it is considered negative and written with a minus sign before the number, such as, -24.3 db.

8-2   THE MICROPHONE

An amplifier can only amplify an electrical frequency. Therefore, a sound frequency such as music or voice must first be converted into an equivalent electrical frequency in order that it may be amplified.

A microphone is a device which translates or converts sound impulses into changing electrical potentials called the signal. The signal, which is now of an electrical nature, can be impressed between the grid and cathode of the first amplifier tube for purposes of amplification. There are many types of microphones in use today; we shall discuss a few of the common ones.

8-3   THE SINGLE BUTTON CARBON MICROPHONE

Construction: The active element consists of a hollow button filled with packed carbon granules (see Figure 8-1). A 6-volt battery is connected in series with the button, so that any current flowing in the battery circuit must flow through the carbon granules.

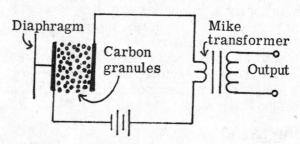

Figure 8-1.   Single-button carbon microphone.

Operation: The resistance of the single button, carbon microphone changes with mechanical pressure. This is because a change in mechanical pressure causes the packing of the carbon granules inside the button to vary. If the packing varies, the resistance of the carbon button will vary. When the sound input strikes the diaphragm of the microphone, it vibrates at the frequency of the sound. This vibration causes the resistance of the carbon inside the diaphragm to vary at the same frequency. The varying resistance will cause the current in the series circuit to vary in the same manner. The result is that an audio current, with the same frequency as the sound, flows through the primary of the microphone transformer.

Connection: The impedance of the button is about 100 ohms. A microphone transformer is used to match this low impedance to the high grid impedance of the first stage.

Frequency Response: The single button carbon microphone responds well to audio frequencies between 250 to 2700 Hz. Since many of the tones of musical instruments lie above 2700 Hz, the carbon microphone is suitable only for voice pick-up. As stated previously, the general range of voice frequencies is below 3000 Hz.

Other Characteristics:

1. The carbon microphone is the most sensitive of all microphones in use at the present time. For a given level of sound input, this microphone will generate a higher signal voltage than any other microphone.

2. The carbon microphone is not directional; it picks up sound impulses equally well from all directions.

3. Constant current through the granules gives rise to an annoying background hiss.

4. Excessive current should not be passed through the carbon granules, or the carbon button jarred while the current is on, because packing of the carbon granules will result. The microphone then becomes inoperative.

Advantages: The main advantage of the single button carbon microphone is that it does not require the careful adjustment of button balance necessary in the double button type. Other advantages are its relatively low cost, very high output and low current consumption.

8-4 THE RIBBON OR VELOCITY MICROPHONE

Construction: This microphone is activated by moving air particles. A thin, corrugated, metallic ribbon is suspended between the poles of a strong permanent magnet.

Operation: Sound energy strikes the ribbon which vibrates back and forth, cutting the magnetic field. The cutting action induces an EMF in the ribbon; this EMF is the audio signal. The EMF frequency is determined by the frequency of the sound wave which strikes the ribbon. The impedance of the short piece of ribbon may be as low as 0.5 ohms. A matching transformer is employed to match the low impedance of the ribbon microphone to the high grid input impedance.

Frequency Response: The frequency response is from 30 to 12,000 Hz. This wide frequency range is satisfactory for the transmission of music as well as voice.

Comments: To prevent a booming effect, the microphone should be placed at least 14 inches away from the source of the sound. This microphone is bi-directional; maximum pick-up occurs at the front and back of the head. It is desirable as a broadcast microphone because it has a flat frequency response.

8-5 THE CRYSTAL MICROPHONE

Construction: The active element in a crystal microphone is a crystalline material, usually Rochelle salts. Other crystals that may be used are quartz and tourmaline. There are two types of crystal microphones:

1. Diaphragm type in which a thin diaphragm is rigidly fixed to one of the major faces of the crystal.

2. Sound cell type in which a series of crystals are excited by sound pressure directly, without the use of a diaphragm. We shall examine the sound cell type of crystal microphone as it is the most commonly used of the two types of crystal microphones.

Operation: Certain crystals, like Rochelle salts, develop a potential difference between two surfaces when a mechanical pressure is applied to their opposite surfaces. Sound pressure applied to a crystal surface will develop a varying electric potential across the opposite surfaces at the frequency of the sound wave. In this manner, sound energy is converted into electrical energy. The varying potential that is developed is applied to the grid circuit of an amplifier for further amplification.

Connection: The crystal microphone is the simplest of all the types discussed. It requires no battery, since it generates its own potential. The crystal microphone requires no transformer, since it has a high impedance of over one megohm; it is, therefore, a perfect match to the high impedance of the grid circuit.

Frequency Response: The frequency response of the crystal microphone is from 50 to 8000 Hz. This is satisfactory for speech reproduction, but not quite satisfactory for music.

Comments: A crystal microphone should be handled with care because any shock is liable to impair its operation. It should not be exposed to excessive temperature and humidity changes. It is used in portable, mobile and police fixed station equipment. A single sound cell is not directional. Multiple cell types can be designed for directional use.

8-6 THE REPRODUCER

The process of amplification consists of three individual steps:

1. Conversion of sound energy to electrical energy by the microphone.

2. Amplification of the converted electrical energy.

3. Conversion of the amplified electrical energy back into sound energy through the reproducer.

Of the many types of reproducers in use today, we will study the headphones, the electromagnetic dynamic loudspeaker and the permanent magnetic dynamic loudspeaker.

8-7 THE RADIO HEADPHONE

The radio headphone or telephone receiver is the simplest type of reproducer. (See Figure 8-2). Its construction is as follows: the leads are connected to a pair of electromagnets inside the case. Separated from the magnets by a few thousandths of an inch is an iron diaphragm which is made to vibrate. Audio currents sent through the field of the electromagnet alternately weaken and strengthen its magnetic field; this, in turn, causes the diaphragm to vibrate. This vibration sets the surrounding air into motion. The air transmits these sound vibrations to the ear of the listener.

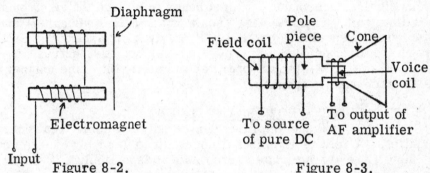

Figure 8-2.
Simplified diagram of headphone.

Figure 8-3.
The electrodynamic speaker.

The impedance of the electromagnetic headphones is about 2000 ohms. This value is high enough for the headphones to be used directly as a plate load for a voltage amplifier triode, without the need of a matching transformer.

8-8 THE ELECTRO-DYNAMIC LOUD-SPEAKER

The major parts of the electro-dynamic loud-speaker are: (See Figure 8-3).

1. The Field Coil: The field coil is a powerful electromagnet which must be energized from a pure DC source. The DC is usually obtained from the same power supply that supplies power to the amplifier or radio.

2. The Voice Coil: This coil is one of few turns; it has an impedance of from 2 to 20 ohms. The coil is wound around a small cardboard cylinder which fits closely around the pole piece of the field magnet. The voice coil is the only part of the system which is free to vibrate.

3. The Spider: The voice coil is suspended around the pole piece by a very flexible support called the "spider".

4. The Cone: The cone of the speaker is firmly attached to the voice coil. The outer edges of the cone are secured to the metal frame of the speaker housing.

8-9 OPERATION OF THE ELECTRO-DYNAMIC LOUD-SPEAKER

Since the voice coil impedance is low, the coil must be connec-

131

ted to the output tube through a matching transformer. (Refer back to Figure 7-5). The operation of the speaker is similar to the operation of the headphones. Audio currents flow through the voice coil and set up a varying magnetic field around the voice coil. The magnetic reaction between the voice coil and the field coil causes the voice coil, together with the cone, to vibrate at the audio frequency. The vibrating cone transmits its energy to the air in the form of sound waves.

8-10 PERMANENT MAGNETIC DYNAMIC SPEAKERS

With the development of powerful magnetic alloys, such as Alnico steel, the permanent magnet began to replace the electromagnetic field coil. The resulting speakers are called permanent magnetic dynamic speakers, or simply P.M. dynamic speakers. Except for the fact that a permanent magnet has replaced the electromagnetic field coil, the P.M. speaker operates in exactly the same manner as the electromagnetic speaker.

8-11 THE CLASS A POWER AMPLIFIER

A Class A voltage amplifier serves only to amplify weak voltage variations. A voltage amplifier is not required to supply a large power output. The average plate current of a voltage amplifier is, therefore, comparatively low in value. (A representative value would be about 5 ma.). A loudspeaker, however, needs a comparatively large current variation through its voice coil in order to operate successfully. The tube which is to drive the loudspeaker must be capable of handling a large plate current swing. Such a tube is known as a POWER AMPLIFIER. The plate current of a receiver power amplifier tube may be about 50 ma.

The characteristics of a power amplifier tube are as follows:

1. A low plate resistance: Since a power tube must be able to supply large power output, it must be capable of conducting a large plate current. An amplifier tube acts like a resistor. A low plate resistance will enable a large plate current to flow. For example: The plate resistance of the 6SJ7 voltage amplifier is 700,000 ohms and the plate current is 3.0 ma.; whereas the plate resistance of the 6F6 power amplifier is 78,000 ohms and the plate current is about 35 ma.

2. Large signal handling ability: A large signal on the grid means a large plate current variation. The tube must be capable of handling a large signal without going into cut-off or drawing grid current. This means that the grid will normally operate with a comparatively large bias voltage. The bias voltage for the 6F6 power amplifier is -16 volts, as compared to -3 volts for the 6SJ7 voltage amplifier.

3. A low amplification factor: The amplification factor is directly related to the plate resistance. If the plate resistance is low, the amplification factor will be low. The 2A3 triode power amplifier has an amplification factor of only 4.2.

4. Large cathode structure: The cathode structure must be large in order to be able to supply the large plate current requirements.

5. Large plate surface structure: The plate surface must be large to enable it to radiate the heat generated by the large plate current flow.

8-12 THE CLASS B POWER AMPLIFIER

A power amplifier operated Class A has a comparatively poor operating efficiency. The reason for this is that the tube conducts for the entire cycle of the input signal; this results in a continuous dissipation of heat by the plate. Consequently, the maximum power output possibilities of the Class A amplifier are never fully realized.

The modulator stages of radio-telephone transmitters require power audio amplifiers capable of delivering large power output. Class A power amplifiers would not be practical for such an application because of their poor operating efficiency. The Class B power amplifier is, therefore, used because of its higher operating efficiency. A Class B amplifier is biased to cut-off so that plate current is practically zero. Figure 8-4 illustrates Class B operation on the E_g-I_p curve.

8-13 THE CHARACTERISTICS OF THE CLASS B AMPLIFIER

The characteristics of the Class B amplifier are as follows:

(1) Plate current flows only during the positive half of the signal period. The negative half of the signal cuts off the tube. (See Figure 8-4). The amplifier operates in a manner similar to that of a rectifier in that it conducts only when the signal is positive.

(2) The amplifier is operated over the entire length of its characteristic curve so that large plate current swings can be obtained. The large plate current swing is necessary if large power output is to be realized.

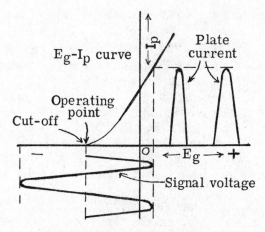

Figure 8-4. Class B operation.

133

(3) The efficiency of a Class B amplifier is in the order of 40 to 55%. It is much higher than that for a Class A for two reasons:

  (a) Plate current flows for half a cycle, so that the power wasted in heating the plate is very much reduced.
  (b) Efficiency of operation increases when a greater portion of the length of the characteristic curve is utilized. The Class B amplifier uses a greater portion of its characteristic curve, as compared to a Class A amplifier.

8-14 CLASS B PUSH-PULL POWER AMPLIFIER

A Class B amplifier tube, when used alone, will distort the signal because only one half of the input cycle is amplified. Therefore, two tubes are necessary to amplify both halves of the input cycle. The plate output of each tube is combined with the other to form one continuous wave. This system of amplification is known as push-pull amplification.

Let us study Figure 8-5 to visualize the operation of a Class B push-pull amplifier: T_1 is the input transformer. During the posi-

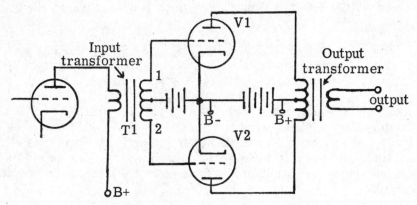

Figure 8-5. Class B push-pull amplifier.

tive half of the input signal, let us say that the grid of V_1 (point #1) goes positive, and the grid of V_2 (point #2) goes negative with respect to the center-tap of the transformer secondary. V_1 conducts while V_2 cuts-off. V_1 will therefore amplify the positive half of the signal. During the negative half of the input signal, the grid of V_1 goes negative while the grid of V_2 goes positive. Now V_1 cuts-off and V_2 conducts. V_2, therefore, amplifies the negative half of the input signal. The negative plate signal of V_2 and positive plate signal of V_1 combine in the output to form a complete amplified cycle, which is illustrated in Figure 8-6.

Push-pull operation has enabled us to utilize the high efficiency of a Class B amplifier while, at the same time, eliminating the distortion inherent in Class B operation.

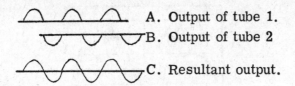

A. Output of tube 1.

B. Output of tube 2

C. Resultant output.

Figure 8-6. Output of a Class B push-pull amplifier.

8-15 <u>SECOND HARMONIC DISTORTION</u>

Any distorted waveform may be analyzed and found to consist of a fundamental frequency plus a number of harmonics. Harmonic frequencies are multiples of the fundamental frequency. For example: Let us suppose the original undistorted signal is a 1000 cycle wave. This signal upon being amplified, becomes distorted due to the addition of harmonic frequencies to the original waveform during the process of amplification. In our example, the amplified distorted wave form would be found to consist of the original fundamental frequency of 1000 cycles, a second harmonic component of 2000 cycles, a third harmonic component of 3000 cycles, etc. The fundamental and the harmonics all add together to give us the resulting distorted waveshape. The second harmonic is usually the most predominant of all the harmonics present. Figure 8-7 illustrates a distorted wave as the point by point sum of a fundamental, plus a second harmonic component.

In an audio amplifier, the distorted signal frequency is converted by the speaker into a distorted sound frequency which sounds unpleasant to the ear. If we could remove this second harmonic from the amplified signal before it reaches the speaker, we would end up with the original undistorted waveform.

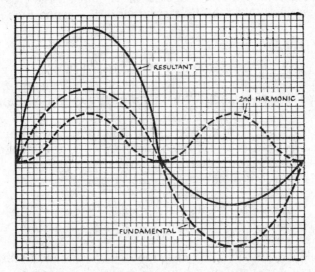

Figure 8-7. Second harmonic distortion.

135

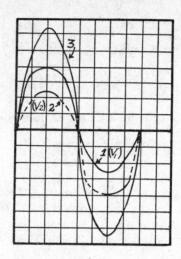

Figure 8-8. Push-pull operation eliminating second harmonic.

Push-pull operation eliminates second harmonic distortion. Figure 8-8 illustrates the distorted output of two Class A amplifiers connected in push-pull. A Class "A" push-pull amplifier differs from a Class "B" push-pull amplifier in that both tubes in the Class "A" push-pull amplifier conduct current continuously. Both tubes combine their output during both the positive as well as the negative cycles to give us the resulting waveshape. Notice that the two curves combine together, point by point, to produce the resultant undistorted output curve. The second harmonics of V_1 and V_2 are out of phase with each other across the transformer primary and consequently, cancel each other out. By eliminating even (2nd, 4th, 6th, etc.) harmonic distortion, push-pull operation improves the fidelity of reproduction considerably over that obtainable from one tube (single-ended) operation.

8-16 TYPES OF DISTORTION IN AMPLIFIERS

Distortion may take many forms in audio amplifiers and may arise from many sources. We will discuss the more important types of distortion.

(1) HARMONIC DISTORTION: This type of distortion was discussed under push-pull amplifier systems. It is sometimes referred to as non-linear distortion. Non-linear distortion arises when an electron tube is operated on the non-linear portion of its characteristic curve.

(2) FREQUENCY DISTORTION: Frequency distortion is the result of the inability of an amplifier to amplify all signal frequencies by the same amount. For a clearer picture of this type of distortion, refer back to Lesson 7, Paragraph 15. Frequency distortion is due to the characteristics of tubes and coupling systems, which cause a decrease in gain at the high and low frequencies within the audio range.

(3) <u>PHASE DISTORTION</u>: In passing through an amplification system, signals always encounter a certain amount of delay. If the delay time is different for the different frequencies which go to make up a musical tone, the result will be an alteration of the wave form. The harmonics in the output wave will appear at different phase angles with respect to the fundamental. As a result, the amplified wave, which is the sum of the fundamental and harmonics, has a different waveshape than the input waveform. This distortion is hardly discernible by ear, but it takes on great importance in television.

8-17 INVERSE FEEDBACK

Figure 8-9 shows a circuit in which part of the output signal on the plate of the power tube is fed back to the grid through a resistor

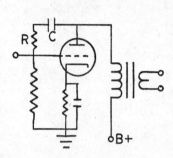

Figure 8-9.
Negative feedback.

and capacitor. Since the plate and grid voltages are out of phase, the feedback signal will be out of phase with the grid signal. If the amount of feedback is correctly adjusted, the harmonics causing distortion may be partially cancelled out. Since a portion of the original signal is also being fed back out of phase, the overall gain of the system is reduced. This disadvantage can be overcome by using either high mu tubes or another stage of amplification. As a result of inverse feedback, the distortion is reduced to a great extent.

Inverse feedback is also known as negative feedback and degenerative feedback.

8-18 CATHODE FOLLOWER AMPLIFIER

A circuit of a cathode follower amplifier is shown in Fig. 8-10. The significant feature of the cathode follower is that the output is obtained at the cathode of the tube. The term "cathode follower" comes from the fact that the output follows the input voltage. There is no phase difference between the output and input as there is in the conventional amplifier. The reason for this is as follows: When the signal applied to the input goes positive, the plate current, which flows through the cathode resistor, increases. This increases the

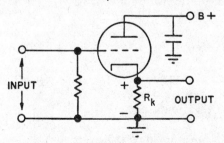

Figure 8-10. A cathode follower amplifier.

137

voltage across R_k and consequently, the output increases. This means that the output is in phase with the input voltage.

The voltage gain of the cathode follower is slightly less than one; the cathode follower therefore, has no value as a voltage amplifier. The value of this circuit lies in its excellent frequency response. In fact, for certain tubes, the frequency response is excellent up to 200 megacycles. It is often used in video and oscilloscope circuits.

Moreover, the cathode follower circuit has a high input impedance and a low output impedance. It is, therefore, useful as an impedance transformer. The power gain of the cathode follower is equal to the ratio of the output resistance to the input resistance.

The plate of the cathode follower is at ground (AC) potential. This is why the cathode follower is sometimes called a grounded plate amplifier.

PRACTICE QUESTIONS - LESSON 8
(For answers, refer to Appendix 6)

8-1 One of the advantages of push-pull operation is that:
    a. two tubes are required rather than one
    b. it eliminates second harmonic distortion
    c. it eliminates the fundamental frequency from the output
    d. the amplification is decreased

8-2* Harmonic distortion is caused by:
    a. operating on the non-linear section of the tube characteristic curve
    b. using pentode tubes
    c. Class A operation
    d. push-pull operation

8-3* The second harmonic of 500 Hz. is:
    a. 500 Hz.   b. 1500 Hz.   c. 1000 Hz.   d. 250 Hz.

8-4* The fifth harmonic is a frequency which is:
    a. one-fifth of the fundamental
    b. 10 times the fundamental
    c. 20 times the fundamental
    d. 5 times the fundamental

8-5* The third harmonic of 350 Hz. is:
    a. 117 Hz.   b. 250 Hz.   c. 700 Hz.   d. 1050 Hz.

8-6* One of the advantages of a Class B amplifier over a Class A
amplifier is:
a. low efficiency   c. higher operating efficiency
b. high gain   d. low plate voltage

8-7* One of the advantages of a Class B amplifier over a Class A
amplifier is:
a. less plate dissipation   c. low B voltage
b. low plate resistance   d. does not require feedback

8-8* One of the advantages of Class B amplification over Class A
amplification is:
a. higher power output can be realized
b. high transconductance
c. low interelectrode capacity
d. low plate resistance

8-9 A microphone:
a. amplifies a sound
b. converts electricity
c. converts sound energy into electrical energy
d. amplifies electrical frequencies

8-10* Frequency distortion is:
a. delay of harmonic frequencies during amplification
b. harmonic distortion
c. non-linear distortion
d. unequal amplification of the signal frequencies present at
the input

8-11* What is the formula for determining the db power gain in a
circuit?
a. $\log 20 \dfrac{P1}{P2}$ c. $10 \log \dfrac{P1}{P2}$

b. $\log 10 \dfrac{P1}{P2}$ d. $20 \log \dfrac{P1}{P2}$

8-12* In a cathode follower:
a. the output is in phase with the input
b. the output impedance is high
c. the voltage gain is medium
d. the input impedance is low

STUDY GUIDE – SECTION II

You should use the following outline as a guide to the lesson material in Section II that you most likely will be questioned about on the government license examination.

A. LESSON 4 - THE DIODE
Be sure to understand thoroughly the theory of the diode tube before proceeding to Lesson 5 (Rectification), which is based upon the operation of the diode. (Refer to Practice Question 1).

You should know the operation and schematic of a solid state semi-conductor.

B. LESSON 5 - RECTIFICATION AND FILTERING
Lesson 5 is an important lesson since every transmitter and receiver contains a power supply. You should know exactly how rectification changes AC to DC. You should know the operation and the advantages and disadvantages of an electrolytic capacitor.

C. LESSON 6 - TRIODES, TETRODES, PENTODES AND
            TRANSISTORS
(1) You should know how to calculate the DC plate power input to a tube when given the DC plate voltage and DC plate current. (Refer to Paragraph 6-8). (Refer to Practice Questions 7, 8, 9 and 10).

(2) You should know the number of elements which make up the triode, tetrode and pentode. (Refer to Practice Questions 4, 15 and 16). You should be familiar with the schematic of a transistor and its similarity to a vacuum tube.

(3) You should know the advantages of a tetrode over a triode (Paragraph 6-11). (Refer to Practice Questions 13 and 18).

(4) Understand what is meant by the term "maximum plate dissipation" in reference to a tube (Paragraph 6-9). Refer to Question 17).

(5) Be able to work out problems similar to practice problems 19 and 20. Here are some hints to assist you in working out problem 19 (Refer to Figure 6-23). Notice that the only current which flows through R_1 is the total supply current of 35 ma. Therefore, $E_g = I_s \times R_1$. Notice also that the current flowing through the bleeder resistor, R_2, is the difference between the supply current and the plate current $(I_s - I_p)$. By Ohm's law, $E_b = (I_s - I_p) \times R_2$. The supply voltage is simply the sum of the voltage drops across the two resistors, R_1 and R_2; $E_{bb} = E_g + E_b$.

D. LESSON 7 - AUDIO AMPLIFIERS
    (1) You must thoroughly understand the operation of a Class A amplifier. You must be familiar with the resulting distortion caused by improper bias operation. Review carefully Paragraphs 7-6, 7-7, 7-16 and 7-17. Be sure that you can answer Practice Questions 2, 3, 4, 5, 6, 7, 11, 12 and 13.
    (2) a. You should be able to draw a circuit diagram of a two-stage, resistance-coupled amplifier. (Some of the questions on the government examination may involve the drawing of a circuit diagram). (Refer to Figure 7-5).
        b. You should be able to draw the schematic diagram asked for in Practice Question 9.
    (3) You should know that the plate efficiency of a Class A amplifier is relatively low. (Paragraph 7-6). (Refer to Practice Question 8).
    (4) You should be able to calculate the bias voltage of a cathode biased amplifier (Paragraph 7-8). (Refer to Practice Question 10).

E. LESSON 8 - MICROPHONES, REPRODUCERS, POWER AMPLIFIERS
    (1) You must thoroughly understand the operation of the Class B amplifier. (Paragraphs 8-12 and 8-13). You should know all the advantages that a Class B amplifier has over a Class A amplifier. (Refer to Practice Questions 6, 7 and 8).
    (2) You should be familiar with the theory of the push-pull amplifier (Paragraph 8-14).
    (3) You should know what is meant by second harmonic distortion (Paragraph 8-15). Be able to answer questions similar to Practice Questions 2, 3, 4 and 5.
    (4) You should know that a push-pull amplifier cancels out the second harmonic in the plate circuit (Paragraph 8-15). (Refer to Practice Question 1).
    (5) You should know the range of audio frequencies used for voice communications. You should be familiar with decibels.
    (6) You should understand the operation of the cathode follower (grounded plate amplifier).

1.* One of the advantages of a Class B amplifier over a Class A amplifier is:
 a. a higher transconductance
 b. lower interelectrode capacity
 c. a higher power output can be realized
 d. low plate resistance

2.* The second harmonic of 350 cps. is:
 a. 117 cps. b. 250 cps. c. 700 cps. d. 1050 cps.

3.* One of the advantages of a Class B amplifier over a Class A amplifier is:
 a. high gain   c. low plate current
 b. low power output   d. higher operating efficiency

4. Push-pull operation:
 a. doubles the second harmonic in the grid circuit
 b. improves the signal strength
 c. cancels out the second harmonic in the plate circuit
 d. cancels the third harmonic in the plate circuit

5.* Refer to Figure 6-23 of Lesson 6 (Practice Question 19). Let: R_1 = 300 ohms, R_2 = 15,000 ohms, I_p = 10 ma., I_s = 15 ma. What is the total supply voltage?

6. Maximum plate dissipation refers to:
 a. maximum safe heat radiation capability of the plate in watts
 b. transconductance expressed in watts
 c. power gain of an amplifier
 d. power sensitivity of a tetrode

7. A pentode has:
 a. 6 grids   b. 4 grids   c. 3 grids   d. 8 grids

8.* A tetrode is superior to a triode as a radio-frequency amplifier because of its:
 a. suppressor grid
 b. increased cathode emission
 c. high plate resistance
 d. reduced possibility of oscillations

9.* The DC power input to the plate of a tube having a plate voltage of 800 volts and a plate current of 85 ma. is:
 a. 68 W.   c. 6.8 W.
 b. 680 W.   d. 68,000 W.

10. AC is changed to DC by means of a:
   a. generator   c. filter
   b. transformer   d. rectifier

11. A choke input filter:
   a. increases the output voltage
   b. lowers the ripple frequency
   c. provides the best voltage regulation
   d. doubles the ripple frequency

12. The filament is always allowed to warm up before applying plate voltage with a:
   a. mercury vapor tube   c. cold-cathode, gas-filled rectifier
   b. high vacuum rectifier d. beam power pentode

13. If a filter capacitor shorts:
   a. the ripple frequency is increased
   b. the rectifier tube will probably burn out
   c. the output current will vary
   d. B+ voltage will tend to increase

14. A bleeder resistor:
   a. improves the voltage regulation
   b. limits the output voltage
   c. does not help the voltage regulation
   d. does not help discharge filter capacitors

15. Connecting the primary of a power transformer to the DC line:
   a. burns out the primary winding
   b. burns out the secondary winding
   c. burns out the rectifier tube
   d. blows the filter capacitors

16. A mercury-vapor rectifier does not have:
   a. low internal resistance
   b. high current rating
   c. high inverse peak voltage rating
   d. constant internal voltage drop

17. A filter circuit in a power supply does not:
   a. filter out the AC   c. use electrolytic capacitors
   b. filter out the DC   d. provide a DC voltage

18. A full-wave, bridge rectifier system, using the same power transformer as a full-wave rectifier system, would have:
   a. one-half the output voltage   c. triple the output voltage
   b. double the output voltage   d. the same output voltage

19. The ripple frequency of a half-wave rectifier system is:
   a. the same as that of a full-wave rectifier
   b. twice that of a full-wave rectifier

c. one-half that of a full-wave rectifier
d. 120 cycles per second

20.* The approximate values of the filter capacitors in a transmitter power supply are between:
a. 20 to 40 µf.
b. 100 to 200 µf.
c. 2 to 4 µf.
d. 200 to 400 µf.

21.* In a Class A amplifier, the grid bias is adjusted for operation over:
a. the linear range of the characteristic curve
b. the bottom range of the characteristic curve
c. the top range of the characteristic curve
d. the entire range of the characteristic curve

22.* In a cathode follower:
a. the gain is high
b. the output impedance is high
c. the grid is at ground potential
d. the frequency response is very good

23.* In a Class A amplifier:
a. the signal never drives the grid into cut-off or grid current
b. the grid draws current
c. the grid operates at cut-off
d. the grid operates at a positive bias

24. In a Class A amplifier, the average plate current:
a. increases with signal application
b. decreases with signal application
c. drops to zero with signal application
d. remains constant with signal application

25.* The plate efficiency of a Class A amplifier is:
a. quite high
b. relatively low
c. the best of all the amplifiers
d. 100%

26.* Improper Class A bias results in:
a. phase distortion
b. improved operation
c. distortion of the output waveform
d. decrease in amplification

27.* A decrease in the Class A average plate current reading with signal application indicates:
a. positive grid bias
b. proper operation
c. insufficient negative grid bias
d. excessive grid bias

28.* The decibel is not used to describe:
a. voltage regulation
b. microphone gain
c. amplifier loss
d. amplifier gain

144

SECTION III — LESSON 9
OSCILLATORS

INTRODUCTION TO TRANSMISSION AND RECEPTION
    The first eight lessons of this course were devoted to the study of vacuum tubes, fundamental radio theory and basic circuits. These lessons contain the background material for our discussion of transmitters and receivers. However, before we go into a detailed study of actual transmitter circuits, we will take a bird's eye view of a complete communications system. Instead of drawing out the individual circuits for you, we will draw a series of boxes, each box representing a stage. (A stage is a tube with its associated parts). The function of each stage will be printed inside the box. Such a diagram is known as a block diagram.
    Fig. 1-A illustrates a block diagram of a radio-telephone transmitter. Let us see briefly what the function is of each stage outlined in the block diagram. The heart of the transmitter is the oscillator.

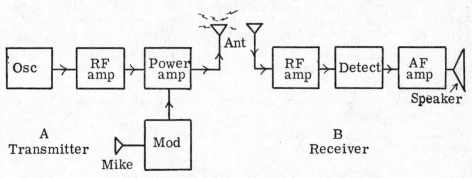

Figure 1. Radio transmitter and receiver.

Its sole purpose is to generate a high frequency alternating current. This high frequency AC is called radio frequency or RF. The output of the oscillator is fed to the radio frequency amplifier which simply amplifies the RF output from the oscillator. The output of the RF amplifier is then fed to the RF power amplifier. The RF power amplifier amplifies the RF in terms of power. The power amplifier then supplies the antenna with the RF power that is to be radiated into space. Up to this point, we have only discussed the generation and transmission of a radio frequency wave which, by itself, contains no intelligence. The intelligence that we desire to transmit is the audio in the form of voice or music. Let us see how the audio is radiated into space.
    The microphone has already been taken up in detail. Its function is to convert sound energy into electrical energy. The output of the microphone is applied to the modulator, which is simply an audio

amplifier. The modulator serves two functions: (1) it amplifies the weak audio output of the microphone and (2) it superimposes the audio on to the radio frequency energy that is present at the power amplifier stage by a process called modulation. The audio is combined with the RF wave because an audio wave by itself is not capable of traveling through space. High frequency such as RF, however, is capable of traveling through space. Therefore, the RF acts as the "carrier" for the audio; the RF carries the audio from the transmitter to the receiver. The combined audio RF output of the power amplifier is fed to the antenna where it is radiated out into space in the form of electromagnetic waves.

At the receiving end of the communications system, the electromagnetic waves induce small voltages into the receiving antenna. These signal voltages are quite weak because the electromagnetic waves have travelled some distance before striking the receiving antenna. Therefore, the signal voltages must be amplified; this is the function of the first stage in the receiver called the RF amplifier. The output of this stage is applied to the detector. Just as the oscillator is the heart of the transmitter, the detector is the heart of the receiver. The detector stage separates the audio from the RF carrier. The carrier has served its purpose in bringing the audio to the receiver. Now, all we are interested in is the audio. The audio output of the detector is then fed to an audio amplifier stage to be amplified. The amplified audio is applied to a speaker which converts the audio electrical variations back into the original sound that energized the microphone of the transmitter.

Thus, we have briefly described the overall picture of a communications system. The remaining lessons will go into the details of each stage of a communications system. We will first consider the oscillator of the transmitter.

9-1 INTRODUCTION TO OSCILLATORS

Simply speaking, a vacuum tube oscillator is an electronic alternating current generator. It is a device used to generate an alternating current of any desired frequency. All transmitters and practically all receivers make use of a vacuum tube oscillator. Vacuum tube oscillators are also employed in various types of instruments used for testing and adjusting radio equipment. Because oscillators find so many applications, various types of oscillator circuits have been developed. However, the operation of the different types of oscillators is fundamentally the same.

9-2 THE OSCILLATING TUNED CIRCUIT

The heart of an oscillator is a TUNED CIRCUIT, which consists of a coil and capacitor in parallel. In order to understand how a complete oscillator works, it is first necessary to see how a simple tuned circuit can produce alternating current oscillations. An elementary oscillatory circuit is shown in Figure 9-1. When the switch is thrown to the left, the capacitor "C" is placed across the battery.

146

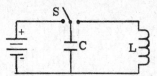

Figure 9-1. An elementary oscillatory circuit.

The coil "L" is out of the circuit. "C" will immediately charge up to the voltage of the battery. The upper plate of "C" will become positive and the lower plate will become negative. A certain amount of electrical energy is, therefore, stored up on the plates of the capacitor by the charging process. If the switch is then thrown to the right, the capacitor will discharge through the coil "L". The electrons will flow from the lower plate of "C", through the coil and back to the upper plate of "C". The flow of electrons will build up a magnetic field around "L". The energy which was stored in the capacitor has been transferred over to the magnetic field surrounding the coil. . When "C" is discharged completely, the flow of electrons through "L" tends to cease, causing the magnetic field to start collapsing. The collapsing magnetic field induces a voltage of such a polarity across "L" that it maintains the flow of electrons to the upper plate of the capacitor. This occurs because the magnetic field acts to prevent a change in the flow of current (Lenz's Law). For a review of Lenz's Law and the action of an inductance, refer to Paragraph 3-8. The flow of electrons to the upper plate continues until it is negative with respect to the bottom plate. When the magnetic field has completely collapsed, the energy which was in the magnetic field has been transferred over to the capacitor in the form of a stored charge. The capacitor is now charged in the opposite polarity to its original charge. The capacitor again discharges through "L", and the entire action as outlined above repeats itself. Thus we can see that the current OSCILLATES back and forth between the coil and the capacitor, alternately charging "C", first in one direction and then in the other. This alternating current will produce an alternating voltage across the tuned circuit. The frequency of this AC voltage is determined by the values of "L" and "C".

9-3   THE DAMPED AND UNDAMPED WAVE
If there were no resistance in either the coil or the capacitor, there would be no energy loss in the form of heat. The oscillations would, therefore, continue forever at a constant amplitude. A graph illustrating this condition is shown in Figure 9-2A. The wave is called an UNDAMPED WAVE (continuous oscillations). However, such a situation is impossible in actual practice. Some resistance is always present in radio components, especially in a coil. This resistance causes some of the energy which oscillates back and forth in the tuned circuit to be transformed into heat. The heat, of course, is a loss of energy. Therefore, with each succeeding cycle, the amplitude of the oscillating voltage decreases until all of the energy has been dis-

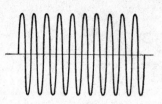 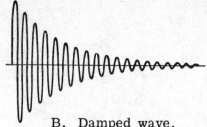

A. Undamped wave.   B. Damped wave.

Figure 9-2. Oscillations.

sipated in the form of heat. Figure 9-2B illustrates the diminishing oscillations which are called a DAMPED WAVE.

9-4 CONDITION FOR OSCILLATION

In radio, it is necessary that the tuned circuit oscillations continue at a constant amplitude (just like the undamped wave of Figure 9-2A). If we want the oscillations to continue, we must make up for the resistance losses which occur in the L-C circuit. We must somehow inject electrical energy back into the L-C circuit to sustain the oscillations. Where is this energy to come from and how do we inject it properly into the L-C circuit? To clarify this question in our mind, we can compare the oscillations of energy in the tuned circuit to a child on a swing. In order that the child keep swinging at a constant height, it is necessary that someone give the swing a little push each time the child reaches the top of his swing. In other words, energy must be added to the swing at the right time and of the right amount to overcome the friction in the hinges, otherwise the swing will gradually come to rest, just like the damped wave oscillations.

In radio, the answer to the question of how to maintain oscillations lies in the use of the amplifying ability of the electron tube. When a vacuum tube is hooked up to a power supply, the AC energy developed in the plate circuit is much greater than that applied to the grid circuit; this is due to the tube amplification. If the oscillating circuit of Figure 9-1 were to be connected to the grid circuit of a vacuum tube, an amplified version of the oscillating voltage would appear in the plate circuit. If we could somehow continuously feed back some energy from the plate circuit to the grid circuit to compensate for the resistance losses in the L-C grid circuit, oscillations could continue like the undamped wave of Figure 9-2A. A simple method of doing this is shown in Figure 9-3. L_1 and C_1 represent the tuned circuit, sometimes called the TANK CIRCUIT. V_1 is the triode amplifier tube. L_p is a coil of wire wound on the same form and next to L_1. Since L_p is in the plate circuit, it is easy to see that some of the amplified energy from the plate circuit is fed back to the grid circuit through the magnetic coupling between the two coils. If this energy can overcome the losses in the tank circuit, oscillations will be maintained.

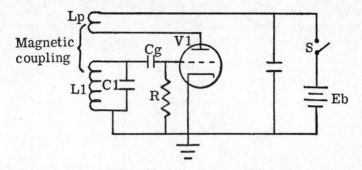

Figure 9-3.   Tickler-coil oscillator or Armstrong oscillator.

The entire circuit of Figure 9-3 is called a vacuum tube oscillator. This particular oscillator has found wide practical use, especially in modern receivers. It is known by the names of: TUNED GRID OSCILLATOR, TICKLER COIL OSCILLATOR, or ARMSTRONG OSCILLATOR. We shall now discuss in detail the operation of this vacuum tube oscillator.

9-5   OPERATION OF A VACUUM TUBE OSCILLATOR

As soon as the switch "S" is turned on, a surge of plate current flows through the plate coil, L_p. This surging current builds up an expanding magnetic field around L_p. The expanding field cuts through L_1 and induces an EMF in it. The induced EMF across the coil will now charge the capacitor of the tuned circuit. The capacitor then discharges through L_1 and the oscillatory action, previously described, has now begun. The losses in the tank circuit are overcome by a feedback of energy from the plate circuit to the grid circuit by means of magnetic coupling between L_p and L_1, indicated by the letter M. In this manner, the oscillations of the tuned circuit are maintained at a constant amplitude.

L_p, called the TICKLER COIL, must be wound in such a direction so that an expanding field about it induces a voltage in L_1 so that the grid goes positive. A positive grid will cause the plate current and the field around L_p to further increase, and induce energy back into L_1. The process of transferring energy from L_p of the plate circuit to L_1 of the grid circuit is called INDUCTIVE FEEDBACK or MAGNETIC FEEDBACK. Since the energy fed back to the tuned circuit is sufficient to make up for the energy lost in the resistance of the tank circuit, the oscillations will continue and will not die down. If the tickler coil is wound in such a direction so as to make the grid negative, the oscillator will NOT start oscillating at all.

From the above explanation, we realize that the vacuum tube itself does not oscillate. The oscillations actually take place in the tuned circuit. The vacuum tube simply functions as an electrical valve, which automatically controls the release of energy back into the tuned circuit. The feed-back energy overcomes losses and maintains

149

oscillations. The above explanation of the operation of an oscillator is basic to all oscillator circuits that will be covered in this lesson.

Figure 9-3A illustrates the Armstrong oscillator using a transistor instead of a tube.

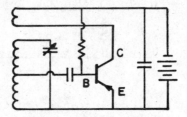

Figure 9-3A. Armstrong oscillator using a transistor.

9-6 FEED-BACK

Let us continue further with the explanation of how the oscillator works. We will now discuss the question of how much feed-back is necessary to sustain oscillations. Is it necessary to feed back energy continuously from the plate circuit to the grid circuit during the entire cycle of oscillation? Because the grid tank circuit has electrical inertia, this becomes unnecessary. (A swing has mechanical inertia; things set in motion tend to continue in motion by their own momentum). The tank circuit will oscillate properly if it receives energy during only a small portion of the AC cycle; just as a man pushing a swing need only give the swing a push when it comes to him. The swing continues oscillating back and forth as long as it receives one push during its entire cycle.

Since it is not necessary to feed back energy from the plate to the grid circuit for an entire cycle, plate current need not flow for an entire cycle. All that is required is pulses of plate current which will feed back pulses of energy to the tank circuit. If plate current were to flow for the entire cycle, there would be too much feed-back to the grid circuit, and the efficiency of the oscillator would thereby be reduced because any unnecessary flow of plate current represents

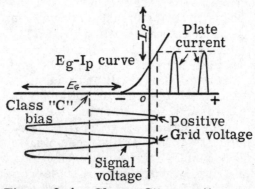

Figure 9-4. Class "C" operation.

150

a waste of power. In a properly designed oscillator, the plate current flows for about 1/4 of a cycle (90⁰). Therefore, the plate current must be cut-off during the remainder of the cycle (270⁰).

Figure 9-4 shows the operating characteristics of an oscillator. Notice that only the peaks of the oscillations bring the tube out of cut-off and cause current to flow. A tube that is biased beyond the cut-off point is said to have CLASS C bias.

9-7   GRID-LEAK BIAS

There are several ways of obtaining high negative bias, as required for Class C operation. One way is by means of a battery; another is by means of a negative voltage power supply. However, in the case of an oscillator, the only practical way of obtaining this high negative bias is by means of a resistor and capacitor $(R \& C_g)$ connected in the grid circuit, as shown in Figure 9-3. This type of bias is known as GRID-LEAK BIAS. Grid-leak bias is used in all oscillators and in many Class C RF amplifiers. A simple explanation of grid-leak bias is as follows:

When the peaks of the oscillations in the tank circuit drive the grid positive with respect to the cathode, grid current, I_g, flows in the grid circuit. A positive grid attracts electrons, as does a positive plate. The grid current flow charges up capacitor C_g in the manner shown in Figure 9-5A. During the remainder of the cycle, the grid does not conduct and the capacitor discharges through R, as shown in Figure 9-5B. Current flowing through R produces a voltage such that the top or grid side of R becomes negative with respect to the bottom or cathode side. This voltage is the grid-leak bias voltage, which makes the control grid negative with respect to the cathode.

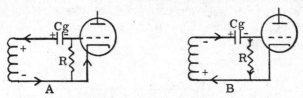

Figure 9-5.   Grid-leak bias.

Because of the heavy grid-leak bias, plate current flows in pulses during the positive peaks of the oscillations. Since the plate current flows for only a small part of a cycle, the average power wasted inside the tube is reduced and the efficiency of the oscillator is increased. The fact that the plate current does not flow continuously does not hinder oscillations because it is only necessary to feed back small pulses of energy in every cycle to sustain the oscillations.

9-8   FREQUENCY OF OSCILLATION

The larger the value of the inductance in the tuned circuit, the longer it will take for the capacitor to discharge through the inductance. Likewise, the larger the capacitance, the longer it will take the capacitor to charge or discharge. Since the time of a cycle of oscillations depends upon the charge and discharge time, it can be seen that the frequency of the oscillator goes down as the inductance or capacitance is increased. On the other hand, the frequency goes up if the inductance or capacitance is made smaller. The formula for the frequency of an oscillator is:

$$9\text{-}1)\ \ F = \frac{1}{2\,\pi\,\sqrt{LC}}$$

where: F is the frequency in cycles
L is the tank inductance in henries
C is the tank capacitance in farads

In order to vary the frequency of the oscillator, it is necessary to vary the value of the inductance or the capacitance. In most receivers and transmitters, a variable capacitor is used in the tank circuit to vary the frequency of the oscillator.

9-9   SERIES-FED AND PARALLEL-FED OSCILLATORS

Figure 9-3 is a schematic of a series-fed Armstrong oscillator. It is called a SERIES-FED OSCILLATOR because the DC plate current flows through the plate coil, L_p. In some cases, it is desirable to arrange the circuit so that the DC component of the plate current does not flow through the plate coil. This is shown in Figure 9-6. In this circuit, the high plate voltage is blocked from the tickler or plate coil by capacitor C_2. Only the AC component of the plate current flows through capacitor C_2 and the plate coil, and generates the magnetic field which is needed for feedback purposes. The oscillator of Figure 9-6 is known as a PARALLEL-FED or SHUNT-FED OSCILLATOR. The coil labeled RFC (L_2) is known as a radio frequency choke. It is designed to have a high impedance to RF. The purpose of the radio frequency choke is to prevent the RF currents from flowing to B+. Because the RF currents are blocked by coil L_2, they flow through the DC blocking capacitor C_2 and through the tickler feedback coil to ground.

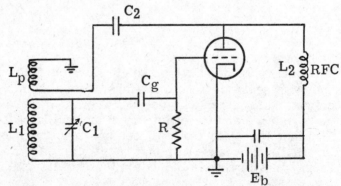

Figure 9-6. Shunt-fed Armstrong oscillator.

To summarize: If the DC component of the plate current flows through the plate coil, the oscillator is series-fed. If the plate current does not flow through the plate coil, the oscillator is shunt-fed.

9-10 THE HARTLEY OSCILLATOR

A popular oscillator that is frequently used in electronic circuits is the HARTLEY OSCILLATOR. Its principle of operation is
very similar to that of the Armstrong Oscillator. Instead of having
two separate plate and grid coils, the Hartley oscillator has a single
coil which is tapped. The Hartley oscillator can always be recognized
by its tapped coil. (See Figures 9-7 and 9-8).

One part of the coil (L_p) is in the plate circuit and the other
part (L_g) is in the grid circuit. Capacitor, C, is across the entire
coil. The resonant frequency of this oscillator is determined by C
and L_g and L_p in series. You will recall that in the Armstrong os-

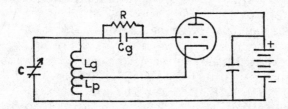

Figure 9-7. Series-fed Hartley oscillator.

cillator, energy is fed back by inductive coupling between the tickler
coil and the grid coil. The feedback in the Hartley oscillator is also
due to inductive coupling (between L_p and L_g). The tickler coil may
be represented by L_p. The amount of feedback can be controlled by
varying the position of the tap on the coil. The theory of operation of
the Hartley oscillator is exactly the same as the Armstrong oscillator. Figure 9-7 shows a series-fed Hartley oscillator and Figure
9-8 shows a shunt-fed Hartley oscillator. As previously mentioned,
the purpose of the RF choke in Figure 9-8 is to keep the RF out of the
power supply.

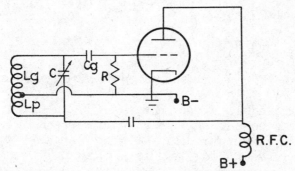

Figure 9-8. Shunt-fed Hartley oscillator.

9-11 THE COLPITTS OSCILLATOR

Figure 9-9A illustrates a shunt-fed COLPITTS OSCILLATOR.
The only difference between the Colpitts oscillator and the Hartley
oscillator is that the Colpitts oscillator has a split tank capacitor,

153

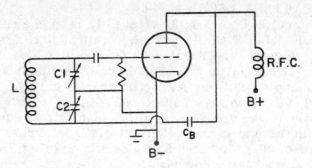

Figure 9-9A. Colpitts oscillator.

whereas the Hartley oscillator has a split tank coil. Capacitor C_2 is in the plate circuit and C_1 is in the grid circuit. Energy is fed back from the plate circuit to the grid circuit by means of capacity coupling between capacitors C_2 and C_1. This type of feed-back is called CAPACITIVE FEEDBACK. The amount of feed-back is controlled by varying the ratio between the two capacitors. The frequency of this oscillator can be varied by either varying the capacities of the capacitors or the inductance of the coil. If the capacitors are made variable, they are usually ganged.

Fig. 9-9B illustrates a TRANSISTORIZED COLPITTS OSCIL-LATOR. It operates in a manner similar to that of the tube type of Colpitts oscillator. The output of the oscillator is taken from tank circuit C1L1. C2 and C3 form the split capacitor arrangement that

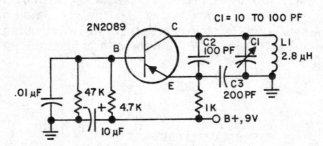

Figure 9-9B. A transistorized Colpitts-type oscillator.

accomplishes feedback. The 1K resistor is the emitter bias and the combination of the 47K and 4.7K resistor represents the base bias.

Note the circuit similarity between the transistorized version and the tube version of the Colpitts oscillator. One end of the tuned circuit of the tube type goes to the plate. The other end goes to the grid. In the transistorized type, note that one end goes to the collector and the other end goes to the base through ground and the .01 capacitor. In the tube type, the junction of C1 and C2 goes to the cathode. In the transistorized type, the junction of C2 and C3 goes to the emitter.

154

The values given would allow the transistorized oscillator to operate at about 10 MHz.

9-12 TUNED PLATE - TUNED GRID OSCILLATOR

Figure 9-10 represents a series-fed, TUNED PLATE - TUNED GRID OSCILLATOR with the plate and grid circuits tuned separately. The plate coil L_p and the grid coil L_g are not magnetically coupled to each other. Physically, they may be quite some distance from each other. How then, is energy transferred from the plate circuit back to the grid circuit to sustain oscillations? The answer is to be found in the internal grid to plate capacitance of the triode. Since the plate and grid are, in effect, two conductors separated by an insulator (di-

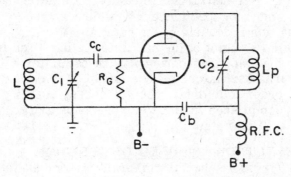

Figure 9-10. Tuned-plate, tuned-grid oscillator.

electric), we have a capacity effect existing between the grid and plate. This capacity is known as the grid to plate interelectrode capacity; the symbol for which is C_{g-p}. The feed-back energy is fed back from the plate circuit to the grid circuit through this interelectrode capacitance. As a result, oscillations are sustained. Both the plate and grid circuits are tuned approximately to the same frequency.

9-13 FREQUENCY STABILITY OF OSCILLATORS

If an oscillator remains in operation continuously, it will be found that the frequency of the oscillator drifts with time. For example, when an oscillator is first turned on, it may start to oscillate at a frequency of 1000 Kc. After the oscillator warms up, the frequency may drift either above or below 1000 kHz by as much as 10 kHz. Frequency drift is highly undesirable in a broadcast transmitter since it would cause fading of the signal at the receiver end. Similarly, oscillators in test equipment must have a minimum of frequency drift if the equipment is to serve any useful purpose. The causes of oscillator drift and its prevention are subjects of importance to all radio men, especially amateur radio operators.

Oscillator frequency drift may be caused by the following factors: (1) Improper design of the oscillator circuit.
      (a) choosing the wrong combination of L and C for the tank circuit.

(2) Poor voltage regulation of the oscillator power supply.
  (a) changes in B+ voltage will cause voltage variations at the screen and plate, which will vary the gain of the tube. Changes in gain will vary the oscillator frequency. A well regulated oscillator power supply is, therefore, necessary for good frequency stability.
(3) Changes in plate resistance and interelectrode capacitance of a tube will cause the frequency to vary.
(4) Changes in temperature will cause the inductance and capacitance of the tank circuit to vary. A physical change in either L or C will change the oscillating frequency.
  (a) negative-temperature coefficient capacitors are used in the tuned circuit to compensate for changes in inductance or capacitance with temperature.
(5) Changes in loading of the oscillator.
  (a) If the output of the oscillator is fed directly into a varying load, the frequency of the oscillator will be affected. The oscillator must be isolated from the varying load in order to maintain good frequency stability. This is accomplished in the electron-coupled oscillator which we will now study.

9-14 THE ELECTRON-COUPLED OSCILLATOR

Figure 9-11 is a schematic diagram of a series-fed ELECTRON COUPLED OSCILLATOR. The tank circuits, in the plate and in the grid, are tuned to the same frequency. If you examine the circuit carefully, you will see that the cathode, control grid and screen grid circuits by themselves form a Hartley oscillator. The screen grid acts as the plate of the oscillator. The plate of the tube serves only to couple energy from the oscillator to the load in the plate circuit.

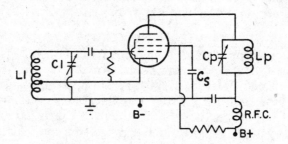

Figure 9-11. Electron-coupled oscillator.

It simply collects the electrons from the cathode and transfers them to the $C_p L_p$ tuned circuit. The electrons flowing from the cathode to the plate are acted upon by the AC voltage which appears at the grid of the oscillator. Thus, the electron stream, in flowing to the real plate, is caused to vary at the frequency of the Hartley oscillator. The plate current, in flowing through the tuned plate circuit (L_p, C_p),

156

injects energy into it and causes it to oscillate at the same frequency as the grid tuned circuit (L_1, C_1). The oscillations in the plate tank circuit are sustained by pulses of energy, which are coupled to the plate from the oscillator section via the electron stream of the tube. This is how this type of oscillator came to be called an "electron-coupled oscillator" (E.C.O.).

The frequency of the E.C.O. is determined by the tuned circuit in the control grid section. Load variations in the plate section will not reflect back to the grid circuit to vary the oscillator frequency, because the only means of coupling between the two parts of the oscillator is through the electron stream which flows only from cathode to plate. There is no interelectrode capacitive coupling between the plate and control grid because electrostatic shielding is offered by the screen grid. The screen grid acts as an electrostatic shield because capacitor C_S places it at ground potential with respect to RF. Thus we see that the tuned circuit in the grid section is well isolated from load variations and therefore, can maintain a constant frequency.

The frequency stability of the electron-coupled oscillator is not affected by voltage variations occurring in the power supply. An increase in the screen voltage causes the oscillator's frequency to shift in one direction, while at the same time, an increase in the plate voltage causes the frequency to shift in the opposite direction. Since the screen grid and plate receive their voltages from the same power supply, any frequency shift due to a varying plate voltage will be cancelled out by an opposite frequency shift, which is due to the varying screen voltage. Thus, the frequency of the electron-coupled oscillator will be maintained fairly constant in spite of B+ voltage fluctuations. The screen grid voltage is adjusted by means of the tap on resistor R for maximum frequency stability.

Because of its excellent stability, the electron-coupled oscillator is used extensively in instruments and devices which require a stable oscillator.

9-15 CRYSTAL-CONTROLLED OSCILLATORS

The most stable of all oscillators is the CRYSTAL-CONTROLLED OSCILLATOR. The most important difference between the oscillators studied to date and the crystal oscillator is that the oscillator tuned circuit consisting of L and C is replaced by a crystal substance. This crystal is usually made out of quartz, a mineral found in the earth. The quartz crystal has the following peculiar property. If a mechanical vibration is applied to the quartz crystal, an electrical voltage will be developed across its surfaces. On the other hand, if we apply an alternating voltage to the surfaces of the quartz crystal, it will vibrate mechanically at the frequency of the AC voltage. This property of the quartz is known as the PIEZO-ELECTRIC EFFECT.

The effective Q of a crystal is much higher than the Q of a tuned circuit. To a great extent, the Q of the tuned circuit determines the stability of the oscillator. Crystal controlled oscillators, therefore, have much greater frequency stability than the L-C type oscillators.

157

If we momentarily apply an AC voltage to two parallel surfaces of the crystal, it will start to vibrate mechanically; this mechanical vibration will, in turn, generate an AC voltage. This AC voltage will again cause the crystal to vibrate, etc., etc. This process will continue until all of the energy which was injected into the crystal is used up. The crystal, from an electrical viewpoint, acts in the same manner as a tuned circuit. If energy is injected into a crystal, an electrical oscillation is generated across the crystal surface, which continues until all of the energy has been used up. Since the vibrating crystal is similar to a tuned circuit, it can be placed in the grid circuit of the tuned plate-tuned grid oscillator, in place of the actual tuned grid circuit. A schematic of a triode crystal oscillator is shown in Figure 9-12. Energy from the plate tuned circuit is fed back to the grid circuit through the grid-plate capacitance of the tube. The energy that is fed back to the grid circuit keeps the crystal oscillating. The oscillations occur at the resonant frequency of the crystal, and the plate circuit is tuned approximately to this frequency. The resonant frequency of a crystal is determined by its physical dimensions.

During oscillations, the crystal vibrates at its resonant frequency. The strength of these vibrations depends upon the voltage

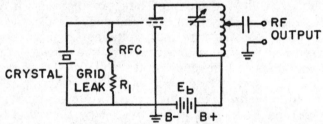

Figure 9-12. Crystal-controlled oscillator.

being fed back to the crystal. If the feed-back is too great, the vibrations may become strong enough to crack or shatter the crystal. The use of a tetrode or pentode (see Figure 9-13) overcomes this difficulty because the screen grid reduces the grid-plate capacitance. This, of course, reduces the feed-back. However, the little energy that does get back is sufficient to sustain the crystal's oscillations. Tetrodes and pentodes are also more sensitive than triodes and require less grid voltage for satisfactory oscillator operation. If the interelectrode capacity feed-back from plate to grid is insufficient to sustain the oscillations of the crystal, a small capacitor may be placed between the grid and plate to increase the amount of feed-back.

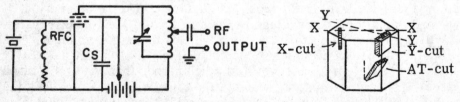

Figure 9-13 Tetrode crystal oscillator.   Figure 9-14 Crystal cuts.

158

The purpose of the RF choke in Figure 9-12 is to make sure that the feed-back energy gets to the crystal and is not by-passed to ground through R_1.

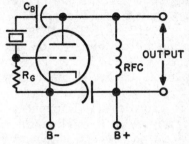

Figure 9-15 Pierce oscillator.

Figure 9-15 illustrates an oscillator that is in widespread use. It is called a Pierce oscillator. It is essentially a Colpitts oscillator with a crystal. The interelectrode cathode-to-grid and cathode-to-plate capacitances act as the split capacitors of the basic Colpitts oscillator. The basic Pierce oscillator is novel in that it does not require an L-C tank circuit.

9-16 RESONANT FREQUENCY OF CRYSTAL

The frequency at which the crystal vibrates and generates an alternating voltage is known as the crystal's RESONANT FREQUENCY. This resonant frequency is determined primarily by the THICKNESS of the crystal. The thinner the crystal, the higher is its resonant frequency; the thicker the crystal, the lower is its resonant frequency.

Quartz crystals, used in oscillator circuits, must be cut and ground to extremely accurate dimensions. For example, the dimensions of a crystal resonant to 1000 Kc. would be between one-half inch and one inch square. The thickness would be 0.1125 inch. Electrical contact with the quartz crystal is obtained by means of a special crystal holder which has two metal plates. The crystal is placed between these two metal plates and a spring device exerts mechanical pressure against the metal plates.

9-17 CRYSTAL CUTS

The frequency of a crystal is affected by the temperature of the air surrounding it. Different types of crystals show different reactions to temperature changes. Crystals are classified according to the manner in which they are cut from the original raw crystal rock. The different crystal cuts from the raw crystal rock are shown in Figure 9-14. Note that an X cut crystal is one that is cut perpendicular to the X axis; a Y cut crystal is one that is cut perpendicular to the Y axis; and an AT cut crystal is one that is cut at a 35 degree angle to the Y cut crystal.

The X cut crystal has a NEGATIVE TEMPERATURE COEFFICIENT. This means that the natural resonant frequency of the crystal goes down as the temperature goes up; and its natural resonant frequency goes up as the temperature goes down. In actual practice, the temperature coefficient of an X cut crystal varies from 10 to 25 cycles per megacycle for each degree centigrade change. For example, if the temperature of a 4 MHz crystal were to change from 35° centigrade to 45° centigrade, the actual change in frequency would be found by multiplying the number of degrees change of temperature by the number of megacycles of the crystal. The result of this multiplication is then, in turn, multiplied by the actual temperature coefficient. See Paragraph 9-20 for actual problems. X cut crystals have more thickness for a given frequency than Y or AT crystals.

Y cut crystals have a POSITIVE TEMPERATURE COEFFICIENT. The frequency of vibration goes up as the temperature goes up, and the frequency goes down as the temperature goes down. However, the Y cut crystal has some undesirable operating characteristics.

(1) The Y crystal has a tendency to vibrate simultaneously at two different frequencies which may be fairly close to each other.

(2) A slight load or temperature variation may cause the crystal to jump from one frequency to another. This makes the oscillator extremely unstable.

(3) Instability due to a relatively large temperature coefficient which may be as high as 100 cycles per megacycle per degree centigrade. The frequency of the Y cut crystal does not vary smoothly with changes in temperature. A slight change in temperature may cause a sudden large frequency shift.

All three factors would result in unstable oscillator operation.

Both the X cut and the Y cut crystals have been superseded by crystals having a LOW TEMPERATURE COEFFICIENT. This type of crystal is called the AT cut crystal (sometimes called A cut). A low temperature coefficient means that the frequency of vibration varies very little with temperature changes. The frequency drift of an AT cut crystal oscillator is, therefore, very small. An AT cut crystal oscillator is also capable of a comparatively high output. The AT cut crystal is used extensively in the frequency range from 1/2 MHz to 10 MHz.

9-18 CARE OF CRYSTALS

The care and treatment of quartz crystals is very important for their efficient operation in oscillator circuits. It should be pointed out at this time that a crystal is thin and fragile and should normally never be removed from the crystal holder. If the crystal is dirty and fails to operate, it is necessary to remove it from its holder and clean it. An excellent cleaning agent for quartz crystals is carbon tetrachloride. Soap and water or alcohol can also be used. After cleaning, the crystal should be washed with water and then dried with a clean, lint-free cloth. The fingers should not come in contact with the faces of the crystal, since oil or dirt getting on to the crystal surface may prevent it from oscillating. The crystal should be handled by grasping the edges, NEVER THE FACES.

Care must be taken not to allow a DC voltage to be placed across a crystal If a DC potential is applied to a crystal, the crystal will be physically strained. If the applied DC potential is strong enough, it might actually crack the crystal.

9-19 ADJUSTMENT OF A CRYSTAL CONTROLLED OSCILLATOR

The most accurate way of adjusting a crystal controlled oscillator for stable operation is to use a DC milliammeter placed in the
plate circuit. When the plate tank circuit is tuned to the resonant frequency of the crystal, the plate current will drop to a low value. However, as we vary the tuning capacitor either side of the resonance
point, the rise in plate current on both sides of the resonance point
will not be uniform. If you will examine Figure 9-16, you will notice
that as the tuning capacitance (high frequency to a low frequency) increases, the plate current slowly decreases to point C, then suddenly

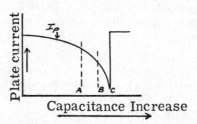

Figure 9-16. Crystal-oscillator, plate current tuning curve.

jumps up to some high value, at which time oscillations cease. Between points A and C, the circuit is oscillating. Before point A and
beyond point C, the circuit stops oscillating. At point C, the plate
circuit is tuned to the resonant frequency of the crystal, and the efficiency and output of the plate tank circuit are at a maximum. However, the oscillator is unstable because any slight change in the loading conditions or any slight increase in the tuning capacitance might
move the operating point beyond point C and cause the oscillator to
stop oscillating. The oscillator is usually operated in the region
between A and B. In this region, the oscillator will continue to
function properly, even with slight changes in load conditions.

9-20 PROBLEMS RELATING TO CRYSTAL FREQUENCIES

In order to operate a transmitter properly, it is important to
know the exact frequency of the crystal oscillator. Since temperature
changes affect the frequency of the crystal, we must be able to figure
out the new crystal frequency for a given temperature change. The
following problems will illustrate how this is done:

Problem 1. A Y cut crystal that is marked 1000 Kc. has a positive temperature coefficient of 75 cycles per degree centigrade, and
is started in operation at 50 degrees centigrade. If the temperature-
frequency characteristic is linear, what will the new crystal frequency
be at 30°centigrade?

Solution: A linear temperature-frequency characteristic means
that the 75 cycles change in crystal frequency will remain constant
for each degree change in temperature. The temperature change is
20 degrees (50° - 30° = 20°). Since the temperature coefficient is 75

cycles per degree centigrade, the crystal frequency shift is 1500 cycles (20 x 75) or 1.5 Kc. The new crystal frequency will therefore be the original frequency minus the frequency drift. (1000 Kc. - 1.5 Kc.) or 998.5 Kc.

Problem 2. A 3000 Kc. low drift crystal has a negative temperature coefficient of 4 cycles per megacycle per degree centigrade. The crystal is started in operation at 40°C. If the temperature-frequency characteristic is linear, what will be the frequency at 50° centigrade?

Solution: A 3000 Kc. crystal is the same as a 3 megacycle crystal, since 1 Mc. equals 1000 Kc. To convert the temperature coefficient (4 cycles per megacycle per degree centigrade) into cycles change per degree centigrade, we multiply the temperature coefficient by the crystal frequency in megacycles. The product is a 12 cycle change per degree centigrade (4 x 3 = 12). The change in temperature is 10°C. (50° - 40° = 10°). The frequency change is therefore 10°C. x 12 cycles per degree = 120 cycles or 0.12 Kc. To convert cycles into kilocycles, we divide the number of cycles by 1000. Therefore:

$$120 \text{ cycles } = \frac{120}{1000} \text{ Kc. } = 0.12 \text{ Kc.}$$

Since the temperature went up, the frequency of this negative temperature coefficient crystal will go down. The new frequency will therefore be 2999.88 Kc. (3000 Kc. - 0.12 Kc).

There are many times when an amateur operator may wish to operate as close to the edge of the frequency band as possible. He may do this in order to establish more contacts. The high and low ends of a particular band are often less crowded with calls than is the center of the band. A signal is therefore subject to less interference at the edges of the band. The one danger in operating at the edge of the band is that a slight shift in the oscillator frequency will throw the transmitted signal frequency outside of the particular band in question. Operating outside of an amateur band is unlawful, according to the rules and regulations of the Federal Communications Commission. Operating at the edge of the band is, therefore, a problem to be considered. Let us assume that you are operating in the 20 meter band. The frequency limits for this band are 14,000 Kc. and 14,350 Kc. Let us further assume that you wish to operate as close to the 14,000 Kc. edge as possible. Would you, therefore, use a crystal rated at exactly 14,000 Kc.? Of course not! No manufacturer can guarantee a crystal to be 100% accurate. A crystal stamped 14,000 Kc. may actually oscillate below 14,000 Kc. Or, if the crystal is cut to exactly 14,000 Kc., temperature changes may shift the crystal's frequency below 14,000 Kc. In both instances, you would be operating outside of the allocated band. In order to be on the safe side, you would have to purchase a crystal rated a few kilocycles above 14,000 Kc. Exactly how much above depends upon the accuracy rating and the temperature coefficient of the crystal in question. A few problems will illustrate these principles:

Problem 1: A crystal manufacturer guarantees his crystals cut for the 7000 Kc. - 7300 Kc. amateur band to be accurate to within .03% of their specified frequency. If you desire to operate as close as possible to 7000 Kc., for what whole number frequency in kilocycles should you order your crystal cut? (In ordering, you would also allow for one additional kilocycle to take care of variations in temperature and circuit constants).

Solution: We first find the crystal frequency tolerance in cycles.

(1) .03% of 7000 Kc. $= \dfrac{.03}{100}$ of 7000 Kc. or:

.0003 x 7000 Kc. = 2.1 Kc.

(2) To the 2.1 Kc. we add 1 Kc. for possible variation due to circuit and temperature constants. 2.1 Kc. + 1 Kc. = 3.1 Kc. (3.1 Kc. is theoretically the maximum frequency variation of a crystal from its specified frequency of 7000 Kc.).

(3) Since the problem asks for a whole number frequency in Kc., we go to the next higher whole number from 3.1 Kc. which is 4 Kc. Therefore, we would order a 7000 Kc. + 4 Kc. or a 7004 Kc. crystal with a .03% tolerance.

Problem 2: A low drift crystal for the 3500 Kc. - 4000 Kc. amateur band is guaranteed by a manufacturer to be calibrated to within .05% of its specified frequency. If you wish to operate as close as possible to the upper edge of the band, for what whole number frequency should you order your crystal? Allow one extra kilocycle for variations from temperature and circuit constants.

Solution: (1) The crystal frequency tolerance at 4000 Kc. in cycles is: $.05\%$ of $4000 = \dfrac{.05}{100} \times 4000 = 2$ Kc.

(2) To the 2 Kc., we add 1 Kc. for possible variations due to circuit and temperature constants: 2 Kc. + 1 Kc. = 3 Kc. (this is a whole number and we leave it at that). We would order a 3997 Mc. crystal (4000 - 3).

Problem 3: For what frequency would you order your crystal for operation as close as possible to the lower band limit of 3500 Kc., with the same calibration accuracy and allowance given in problem 2?

Solution: (1) The crystal frequency tolerance at 3500 Kc. in cycles is: $.05\%$ of $3500 = \dfrac{.05}{100} \times 3500 = 1.75$ Kc.

(2) Add 1 Kc. for variations in circuit and temperature constants: 1.75 + 1 = 2.75 Kc.
Since the problem asks for a whole number frequency in kilocycles, we go to the next higher whole number from 2.75 Kc. which is 3 Kc. We would, therefore, order a 3503 Kc. crystal (3500 + 3 = 3503 Kc).

9-1   An X cut crystal, compared to a Y cut of similar frequency is:
a. heavier   b. wider   c. rounder   d. thicker

9-2   A quartz crystal in the oscillator of a transmitter does not:
a. stabilize the output frequency   c. determine the frequency
b. provide a high Q tank circuit   d. amplify the signal

9-3   A desirable operating characteristic of an A cut crystal is:
a. high frequency drift   c. positive temperature coefficient
b. high output capability   d. negative temperature coefficient

9-4   A desirable operating characteristic of an A cut crystal is:
a. low frequency of oscillation   b. light weight
c. low Q (poor selectivity)
d. small temperature-frequency coefficient

9-5* The electron-coupled oscillator, compared to other types:
a. has better frequency stability
b. has variable frequency characteristics
c. has parasitic oscillations   d. oscillates above 100 Mc.

9-6* The electron-coupled oscillator does not have:
a. excellent frequency stability
b. large frequency variations with variations in supply voltage
c. coupling of energy from oscillator section to plate circuit
   by means of the electron stream
d. frequency independent of load variations

9-7* The crystal oscillator is:
a. the least stable of all   b. only a Hartley oscillator
c. less stable than the electron-coupled oscillator
d. the most stable of all the oscillators

9-8* Draw a simple schematic diagram of a piezo-electric crystal-
controlled oscillator using a pentode vacuum tube. Indicate
polarity of supply voltages.

9-9   A certain 28 Mc. Y cut crystal has a positive temperature coefficient of 100 cycles per degree centigrade, and is started in
operation at 40° centigrade. What will the oscillation frequency
be at a temperature of 70° centigrade?

9-10* Which of the following is not required for a circuit to oscillate?
a. feedback   c. piezo-electric effect
b. a tuned circuit   d. amplification

SECTION III — LESSON 10
CONTINUOUS-WAVE TRANSMITTERS

10-1 INTRODUCTION

The function of a radio transmitter is to transmit intelligence by means of a radio frequency wave. The RF wave is radiated into space by an antenna system. An antenna is a device which converts AC energy into electromagnetic radiation known as radio waves. The RF wave traveling through space is then picked up by a receiver which converts the RF signal into an audio output.

Radio transmitters may be divided into two types. One is the CONTINUOUS-WAVE type of transmitter, which we shall now study; the other is the modulated type of transmitter, which we shall study later on.

10-2 CONTINUOUS WAVES

Continuous waves, abbreviated CW, are radio waves of constant amplitude. In the CW transmitter, continuous waves are radiated into space by simply coupling the output of a vacuum tube power oscillator to a suitable antenna system. The International Morse Code is used to convey intelligence by CW communication.

The Morse Code consists of a series of dots and dashes which represent the letters of the alphabet. In order to transmit code, the CW transmission must be interrupted in a dot and dash sequence. This type of emission is actually an RF wave broken up into sections. An oscillator is made to stop and start oscillating by means of a telegraph key. By allowing the oscillator to operate for longer or shorter amounts of time, we can produce dots and dashes. Figure 10-1 shows the output of an oscillator for the letter "D" (dash-dot-dot).

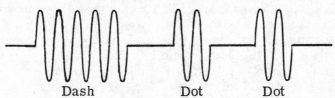

Dash   Dot   Dot

Figure 10-1. Keyed output of an oscillator
for the letter "D" (dash-dot-dot).

The symbol that is used to designate the transmission of code by interrupting a CW transmitter is "A1". The symbols for the various types of transmission can be found on Page 211.

10-3 ONE-TUBE TRANSMITTER

In early type radio transmitters, the oscillator was directly coupled to the antenna system. In order to increase the power output of this type of transmitter, it was necessary to use a larger tube or to increase the operating voltages. There is a limit, however, to the amount of power that one can get from a one-tube transmitter. The power output of an oscillator depends upon RF currents in the oscillator circuit. Since these currents are relatively weak, very little power can be delivered to the antenna. The radiated wave, therefore, will also be weak. Another defect of the simple oscillator type of transmitter is its poor frequency stability. Figure 10-2 shows a one-tube transmitter. Capacitor C_A represents the antenna capacitance to ground which will vary as the antenna swings in the wind. This varying antenna capacitance will be coupled back to the tank circuit and will cause the oscillator frequency to vary. The disadvantage of poor frequency stability can be oversome to a great extent by the use of an intermediate amplifier stage which serves to isolate the antenna from the oscillator. Changes in antenna capacity will therefore, not be reflected back into the oscillator tank circuit. At the same time, the amplifier amplifies the output of the oscillator and feeds a more powerful signal into the antenna.

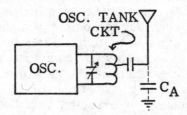

Figure 10-2. One-tube transmitter.

10-4 MASTER-OSCILLATOR POWER-AMPLIFIER

A transmitter consisting of an oscillator and an amplifier (or a series of amplifiers) is called a MASTER-OSCILLATOR POWER-AMPLIFIER, MOPA for short. Such a transmitter is shown in Figure 10-3. The output of the oscillator is amplified by V_2. Capacitor C_1 prevents the high DC voltage on the plate of V_1 from being applied to the grid of V_2. At the same time, it allows the RF energy to get through to the grid of V_2. The RF choke L_1 prevents the RF energy from flowing to ground through R_1. This is because an RF choke opposes the flow of RF currents.

The master-oscillator power-amplifier type of transmitter has a decided advantage over the simple oscillator transmitter in that the frequency stability is greatly improved. High frequency stability is obtained in this system because the oscillator is not coupled directly to the antenna; the oscillator is, therefore, unaffected by any change in the antenna-to-ground capacitance. Changes in antenna-to-ground capacitance will merely react upon the RF power amplifier circuit, resulting in a decrease in the radiated power output. The amplifier in Figure 10-3 may feed the antenna directly, or it may be the first

166

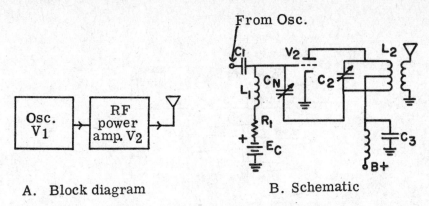

A. Block diagram B. Schematic

Figure 10-3. Master-oscillator, power-amplifier transmitter.

of a series of RF amplifiers, the last of which feeds into an antenna system.

10-5 HIGH EFFICIENCY CLASS C RF AMPLIFIER

In Lesson 7, we studied the biasing methods for audio amplifiers. You will recall that AF amplifiers are operated with cathode bias as Class A voltage amplifiers. The audio amplifier tubes were operated as Class A or Class B amplifiers because we were interested in obtaining good fidelity of reproduction. The Class A amplifier sacrifices efficiency for excellent fidelity. In the case of an RF amplifier, we are not interested in fidelity since we are not amplifying an audio signal. We are interested in efficiency of operation. An RF amplifier operates most efficiently in a transmitter as a Class C amplifier. In order to operate the tube as a Class C amplifier, the bias must be between one and one-half to four times the bias value necessary for cut-off. This condition is shown graphically in Figure 10-4. You will notice that with a pure sine wave applied to the grid, the plate current consists of small pulses which certainly do not resemble the input sine wave. Since the plate current wave does not resemble the grid signal, the fidelity of a Class C amplifier is poor. One important point to notice is that the plate current flows for only a fraction of the period of the input signal. Compare this to a Class A amplifier where the plate current flows continuously. Obviously, more power is wasted in plate dissipation in a Class A amplifier as compared to a Class C amplifier. Since the plate dissipation is decreased in the Class C amplifier (as compared to the Class A amplifier), the useful power output is increased. The efficiency of a Class C amplifier is therefore excellent. It is approximately 70% efficient. The question that always arises at this point is: What good are the plate current pulses if we are interested in obtaining an amplified version of the sine wave input? The answer lies in the ability of the plate tank circuit to reproduce a pure sine wave from pulses of energy which are applied to it every cycle. From the discussion of

167

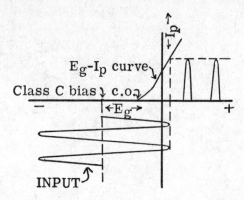

Figure 10-4. Class "C" bias operation.

the oscillatory circuit (Paragraph 9-5), it will be recalled that when the plate tank circuit is tuned to the resonant frequency of the grid circuit, the plate current pulses will reinforce the oscillations in the plate tuned circuit at just the right instant, sustaining oscillations. The surges of plate current give the tank circuit the shot of energy, and the FLYWHEEL EFFECT causes the tuned circuit to make up that portion of the sine wave missing in the plate current pulses. Thus, we see that although the plate current is made up of pulses, the signal fed to the antenna or the next stage is a pure sine wave.

10-6 MINIMIZING HARMONIC OUTPUT

It is very important that the output waveform of an RF amplifier contain a minimum of harmonic components. In other words, the output should be as close to a pure sine wave as possible. If the harmonic components are radiated by the antenna, unlawful interference with adjacent transmissions may result. It is especially important that the output stage of the transmitter produce a minimum amount of harmonic and spurious signals. This is because this output stage feeds the antenna and the harmonic and spurious signals are bound to be transmitted.

A Class C, RF amplifier should have the following characteristics if generation of harmonics is to be kept to a minimum:

1. The plate tank circuit should have a low inductance to capacitance ratio (low L-C ratio).
2. The amplifier should operate with the proper grid bias and grid signal.
3. Push-pull operation will eliminate second harmonic components.
4. Use link coupling where possible.
5. Avoid capacitive coupling.
6. Use tuned circuits where possible.
7. Use proper plate and screen voltages (as low as possible).
8. Use low-pass filters where possible.

9. Use a Faraday shield. See Paragraph 10-25 for a complete discussion of a Faraday shield.

10. Use a high Q plate tank circuit. By increasing the Q of the tank circuit, we increase the selectivity of the circuit. This means that we pass the desired frequency, but exclude the undesired signals (harmonics, etc.).

There is a limit as to how high the Q should be. Too high a Q will result in high internal tank currents and therefore, less power transferred to the next stage or antenna. The ideal Q of an RF power amplifier tank circuit should be between 10 and 20.

10-7 GRID-LEAK BIAS

It was mentioned above that a Class C amplifier requires a bias of from one and one-half to four times the value of cut-off bias. There are several methods of obtaining Class C bias. The first method that we shall discuss is known as GRID-LEAK BIAS. You will recall that grid-leak bias is used in the self-biased oscillator. (Refer back to Paragraph 9-7). Figure 10-3 shows the RF amplifier, V_2, employing grid-leak bias. R_1 is the bias resistor and C_1 is the bias capacitor. Before the signal from the previous stage is applied to the grid of the amplifier tube, the bias on the grid is zero. However, when a signal is applied, a grid bias voltage develops across R_1. Let us see how this comes about: On the positive half of the incoming signal, the grid is driven positive with respect to the cathode. This causes a flow of grid current, which charges up capacitor C_1. On the negative half of the signal, the capacitor discharges through R_1. The discharge current that flows through R_1 develops a DC voltage across R_1. Capacitor C_1 which is effectively in parallel with R_1, tends to keep this voltage constant. Since the current enters R_1 at the top, (the grid side), the top part of the resistor is negative with respect to the bottom part. The top of the resistor is connected to the grid. Therefore, the grid is negatively biased with respect to the cathode.

The amount of grid-leak bias that is developed depends upon the strength of the signal. This may sometimes be a serious disadvantage. If, for some reason, the signal or excitation is lost, the bias will disappear and the plate current may rise to excessively high values.

10-8 FIXED BIAS

Another method of obtaining bias for Class C amplifiers is through the use of a "C" battery. A "C" battery is just an ordinary battery used for biasing purposes. The negative terminal of the "C" battery is connected to the grid and the positive terminal is connected to the cathode. This, of course, makes the grid negative with respect to the cathode. An RF by-pass capacitor is usually shunted across the battery to complete the RF path around the battery. The amount of battery voltage to be used for a particular tube can be found by consulting a transmitting tube manual.

10-9 COMBINATION GRID-LEAK, CATHODE BIAS

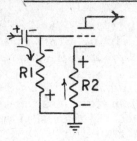

Figure 10-5.

A third method of obtaining bias is shown in Figure 10-5. This method is a combination of grid leak and cathode bias. R_1 provides most of the bias voltage. R_2 is placed in the circuit to act as a protective bias in case the input signal to the stage should fail. Upon loss of grid leak bias, the increased plate current will flow through R_2 developing a heavy bias voltage which will, in turn, limit the plate current to a safe value. R_2 will not cause any appreciable loss of plate voltage, since its value is small. It will simply serve to bias the tube, should the grid leak bias disappear.

10-10 GRID-LEAK AND BATTERY BIAS

The fourth method of obtaining bias for an RF amplifier is shown in Figure 10-3. This method is a combination of grid-leak and battery bias. Again, most of the bias voltage is obtained from the voltage drop across the grid leak resistor. The battery is connected in the circuit simply as a means of keeping some bias voltage on the tube in the event that the grid-leak bias drops to zero. The transmitting tube is thus protected against damage due to excessive plate current flow.

10-11 POWER SUPPLY BIAS

The last biasing method that we will discuss is power supply bias. The only difference between this system and the battery bias system is that the battery has been replaced by a well-regulated negative power supply. If the excitation to the stage fails, the bias is not affected and the plate current does not rise to dangerous values. This method is quite popular in the more expensive transmitters.

10-12 NEUTRALIZATION

Examine the RF amplifier of Figure 10-6. Note that the tank circuit L_2C_2 is not only the plate tank circuit of the oscillator, but can also be considered as the grid tank circuit of the RF amplifier. Notice that the portion of the schematic of Figure 10-6 inside the dotted line is exactly the same as a tuned-plate, tuned-grid oscillator. (Refer to Lesson 9, Figure 9-10). This portion of the circuit will oscillate just like a tuned-plate, tuned-grid oscillator unless certain precautions are taken. An oscillating RF amplifier is very undesirable. An amplifier is only supposed to amplify and not to oscillate. An oscillating amplifier has poor frequency stability. Antenna variations are directly coupled back to the oscillating amplifier, and all sorts of spurious radiations will result. Spurious radiations differ in frequency from the desired RF transmission. They are radiated with the desired frequency transmission and cause interference with stations on nearby frequencies.

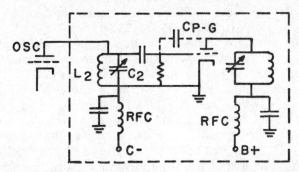

Figure 10-6. Oscillatory circuit in an unneutralized RF amplifier.

There are two general methods of preventing an RF amplifier from oscillating. One is to use a tetrode or pentode instead of a triode. As you have previously learned, the addition of a screen grid reduces the grid-plate capacitance. It would, therefore, be very difficult for a tetrode or pentode to oscillate, since there would be no feedback through the grid-plate capacitance as we have in a triode. However, most high powered RF amplifying tubes are triodes, and therefore, we do have the problem of preventing oscillations from taking place. Therefore, precautions must be taken when triodes are used as RF amplifiers. This brings us to the second method of preventing an RF amplifier from oscillating.

10-13 PLATE NEUTRALIZATION

We realize that as long as we use a triode, we will have feedback from the plate circuit to the grid circuit through the interelectrode plate-grid capacitance. We must, in some manner, cancel out or neutralize this feedback if we are going to prevent oscillations. The remedy is to connect an external capacitor into the circuit to NEUTRALIZE this feedback. Figure 10-7 shows a neutralized triode RF amplifier. Capacitor C_n is the neutralizing capacitor and C_{p-g} is the grid to plate interelectrode capacity. Notice that the B+ is fed to the plate through a center-tap on the plate coil. The center-tap is

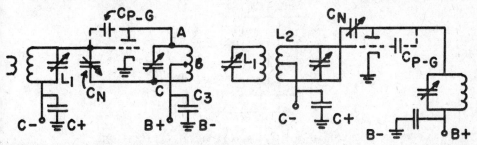

Figure 10-7 Plate neutralization.   Figure 10-8 Grid neutralization.

placed at RF ground (zero) potential through capacitor C_3. The plate RF voltage with respect to ground is the voltage across the top half of the coil; it is the voltage between A and B. This voltage feeds energy back to the grid and tends to make the amplifier oscillate. The RF voltage between points B and C is the neutralizing voltage and is equal to the plate RF voltage. Because potentials at opposite ends of a coil are 180° out of phase with each other, the plate RF voltage is 180° out of phase with the neutralizing voltage. If C_n is made to equal C_{p-g}, the neutralizing voltage will cause a voltage to be fed back to the grid which will be equal and opposite to the voltage fed back by C_{p-g}. The two voltages will cancel each other out, and the amplifier will no longer oscillate. The above system of neutralization is called PLATE NEUTRALIZATION or HAZELTINE NEUTRALIZATION. We can regognize it by the fact that C_n is connected between the bottom of the plate coil and the control grid. This is the system used in Figures 10-3 and 10-7.

10-14 GRID NEUTRALIZATION

Figure 10-8 shows another system of neutralization. It is called GRID NEUTRALIZATION or RICE NEUTRALIZATION. In this case, the grid coil is split and C_n is connected between the bottom of the grid coil and the plate. The operation of the neutralization process in this system is similar to the plate neutralization system. The neutralizing voltage fed back from the plate to the bottom of the grid coil will cancel out the voltage fed back from the plate to the top of the grid coil by the grid to plate capacitance.

10-15 CRISS-CROSS NEUTRALIZATION

Figure 10-9 shows a third system of neutralization. This is the system used to neutralize an RF amplifier stage consisting of two triodes in push-pull. It is called CRISS-CROSS NEUTRALIZATION or BALANTINE NEUTRALIZATION. The plate of tube A is joined with the grid of tube B through a neutralizing capacitor; the plate of tube B is joined with the grid of tube A through another neutralizing capacitor. If you examine the circuit of Figure 10-9, you will see that criss-cross neutralization is really a double Hazeltine system.

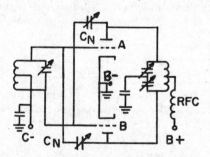

Figure 10-9. Criss-cross neutralization.

10-16 STEPS IN NEUTRALIZING AN RF AMPLIFIER

The previous paragraphs describe the theory of neutralization.

It is important, however, to know the actual practical steps in neutralizing an RF amplifier of a transmitter. There are two methods in general use today. The first method is as follows:

1. Remove the plate voltage from the stage to be neutralized. This is very important since it is impossible to neutralize an amplifier with the plate voltage applied.

2. The stage preceding the stage to be neutralized should have its power on and should be properly tuned to the oscillator frequency. The filament voltage of the stage being neutralized should be on.

3. The grid and plate tank circuits of the stage being neutralized should now be tuned to resonate with the signal coming from the preceding stage. This is done by tuning the grid and plate tank capacitors for a maximum indication of the RF indicator which is coupled to the plate tank circuit. The RF indicator may be a neon bulb or a flashlight bulb connected to a small loop of wire. We can also use a thermocouple ammeter which is connected in series with the plate tank circuit. If a thermocouple ammeter is used, care should be taken not to overload the meter. It is a sensitive instrument that is easily damaged. Any coupling between an indicating instrument and plate tank coil should be made as loose as possible.

4. The neutralizing capacitor or capacitors are then adjusted until the RF indicator shows that the RF energy in the plate tank circuit is at a minimum.

5. Repeat steps 3 and 4 to make sure that the stage is as completely neutralized as possible.

The second method used to neutralize a triode RF amplifier is as follows:

1. Remove the plate voltage from the stage to be neutralized. Keep the filament voltage on.

2. Tune the preceding stages so that there is excitation (a signal input) to the stage to be neutralized.

3. Insert a DC milliammeter in the grid circuit, if one is not already present.

4. Rock the plate tuning capacitor of the stage to be neutralized back and forth, and observe the grid meter. If the grid meter varies, the stage is not neutralized. Then adjust the neutralizing capacitor until rocking of the plate tank capacitor no longer causes the grid meter to vary.

It is not always possible to neutralize an amplifier completely. Therefore, if you neutralize an amplifier by using the first method, do not always expect a zero reading of the RF indicator. It is quite likely that there is stray inductive or capacitive coupling between the stage being neutralized and a preceding stage. The neutralizing capacitor cannot cancel this out. It is also possible that there is insufficient neutralizing capacity or too much stray capacity within the stage itself. Proper wiring and parts layout would remedy this situation to a great extent.

10-16A THE GROUNDED GRID AMPLIFIER

Fig. 10-9A illustrates a grounded grid amplifier. It operates in much the same manner as the ordinary grounded cathode amplifier. The principle difference is that in the grounded grid amplifier, the control grid is grounded, while the cathode is "hot". The signal voltage is applied between the cathode and grid in both cases. The grid bias requirements are the same for both amplifiers. In both cases, the output is taken from the plate circuit.

Neutralization is not required in the grounded grid amplifier because the grid acts as a shield between the output (plate) and the input (cathode). The capacitance between the plate and cathode is about 1/25th of the grid to plate capacity of the same tube in a grounded cathode circuit. The circuit shown in Fig. 10-9A is biased for Class B operation. Class B operation requires that the grid be biased at cutoff. Hence, the plate current will flow only during one-half of the input cycle. However, the L1C2 tank circuit exhibits the "flywheel effect". This means that once the LC circuit is excited, it provides the complete cycle of voltage.

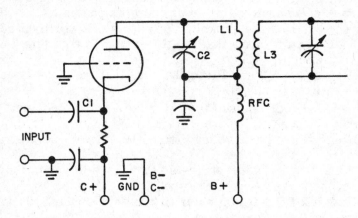

Figure 10-9A. A Class B grounded grid triode amplifier.

The input impedance of the grounded grid amplifier is low and therefore, requires more driver power than a similar circuit using a grounded cathode. The output capacity of the grounded grid system is about one-half that of the grounded cathode system. This allows the grounded grid system to be used at much higher frequencies. The grounded grid amplifier is satisfactory for use as a linear amplifier, for AM, SSB and TV. In the receiving RF amplifier services, the grounded grid amplifier is useful because it is capable of a better noise figure than the grounded cathode system and can therefore be used at much higher frequencies.

A grounded grid amplifier cannot be modulated 100% unless the driver is also modulated about 70%.

10-17 FREQUENCY MULTIPLIERS*

It is not always desirable to have the oscillator of a transmitter generate the frequency which is to be radiated. In order for a crystal controlled oscillator to produce a high frequency, the crystal must be ground very thin. Since a thin crystal can crack easily, it is a good idea to operate the oscillator at a low frequency and to step up the frequency by means of special RF amplifiers. These special RF amplifiers are called FREQUENCY MULTIPLIERS.

Frequency multiplication is made possible by operating a vacuum tube on the non-linear portion of its characteristic curve. As a result, harmonic distortion is developed in the plate circuit. As you have already learned, harmonic distortion results in the generation of new frequencies. These new frequencies are multiples of the original or fundamental frequency. In other words, if we feed 1000 Kc. into the grid circuit of an amplifier which is operated to give strong harmonic distortion, the plate circuit will contain 1000 Kc., 2000 Kc., 3000 Kc., 4000 Kc., etc. The 1000 Kc. is known as the fundamental, 2000 Kc. is the second harmonic, 3000 Kc. is the third harmonic, etc.

Ordinarily, harmonic distortion is to be avoided in an amplifier circuit because distortion alters the waveshape of the original signal. However, when frequency multiplication is required, the signal is deliberately distorted to form strong harmonics. The desired harmonic frequency is then selected with a properly tuned plate circuit. In other words, the plate tank circuit is made resonant to the desired harmonic frequency. The tuned circuit should be sharp enough to accept the desired harmonic, but to reject all other harmonics.

In order to develop strong harmonic distortion, the frequency multiplier tube is heavily biased; even more so than a Class C amplifier. The bias voltage may be as high as ten times the value of cut-off bias. However, this large grid bias requires very strong grid excitation or drive. The signal must be large enough so that the positive peaks of the signal can overcome the large negative grid bias voltage. The plate current consists of positive pulses, but the inertia or flywheel effect of the plate tank circuit will make up the remaining portion of the sine wave of the harmonic frequency peaks.

A unique method of obtaining frequency doubling is to connect up two amplifiers in PUSH-PUSH. In a push-push circuit, the grids are connected in the conventional push-pull arrangement (at opposite ends of a tank circuit). The plates, however, are connected in parallel across a tank circuit which is tuned to double the frequency of the grid input signal. The output of a push-push arrangement is rich in even harmonic components.

---

*Do not confuse the output of a frequency multiplier with PARASITIC OSCILLATIONS. The latter are UNWANTED oscillations not occurring at wanted operating frequencies.

The complete C.W. transmitter of Figure 10-14 contains a FREQUENCY DOUBLER (tube V_2). We call it a frequency doubler because the plate tank circuit is tuned to the second harmonic of the fundamental. If the plate tank were tuned to three times the fundamental, we would call it a FREQUENCY TRIPLER. Note that there is no neutralizing capacitor in the frequency multiplier, even though a triode is being used. This is because the plate and grid circuits of a frequency multiplier are tuned to different frequencies and there is no danger of oscillation due to feedback. Other characteristics of a frequency multiplier, not previously mentioned, are as follows:

1. The plate current flows for approximately 90° or one quarter of the time of an input cycle.

2. The plate efficiency of the frequency multiplier is lower than that of a straight Class C amplifier.

3. The plate tank circuit has a high impedance to the harmonic frequency to which it is tuned (high L to C ratio).

10-18 COUPLING BETWEEN STAGES

There are three types of stage-to-stage coupling used in transmitters. The first type, called CAPACITY COUPLING, is shown in Figure 10-3. It is similar to the resistance capacity coupling used in audio amplifiers. Capacitive coupling, the simplest and least expensive method, consists merely of a coupling capacitor which transfers the RF voltage from the plate of one tube to the grid of the next. In order to match impedances, capacitor C_1 is sometimes connected to a tap on the plate tank coil of the previous stage. The disadvantage of capacity coupling, compared to the other coupling methods, is that undesired harmonics are easily transferred from stage to stage.

Figure 10-8 shows a second method of coupling between stages. It is called INDUCTIVE COUPLING. The RF voltage is magnetically or inductively coupled from L_1 to L_2. Inductive coupling is more expensive than capacitive coupling since it requires two tuned circuits. It also requires additional tuning. The advantage of inductive coupling is that the addition of a tuned grid circuit results in increased gain and power output.

The third method of coupling RF from stage to stage is called LINK COUPLING. Link coupling is a very efficient form of coupling and it may be used between the oscillator and RF amplifier stage, between two RF amplifier stages, between an RF amplifier stage and the final RF amplifier stage and between the final RF amplifier stage and the antenna coupling network. Figure 10-14 shows the doubler (V_2) and the power amplifier (V_3, V_4) link coupled. The actual link coupling consists of a pair of wires with a loop of two or three turns at either end. The chief advantage of this form of coupling is that two stages which are physically some distance from each other, can be coupled. Capacitive or inductive coupling methods could not be used in such a case since long wires cause heavy losses at high frequencies. Long leads have sufficient inductive reactance at high frequen-

176

cies to build up a counter-EMF and cut down the signal strength to the next stage. In link coupling, however, no counter-EMF is induced in the long leads since the current in one leg at a certain instant is opposite in direction to the current in the other leg at the same instant. The resulting magnetic fields are out of phase and therefore, cancel each other. The result is that no back EMF or inductive reactance is created, and the signal is coupled to the next stage without loss.

Notice that each loop is coupled to its respective coil at a point of low RF potential. This is the point where B+ or C- is connected to the tank circuit. B+ and C- are at zero RF potential because the power supply filter capacitors have a negligible impedance to ground at RF. Coupling from points of low RF potential prevents unwanted harmonics from being transferred through the stray capacitive coupling that exists between the tank coils and the link coils.

10-19 KEYING THE TRANSMITTER

At the beginning of this lesson, we learned that the telegraph key is used to start and stop the operation of a CW transmitter. This causes radio waves to be sent out by the antenna in the form of dots and dashes. The telegraph key is merely a switch which opens and closes a circuit or circuits in a transmitter.

While keying may at first thought seem simple, there are many considerations which make it a very important subject for study. These considerations concern not only the simple act of forming dots and dashes by keying, but also the undesired effects that may result from interrupting the operation of the transmitter.

A good keying system should fulfill three requirements:

1. There should be no radiation of energy from the antenna when the key is open (key up). Some energy may get through to the antenna during keying spaces (when the key is open). The energy that is radiated during key-up is called BACKWAVE. A CW signal containing backwave is very difficult to read because a weak signal is heard in the receiver during the space interval between dots and dashes. This signal may be almost as loud as the code reception. A pronounced backwave often results when the keying is done in the amplifier stage feeding the antenna. Backwave may also be caused by incomplete neutralization of the final stage. This allows energy to get to the antenna through the grid-plate capacitance of the tube. A third cause of backwave may be the possible magnetic pickup between the antenna coupling coils and one of the low power stages. Backwave can generally be eliminated by shielding, by proper neutralization, and by rearranging the tank circuits to eliminate unwanted coupling.

2. The keying system should allow the radiation of full power output when the key is closed (key down).

3. The code output should be free of clicks.

When power is applied or removed from a circuit very suddenly, as is the case when a transmitter is keyed, the large amounts of energy that are thus released will surge back and forth and will result in damped oscillations. The damped oscillation will cause interference in nearby receivers. Interference will be present in the form of clicks or thumps, even though the receivers are tuned to different frequencies from that of the transmitter. KEY CLICK FILTERS are used in the keying system of radio transmitters to attenuate or reduce the clicks. A typical key click filter is shown in Figures 10-10 and 10-14. The inductance, L, causes a slight lag in the current which builds up gradually instead of instantly when the key is closed. C and R are connected in series across the key to absorb the spark which tends to occur when the key is opened. The capacitor charges up and prevents a spark from jumping the gap formed by the open key. When the key is closed, the capacitor discharges through R, thereby dissipating the energy of the charged capacitor.

4. The code output should be free of chirps. Chirps occur because the transmitter's output frequency changes when the key contacts are closed and when they are opened. It is difficult to prevent chirps completely because the sudden voltage changes that occur during keying will affect the frequency.

Some of the means by which chirping can be minimized are: use a regulated power supply on the oscillator, key an amplifier rather than the oscillator, use a buffer stage between the keyed amplifier stage and the oscillator stage, use a separate power supply for the oscillator.

10-20 METHODS OF KEYING

Keying takes place in either the oscillator or amplifier stages of the transmitter. A number of different keying systems are in use today. Figure 10-11 illustrates PLATE KEYING. Plate keying may be used in the oscillator or amplifier stages. When the key is open, no plate current can flow and the tube does not operate. When the key is closed, the tube operates and the transmitter sends out RF. The key may be used to control the plate current of one tube or several tubes. Plate keying is usually accomplished in the power amplifier circuit in transmitters which use a crystal controlled oscillator.

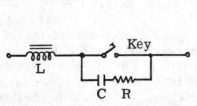

Figure 10-10. Key click filter.

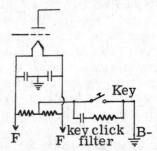

Figure 10-11. Plate keying.

In larger transmitters, the ordinary hand key cannot accom-

178

modate the large plate current flow without excessive arcing. The high plate voltage may also make it too dangerous to operate a hand key in the plate circuit. Therefore, some indirect method of stopping and starting the plate current is called for. Figure 10-12 shows a relay system for indirectly controlling the plate current. When the key is closed, a current from the battery flows through the relay coil. The magnetic field about this coil draws the metal arm, A, towards it. The metal arm moves towards the coil, M, against the tension of the spring, S. As the arm is drawn to M, the relay contact points make contact and the plate current circuit is now complete. When the key is opened for a code space, the coil de-energizes and allows the contact points to be drawn apart by the tension of the spring.

A second method of keying is known as TRANSFORMER PRI-MARY KEYING. In this method, the key is simply inserted in the primary of the high voltage plate transformer which supplied B+ voltage to the stage or stages to be keyed. When the key is depressed, the primary circuit is completed and current will flow through it. The primary current will induce a voltage in the secondary which, in turn, will be rectified as a high B+ voltage and applied to the plate of

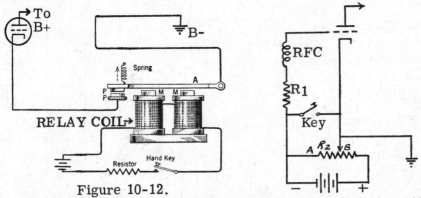

Figure 10-12.
Indirect keying using relay.

Figure 10-13 Blocked-grid keying

the keyed stage. When the key is opened, the primary current will be interrupted and the plate voltage of the keyed stage will drop to zero.

A third and widely used method of keying is called BLOCKED-GRID KEYING. In this method, a high negative bias is applied to the grid of the stage to be keyed. This bias is sufficient to cut off plate current completely, even with excitation applied to the grid. Figure 10-13 illustrates the method of blocked-grid keying. R_1 is the normal grid-leak resistor. R_2 is a voltage dividing resistor across which the entire voltage is placed. When the key is up, the large negative voltage across the AB portion of R_2 is applied to the grid. This voltage is large enough to cut the tube off completely, regardless of the size of the input signal. Therefore, the stage is inoperative and there is no output from the transmitter. When the key is

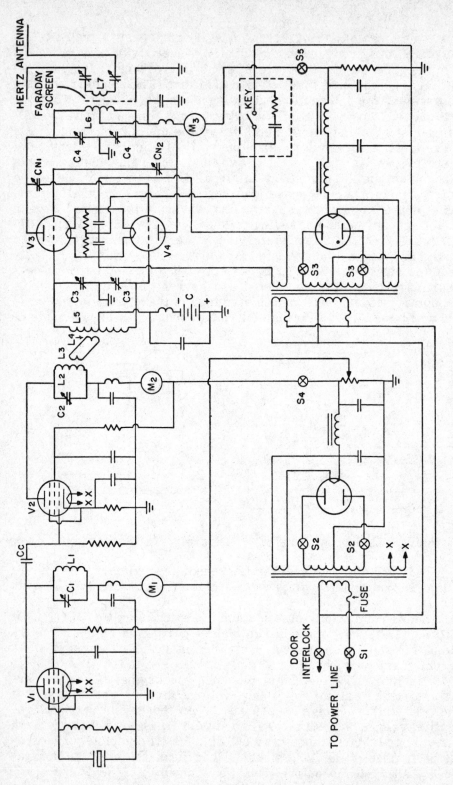

Figure 10-14. Complete CW Transmitter.

depressed, the blocking bias across AB is shorted out, and the only bias in the stage is the grid-leak bias. This is the normal bias for the stage, and the transmitter now radiates its normal output.

10-21 A TYPICAL CW TRANSMITTER

Figure 10-14 is a schematic of a typical MEDIUM POWER CW TRANSMITTER that can be used by amateurs. We will now proceed to discuss in detail the characteristics of this transmitter. The typical CW transmitter, illustrated, consists of two power supplies, an oscillator, a frequency doubler and an RF push-pull amplifier. Let us first discuss the power supplies.

10-22 POWER SUPPLIES

You will notice that there are TWO power supplies in this transmitter instead of one. The oscillator and first RF amplifier (doubler) connect to one power supply, and the power amplifier connects to the second power supply. The reason for having a separate power supply for the oscillator is to prevent the oscillator from becoming unstable. If the oscillator and the final amplifier were to have a common power supply, any load changes which occur in the amplifier would be fed to the oscillator through the common supply. These load changes would cause the voltage on the elements of the oscillator to change. This, in turn, would cause the frequency of the oscillator to vary. The frequency of the output signal would therefore vary. This is a form of undesirable frequency modulation. A transmitter whose frequency drifts or varies is very undesirable because it causes fading at the receiver end and spurious sidebands, which interfere with adjacent frequencies.

One of the requirements for good frequency stability in a transmitter is a well-regulated power supply. A well-regulated power supply consists of a choke input filter and a bleeder. The rectifier tube is usually of the mercury vapor type for two reasons:

1. A mercury vapor rectifier tube has a constant voltage drop regardless of load current changes. This improves the voltage regulation.

2. The mercury vapor tube is capable of supplying the large load current requirements of the transmitter. For a review of power supplies, refer to Lesson 5.

For purposes of safety, a DOOR INTERLOCK SWITCH is used. The door interlock switch shuts off the power to the transmitter when the transmitter door is open. The operator is thereby protected from contact with high voltages inside the transmitter. Notice that the transformer primaries are fused. The fuses protect the various parts of the power supply from damage due to short circuits or overloads. These fuses also prevent power line shut-offs by blowing out before the main power line fuses blow. There is a main on-off switch which turns on filament power for all tubes. Switches S_2 and S_3 in the plate circuit of the rectifier tubes allow the high voltage to be turned on after the mercury vapor rectifiers have had sufficient time to warm

181

up.   Switches S_2 and S_3 in the off-position put the transmitter in "stand-by".

High voltages are present in transmitters. They are dangerous and can cause severe electrical shock, or even death. The following precautions should be observed when working in high voltage circuits:

1. Shut off the power from circuits that you intend to work on.

2. Even if the transmitter has a door interlock switch, check high voltage points with a meter to make sure that the door interlock switch has actually removed the B+ when the door was opened.

3. Short a B+ point to ground with an insulated screw driver to discharge the energy that may remain in the capacitors.

4. If the plate voltage of the final amplifier has to be measured, the meter should be placed between the B+ point and the cathode (or ground) rather than between the plate and cathode. The plate has a high RF voltage on it and there is the danger of arcing or RF burns if anything touches the plate.

In designing electronic equipment that will have high voltages, use bleeder resistors across the power supply filter capacitors. Furthermore, high voltage wires or circuits should not be exposed or in a position where an operator or other person can come in contact with them.

All electronic equipment having high voltage, should be enclosed in metal cabinets. The cabinets should be connected to each other and to a good ground. By a good ground, we mean the cold water system or a ground rod. A description of a ground rod is given in Lesson 12.

10-23 OSCILLATOR AND FREQUENCY DOUBLER

The oscillator in the illustrated CW transmitter is a conventional pentode crystal controlled oscillator. M_1 is a milliammeter which is placed in the plate circuit to measure plate current and to tune the plate tank circuit to resonance with the crystal frequency. Plate tank tuning is indicated by a dip reading (minimum reading) on M_1 (Refer to Lesson 9, Paragraph 9-19). The energy from the oscillator is capacity coupled to the frequency doubler through C_c. The frequency doubler is an RF stage which is tuned to twice the oscillator frequency in the plate circuit. Since it is located between the oscillator and the final amplifier, it is called a buffer stage. It isolates the oscillator from the final amplifier and thereby improves the oscillator frequency stability. Notice that there is no neutralization of the frequency doubler. There are two reasons for this. As we mentioned previously, frequency multipliers do not require neutralization since the grid and plate circuits are tuned to different frequencies. Also, since the tube used is a pentode, the grid-plate capacitance is very small and the plate to grid feedback will therefore be negligible. Neutralization of a pentode or tetrode is only necessary at very high frequencies.

The bias for the frequency doubler stage is a combination of grid-leak bias and cathode bias. Most of the bias voltage comes from the grid-leak resistor; the cathode bias is simply protective bias. The reason for the protective cathode bias is as follows: Among other things, grid-leak bias depends upon the excitation voltage coupled from the preceding stage. If the oscillator were to stop oscillating, there would be no excitation voltage applied to the RF amplifier. The bias would consequently drop from its high negative value to zero, and would cause the plate current to rise to a value high enough to damage the tube. This is a very serious disadvantage of grid-leak bias. The cathode bias that you see in the diagram is a protective bias. It provides for a minimum bias when the grid-leak bias fails. As the plate current rises, the cathode bias also rises.

The buffer RF amplifier is series-fed because the DC component of the plate current flows through the plate coil. RF amplifiers are series fed or shunt fed in the same manner that oscillators are. See Paragraph 9-9 on Page 152. If the buffer RF amplifier is to be designed with a shunt fed circuit, its plate circuit should be similar to the plate circuit of Figure 9-6 on Page 152.

10-24 RF POWER AMPLIFIER

The buffer amplifier is coupled to the final RF amplifier by a link coupling system, as shown in Figure 10-14. Link coupling may be used between any two stages, as well as between the final amplifier and antenna. (Refer to Paragraph 10-18). The output stage is coupled to a simple half-wave antenna (called a Hertz antenna) by means of a tuned line.

The RF power amplifier is connected in push-pull. The advantages to be gathered from push-pull operation are as follows:

1. Even harmonics are cancelled out in the plate circuit, reducing the possibility of serious second harmonic radiation. (Refer to Lesson 8, Paragraph 8-14).

2. The power output is higher than the power output of a single-ended amplifier.

3. There is no need to re-neutralize when the transmitter is tuned from one frequency output to another.

Notice that the RF power amplifier employs:

1. criss-cross neutralization
2. battery bias in the grid circuit
3. key and key-click filter in series with the center-tap return of the filament transformer to ground.

10-25 THE FARADAY SHIELD

One way of reducing or attenuating undesirable radiation of harmonic frequencies is by including a FARADAY SHIELD between the tank coil of the power amplifier and the antenna coupling circuit. In Figure 10-14, the Faraday shield reduces the harmonic transfer of energy through the stray capacity that exists between the inductively coupled coils, L_6 and L_7. The Faraday shield is actually a mesh of metal strips which is grounded to the chassis of the transmitter.

10-26 THE DIRECTLY HEATED POWER AMPLIFIER

Most high power transmitting tubes (see tubes V_3 and V_4 of Figure 10-14) are directly heated triodes using AC for filament power. A directly heated filament presents a problem as far as the return path for the plate and grid circuits are concerned. If we were to connect B- and the bottom of the grid circuit to one side of the filament, the output of the amplifier would have a 60 cycle hum superimposed on the RF. The hum modulation would be radiated and picked up by the receiver as undesirable noise. To prevent hum modulation, the equivalent center point is connected through the key to ground as the return path for the plate and grid circuits (see Figure 10-14). This can also be done by grounding the center tap of the transformer.

10-27 TUNING THE TRANSMITTER

It is very important that the amateur radio operator know how to put a transmitter into operation. We will use the CW transmitter of Figure 10-14 to describe the complete procedure in tuning and operating the transmitter.

We will assume that all the switches are open and that the transmitter has not been used for some time. With the power plug plugged into a 110 AC wall socket, we proceed in the following manner:

1. The main switch S_1 is closed to allow the filaments of all the tubes in the transmitter to heat up. Since the rectifier tubes are of the mercury-vapor type, the filaments of these rectifiers must be heated for several minutes before voltage is applied to the rectifier plates.

2. After the filaments have heated up for a few minutes, switch #2 is closed. Switch #2 is a double pole single throw switch which applies AC voltage to the plates of the rectifier tube of the oscillator-buffer power supply. The oscillator tube now has plate voltage and is ready to be tuned.

3. We tune the oscillator by varying capacitor C_1 and observing meter M_1 for the characteristic crystal oscillator dip. (The tuning procedure for an oscillator was described in Lesson 9, Paragraph 9-19). The oscillator plate tank circuit is now resonant to the crystal frequency and offers maximum impedance to plate current flow.

4. By closing switch #4, we apply B+ voltage to the plate of the buffer-doubler stage. This stage is now ready for tuning.

5. The plate of the buffer-doubler stage is tuned by adjusting C_2 until the plate milliammeter, M_2, dips (reads a minimum). The tuned circuit, $C_2 L_2$, is now resonant to the second harmonic of the oscillator frequency.

6. The push-pull power amplifier stage is now ready to be neutralized. We use either of the two methods of neutralization described in detail in Paragraph 10-15. Neutralizing capacitors N_1 and N_2 are adjusted at the same time.

7. Switch #3 is closed next. This applies AC voltage to the plates of the high voltage rectifier. However, the high B+ voltage is

still not applied to the power amplifier stage. With switch #5 still open, the plate tuning capacitor is turned to the approximate resonant point, as indicated by a marked line on the plate tuning dial. This mark had been previously recorded under operating conditions as being the point of resonance for the plate tank circuit. We can now close switch #5 and be assured that the plate tank is close enough to resonance to prevent excessive plate current flow at the instant the key is closed. Upon closing switch #5, depress the key and immediately adjust C_4 for a minimum reading on M_3. A minimum reading indicates that the tank circuit is at resonance. If the tank circuit is not at resonance, the plate current will rise to a high value.

8. The dummy antenna (not shown) is next hooked up to L_7 and the last stage is then retuned for a minimum reading of M_3.

9. The dummy antenna is removed and the actual antenna is hooked up to the transmitter. C_1, C_2, C_3 and C_4 are retuned slightly and the transmitter is now ready for operation.

10-28 INPUT POWER LIMITATIONS

FOR NOVICE CLASS TRANSMITTERS: Paragraph 97.67(d) of the Federal Communications Commission's Rules and Regulations states as follows: in the frequency bands 3700-3750 kHz, 7100-7150 kHz (7050-7075 kHz when the terrestrial location of the station is not within Region 2), 21,100-21,200 kHz, and 28,100-28,200 kHz, the maximum plate input power which may be utilized is 250 watts. Since these frequencies are those that a Novice may use, the maximum Novice input power is 250 watts.

A few examples will illustrate the method used to calculate the input plate power to a Novice transmitter.

Example #1. What is the input plate power to a Novice transmitter having a final plate voltage of 600 volts, a plate current of 80 ma., a screen voltage of 150 volts, a screen current of 8 ma., a filament voltage of 6.3 volts, a filament current of 500 ma. and a driving power of .6 watts?

Solution: We determine the plate power using the basic power formula:

$$P = EI \qquad \text{where: } \begin{array}{l} P = \text{Plate input power} \\ E = \text{Plate voltage} \\ I = \text{Plate current in amperes} \end{array}$$

$P = 600 \times .08 = 48$ watts.

The other information given in the example is not relevant to the problem. We therefore ignore it.

Example #2. What is the input plate power to a Novice transmitter having a final plate voltage of 750 volts, a plate current of 220 ma., and a filament voltage of 12.6 volts?

$$P = EI \qquad\qquad P = 750 \times .22 = 165 \text{ volts}$$

We ignore the filament voltage since this has nothing to do with the problem.

FOR ALL OTHER CLASSES OF TRANSMITTERS: Paragraph 97.67(a) of the FCC Rules and Regulations states that "....each amateur transmitter may be operated with a power input not exceeding 1 kilowatt to the plate circuit of the final amplifier stage....". Here, the input power is specifically limited to the plate input. Therefore, when we speak of the power input to a transmitter, other than a Novice transmitter, we calculate only the input to the plate and disregard the driving power and the power input to the other elements. The only exception to this rule is when we are dealing with a grounded-grid final amplifier. In this case only, we add the input driving power to the input plate power of the stage.

10-29 THE PI-SECTION OUTPUT CIRCUIT

The Pi-section output circuit is in widespread use in both commercial and amateur transmitters. It provides a certain amount of attenuation of undesired harmonics and it permits the transmitter to be used with a variety of antennas.

Fig. 10-15 illustrates an RF stage using at pi-network output circuit. The pi-network circuit consists of C3, L and C4. This circuit is not too different from the conventional parallel resonant output circuit. C3 is the plate tuning capacitor and C4 is the loading capacitor.

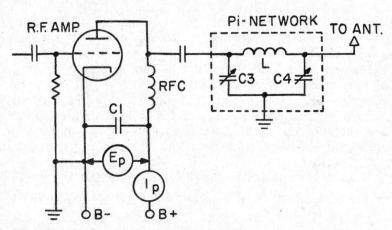

Figure 10-15. An RF amplifier stage using a pi-network output tank circuit. Neutralization is not shown in this diagram.

The proper tune-up procedure for the pi-network output circuit is as follows:

(1) Before power is turned on, adjust C3 and C4 for maximum capacitance.

(2) After the power has been turned on and the circuits ahead of the RF amplifier stage have been tuned up, adjust C3 for minimum reading (dip) on the plate current meter.

(3) Reduce the capacitance of C4 slightly and observe that the

plate current rises.
(4) Readjust C3 for a dip in the plate current.
(5) Reduce the capacity of C4 again and note a further rise in plate current.
(6) Readjust C3 for a dip in plate current.
(7) Repeat steps 5 and 6 until the plate current reading is at its recommended value at the "dip" point. C3 should be the last control to be adjusted.

10-30 RADIO FREQUENCY INTERFERENCE (RFI)

Radio Frequency Interference (RFI) is the interference caused to other equipment by the RF emissions from a transmitter. Amateur stations can cause RF interference to a number of other services. Some of them are: television receivers, standard broadcast receivers, hi-fi equipment and the telephone system.

Television interference (called TVI) is the most important type of interference confronting the amateur. It is discussed in detail in the section 10-31 below. Interference to broadcast receivers and hi-fi equipment is usually due to rectification of the strong RF signal in an early audio stage. This can be cured by shielding and/or by-passing of power leads, speaker leads and other interconnecting leads. By-passing the grid of the first audio tube to the cathode with a .001 mfd. capacitor is important in eliminating this type of interference.

Pickup of the transmitter signal in the telephone lines can usually be cured by RF by-passing of the telephone microphone and their lines.

RFI in P-A systems is handled in a manner similar to that of hi-fi equipment.

10-31 TELEVISION INTERFERENCE

Amateur transmitters frequently cause interference to television receivers. One of the main reasons for this is the fact that the frequencies of the television channels are harmonically related to the amateur band frequencies. An example will make this clear. Let us assume that an amateur is operating at a frequency of 29 Mc. Regardless of how well the transmitter is designed, a certain amount of energy at the second harmonic of 58 Mc. (2 x 29 Mc.) will also be transmitted. Since television Channel 2 is from 54 to 60 Mc., the 58 Mc. signal will cause interference to Channel 2.

One of the important methods of preventing harmonics from being radiated from the transmitter is to install a low pass filter between the transmitter and its antenna. A low pass filter will pass signals below a certain cut-off frequency and block signals above that frequency. In this way, the harmonics will not get through to the antenna to be radiated. In the above example, we would install a low-pass filter with a cut-off frequency of 40 Mc. The 29 Mc. signal would get through, but the 58 Mc. harmonic would be suppressed.

Figure 10-16 illustrates some simple forms of single section

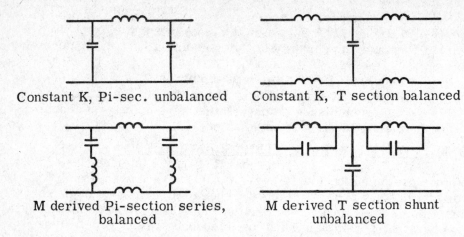

Constant K, Pi-sec. unbalanced   Constant K, T section balanced

M derived Pi-section series,   M derived T section shunt
balanced   unbalanced

Figure 10-16. Various types of low pass filters.

low pass filters, together with the designations of the filters. The designations come about from the fact that the appearance of the various filter configurations resemble letters of the American or Greek alphabet.

Other methods of suppressing spurious and harmonic emissions from the transmitter are as follows:

(1) Use a transmatch or antenna tuner between the transmitter and the transmission line. Fig. 10-17 is a block diagram showing where the filter and tuner are inserted in a transmitter installation.

(2) Use a transmitter circuit design and layout that will not cause harmonic and spurious signals in the TV bands.

(3) Where possible, use link coupling and tuned circuits.

(4) Shield the transmitter adequately. Ground all cabinets to a good common ground such as the cold water pipe or a ground rod.

(5) Keep plate and screen voltages as low as possible.

(6) Reduce excessive grid drive to the final stage.

(7) Check all mechanical joints and connections in the antenna system and ground system. Make sure that they are tight and free of corrosion.

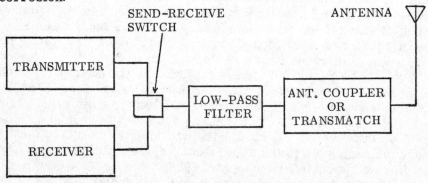

Figure 10-17. Block diagram of a radio station.

The above paragraphs deal with television interference caused by spurious and harmonic output from the transmitter. Television interference can also be caused by receiver deficiencies. A receiver that is not highly selective will respond to interfering signals outside of its frequency band. This is usually true of TV receivers located in the vicinity of a transmitter. For instance, let us assume that an amateur, operating at 29 MHz, has adequate harmonic suppression and transmits a clean signal. A TV receiver, located close by, will be swamped with the 29 MHz signal. It will overload the receiver's front end and by means of rectification in the receiver, harmonics will be produced. The second harmonic of 29 MHz is 58 MHz, which falls inside of Channel 2 and will cause interference as though the amateur transmitter were transmitting a 58 MHz signal.

The way to prevent this type of interference is to install a high-pass filter at the receiver's antenna terminals in series with the antenna. A high-pass filter will pass signals above a certain cut-off frequency and reject signals below this frequency. We choose a high-pass filter with a cut-off frequency below the television frequencies. For instance, 40 MHz could be used as the cut-off frequency. The television signals will pass through without attenuation, but the signals below the cut-off frequency will not be allowed to pass. In the above example, the 29 MHz Amateur signal would be attenuated while the TV signals, which are above 50 MHz would pass without attenuation. Some typical single section high-pass filters are illustrated in Fig. 10-18. Filters with greater attenuation can be made by combining two or more single section filters in series.

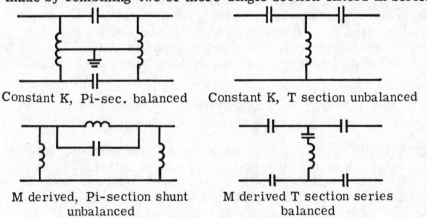

Constant K, Pi-sec. balanced   Constant K, T section unbalanced

M derived, Pi-section shunt   M derived T section series
unbalanced   balanced

Figure 10-18. Various types of high-pass filters.

Other methods of reducing TVI at the receiver end are:
(1) Use wave traps tuned to the transmitting frequency at the antenna and/or the power lines.
(2) Use an AC line filter.
(3) Use a high gain TV receiving antenna.
(4) Use a shielded type of transmission line.

(5) Check the receiving antenna for broken elements, corroded joints and poor electrical and mechanical connections. Corroded joints and poor electrical connections can behave as rectifiers, causing harmonic generation.

10-32 CHOOSING AN OPERATING FREQUENCY.

Radio amateurs are not assigned specific operating frequencies. They can operate anywhere they want to, within specified band limits. In other words, an amateur holding a Novice license, can operate on any frequency within the 3700 kHz to 3750 kHz band. The operating frequency that is chosen depends upon many factors. If he wishes to communicate with Amateur Station W2ABC who is in contact with Amateur Station W6XYZ, he sets his station frequency at or near W6XYZ and waits until the two amateurs have finished their contact. He then calls Station W2ABC. The reason he sets his frequency on W6XYZ's frequency is that W2ABC is listening to the frequency that Station W6XYZ is transmitting on. In most instances, two stations in contact with each other are on the same frequency.

If an amateur wishes to communicate with any other amatuer or if he wishes to communicate with a particular area, he chooses a clear frequency and calls "CQ" or CQ to a particular area. In choosing a clear frequency, he first listens in on the frequency that he wishes to use to make certain that no one is on the frequency.

If an amateur is operating his station close to the edge of the band, he must make absolutely certain that he is not operating outside of the band. Lesson 12 discusses the various methods that are used to determine the exact operating frequency.

The band that an amateur uses depends upon the distance to be covered, the time of day, the time of the year, etc. The chart in Lesson 12 lists the propagation characteristics of the various bands.

PRACTICE QUESTIONS - LESSON 10
(For answers, refer to Appendix 6)

10-1 The purpose of using a center-tap return connection on the secondary of a transmitting tube's filament transformer is to:
    a. allow the filaments to heat up   b. permit power output
    c. prevent modulation of the RF by the AC filament supply
    d. prevent radiation of spurious harmonics

10-2 A separate power supply is used for the oscillator stage of a transmitter:
    a. because the filaments require a separate heating source
    b. because a lower plate voltage is required
    c. to prevent frequency instability due to load variations being fed back through a common power supply
    d. to increase the frequency bandwidth radiated due to a common power supply.

10-3* The principle advantage of a screen-grid type RF amplifier tube over a triode of equal output rating is:
a. it does not require neutralization
b. it has more gain
c. it has higher interelectrode capacity
d. the need for lower operating voltages

10-4* Describe the adjustment procedure for proper neutralization in a radio-frequency power amplifier using an RF indicator coupled to the plate tank circuit.

10-5* A triode radio-frequency power amplifier must be neutralized:
a. to increase power output
b. to prevent self-oscillations
c. to eliminate second harmonic radiation
d. when used as a frequency doubler

10-6* The result of operating an unneutralized RF triode power amplifier would be:
a. decreased output   c. a decrease in harmonic content
b. spurious radiation   d. varying load condition

10-7* One of the characteristics of an RF frequency doubler amplifier is NOT:
a. high negative grid bias   b. large excitation signal
c. high impedance plate circuit tuned to twice the excitation frequency
d. low impedance plate circuit tuned to the same frequency as the excitation voltage

10-8 Where is link coupling applicable in a transmitter?

10-9* The first step in neutralizing an RF amplifier is to:
a. remove the plate voltage
b. tune the plate circuit to resonance
c. adjust the neutralizing capacitor for minimum output on the RF indicator
d. tune the grid circuit to resonance

10-10* The symbol for telegraphy, using unmodulated RF, is:
a. AØ   b. A1   c. A2   d. A3

10-11* A power output RF amplifier SHOULD NOT:
a. be coupled to the antenna system
b. have minimum plate current at resonance
c. couple high harmonics to the antenna
d. be matched to the output circuit impedance

10-12* The plate current of a radio-frequency power amplifier at resonance:
a. is a minimum   c. does not change
b. is a maximum   d. increases a bit over non-resonance

10-13* In a pi-network output circuit, the input capacitor should be:
  a. tuned for minimum antenna current
  b. tuned for maximum plate current
  c. tuned for minimum plate current
  d. a and c are correct

10-14* Draw a simple schematic diagram of a plate-neutralized final triode RF stage coupled to a Hertzian antenna, showing the antenna system and a Faraday screen to reduce harmonic radiation.

10-15* The principle purpose of using door interlock switches is to:
  a. eliminate the need of turning off transmitter
  b. act as an on-off switch
  c. protect equipment against mishandling by incompetent personnel
  d. prevent personnel from being accidentally shocked by dangerous voltages when cage to transmitter is open

10-16* The circuit condition which WILL NOT minimize harmonic components in the output circuit of an RF amplifier is:
  a. low L/C ratio   c. push-pull operation
  b. improper neutralization   d. proper bias voltage

10-17* TVI can be eliminated by a:
  a. high-pass filter at the receiver
  b. high-pass filter at the transmitter
  c. high-pass filter at the receiver and a low-pass filter at the transmitter
  d. low-pass filter at the receiver

10-18* The principle disadvantage to using a grid-leak as the only source of bias in a Class C RF power amplifier is:
  a. poor efficiency
  b. varying bias voltage
  c. it distorts output
  d. loss of excitation will drop bias to zero, resulting in heavy plate current

10-19* An advantage of a grounded grid amplifier is:
  a. the full excitation voltage appears between cathode and ground
  b. low driving power is required
  c. a higher noise figure is possible
  d. the input impedance is high

SECTION III – LESSON 11
THE MODULATED TRANSMITTER

11-1 INTRODUCTION

In the previous lesson, we learned how a CW transmitter operates. Communication by means of CW code transmission is known as RADIOTELEGRAPHY. The disadvantage of radiotelegraphy transmission is that the radio operator must know code. In order that operators who are not familiar with code be able to send and receive messages directly, the transmission of speech is necessary. The transmission of audio (speech) by means of radio communication is known as RADIOTELEPHONY.

A radiotelephone transmitter consists of a CW transmitter (minus the telegraph key), plus an audio frequency amplifier system. The audio frequency system amplifies the audio signals and superimposes them on the RF signal that is generated by the RF oscillator. The process of superimposing the audio on the RF is known as MODULATION. The RF signal is called a CARRIER since it "carries" the audio through space to the receiving antenna. (Refer back to the introduction to transmission and reception at the beginning of Lesson 9).

11-2 AMPLITUDE MODULATION

There are several methods of modulating a carrier. The method which interests us as amateurs is called AMPLITUDE MODULATION.

In amplitude modulation, the modulating frequency is the intelligence (voice or music) which is to be transmitted through space to receivers many miles away. The modulating frequency is audio and, by itself, cannot be transmitted. A radio-frequency wave, however, is capable of being transmitted through space. If we combine or mix an audio-frequency wave with a radio-frequency wave in a special mixing circuit, we obtain an RF output which contains the audio and can be transmitted. Figure 11-1 illustrates a voice modulated radio-

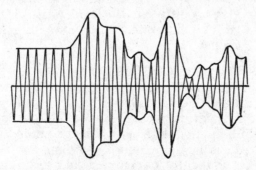

Figure 11-1. Radio wave modulated with voice.

frequency wave whose amplitude varies according to the amplitude of
the audio wave, thus the term "amplitude modulation". The frequency
of this variation is the same as the audio modulating frequency. (The
abbreviation for amplitude modulation is AM). An AM wave is, therefore, a radio-frequency wave which contains in its amplitude variations, the audio or intelligence which we desire to transmit.

11-3 THE AM TRANSMITTER

A block diagram of a typical amplitude modulated radiotelephone
transmitter is shown in Figure 11-2. Above each block is drawn the
waveshape of the voltage output of that particular stage. With the aid
of these waveshapes and the block diagram layout, we shall discuss
the operation of the radiotelephone transmitter.

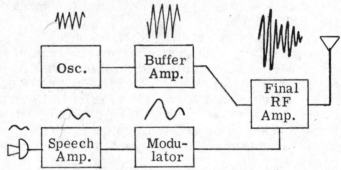

Figure 11-2. Block diagram of amplitude-modulated transmitter.

To begin with, the oscillator stage generates a radio-frequency
voltage called the carrier. Following the oscillator is the buffer-
amplifier stage which amplifies the output of the oscillator and isolates the oscillator from the power amplifier. The final stage is the
power amplifier which delivers energy to the antenna. Notice that the
output waveshape of the final RF stage does not resemble the input
waveshape from the buffer. The RF waveshape has been altered by
modulation. This brings us to the modulation or audio section. The
microphone converts the sound that is to be transmitted into electrical
variations. The weak output of the microphone is fed into an audio
amplifier (speech amplifier). The output of the speech amplifier
drives an audio power amplifier called a MODULATOR. The modulator injects the audio signals into the RF power amplifier to produce
the modulated RF output.

11-4 PERCENTAGE OF MODULATION

The method by which the audio signal is actually injected into
RF amplifier will be discussed later on. We will now explain the
term "amount of modulation" as expressed in a percentage number.

It is possible to modulate with a large audio voltage or with a
small audio voltage. A large modulating voltage causes a large variation in the peaks of the RF carrier, which results in a large percentage of modulation. A small audio voltage causes a small variation

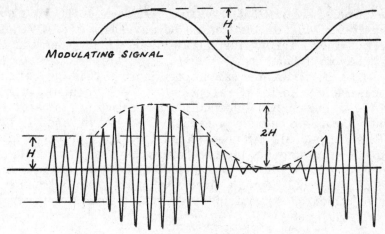

Figure 11-3. 100% amplitude modulation.

in the peaks of the RF carrier, which results in a low percentage of modulation. By examining the waveshape of a modulated carrier, it is possible to determine the numerical percentage of modulation.

For example, Figure 11-3 illustrates a carrier 100% modulated. Notice that the highest peak of the modulated wave is exactly twice as high as the peak of the carrier before modulation. Also notice that the minimum point of the modulated signal is at zero amplitude. In other words, the peaks of the carrier, modulated, vary 100% above and below the peaks of the unmodulated carrier. This is the condition for 100% modulation. Figure 11-4 shows an example of 50% modulation. The carrier of Figure 11-4 is the same in amplitude as the carrier of Figure 11-3. The modulating signal of Figure 11-4 is, however, half the amplitude of the modulating signal of Figure 11-3. The maximum peak of the modulated signal is one and one-half times the peak of the unmodulated carrier, and the minimum peak is one half times the peak of the unmodulated carrier. In other words, the peaks of the modulated carrier vary 50% above and below the peaks of the unmodulated carrier.

If the carrier level is kept the same and the modulating sig-

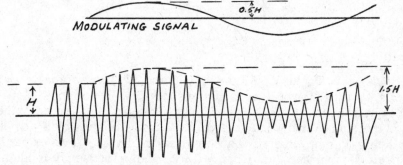

Figure 11-4. 50% amplitude modulation.

195

nal is increased above that of Figure 11-3, we get the wave shown in Figure 11-5. This illustration is the waveshape of an OVERMODU-LATED carrier. During the interval labeled "C", there is actually no output from the antenna.

The 100% modulated carrier of Figure 11-3 is theoretically the most desirable in terms of reception. A 100% modulated signal produces the strongest possible undistorted signal at the receiver end. The 50% modulated carrier of Figure 11-4 is considered an UNDER-MODULATED signal. An undermodulated signal produces an undistorted but weak signal at the receiver end. The overmodulated carrier of Figure 11-5 is highly undesirable since it results in a distorted signal at the receiver end. Overmodulation also produces spurious radiation which causes interference with transmitters operating on nearby frequencies.

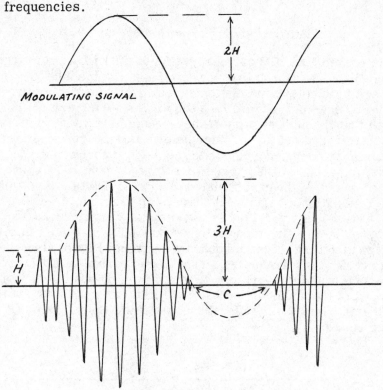

Figure 11-5. Overmodulation.

11-5 SIDEBANDS

The waveshapes of Figures 11-3 and 11-4 are actually the result of a combination of several frequencies. It is not possible to tell, merely by looking at a waveshape, what frequencies are combined to give it the shape that it has. However, these frequencies can be determined by a complicated mathematical analysis. For example, it has been determined that when a 1 Kc. audio-frequency modulates a 1000 Kc. carrier, the resultant signal will be a complex modulated wave containing the following component frequencies:

1 Kc. ⎫
1000 Kc. ⎬ - the original frequencies
1001 Kc. - the sum of the original frequencies
999 Kc. - the difference of the original frequencies

Whenever any two frequencies combine by modulation, the resultant waveshape will contain the <u>original frequencies plus the sum and difference of the original frequencies.</u> These new sum and difference frequencies are known as SIDEBAND FREQUENCIES or simply SIDEBANDS. In the above example, the 1001 Kc. component is known as the UPPER SIDEBAND. The 999 Kc. component is known as the LOWER SIDEBAND. If the audio frequency had been 2 Kc., the upper sideband would have been 1002 Kc., and the lower sideband would have been 998 Kc. The higher the audio modulation frequency, the farther both sidebands are removed from the carrier frequency.

When speech or music is used to modulate a carrier, many audio modulating frequencies are present. Each audio frequency will produce an upper sideband frequency and a lower sideband frequency. Therefore, speech or music modulation generates a wide band of frequencies. The difference in kilocycles between the uppermost side band and lowest sideband is called the BANDWIDTH of the modulated carrier. The bandwidth of a carrier is equal to twice the highest audio modulating frequency used. For example, if the carrier is 1000 Kc. and the highest audio modulating frequency is 5 Kc., the band width is 10 Kc. (1005 Kc. - 995 Kc.). If the highest audio modulating frequency is 3 Kc., the bandwidth is 6 Kc. In other words, the AM signal consisting of a carrier and sidebands actually occupies 6 Kc. of the radio frequency spectrum. Thus, when we say that station W2XYZ is operating on phone at 7250 kHz, what we really mean is that he is occupying that part of the band between 7247 kHz and 7253 kHz. A term used to describe the total width of a signal is the "occupied bandwidth of an emission". A highly technical definition of the "occupied bandwidth of an emission" is "the band of frequencies comprising 99% of the total radiated power, extended to include any discrete frequency on which the power is at least 0.25% of the total radiated power".

Compared to a phone signal, a CW signal consists only of a carrier and therefore, has no bandwidth. (Practically speaking, however, the keying causes a bandwidth of 100 cycles or less, depending on the code speed).

Since the ham bands are congested, it is important to keep the bandwidth of the modulated signal as narrow as possible. We can do this by limiting our audio frequencies to those below 3000 Hz. The bandwidth will thus be limited to 6 kHz. This will not hurt the quality of the signal since the bulk of the voice frequencies are below 3000 Hz.

The fact that an amplitude modulated signal has sidebands should be considered in calculating how close a transmitter can be set to a band's edge. The sidebands, as well as the carrier, must be within the band limits. We must therefore add the maximum possible transmitter tolerance to the highest audio modulating frequency, and stay away from the band edge by at least this amount. An example will make this clear:

How close can we operate to 14,200 Kc. (the lower band limit of the 20 meter phone band) with a transmitter whose accuracy is guaranteed to $\pm$ .01% and whose highest audio modulating frequency is 3 Kc.?

First we find the maximum possible error in the transmitter frequency: 14,200 Kc. x .0001 = 1.42 Kc.

We then add this to 3 Kc.

1.42 Kc. + 3 Kc. = 4.42 Kc.

The 4.42 Kc. is then added to the lower band edge frequency:

4.42 Kc. + 14,200 Kc. = 14,204.42 Kc.

Therefore, the closest we can set the transmitter carrier is 14,204.42 Kc. In the event that the transmitter does have the maximum error in the low frequency direction, the entire signal, including the lower sidebands, will still be inside the band.

11-6 POWER IN THE SIDEBANDS

If the modulator of a radiotelephone transmitter were turned off, the carrier would continue to be radiated as CW transmission by the RF section of the transmitter. As soon as the modulator is turned on, the carrier is amplitude modulated and the sideband frequencies come into existence. Since the modulated wave contains frequencies in addition to the carrier, there must be more power in the modulated wave than in the unmodulated wave. The additional power is supplied by the modulator stage and is contained in the sidebands of the transmission.

11-7 METHODS OF MODULATION

In the last few paragraphs, we have discussed the general principles of amplitude modulation. We are now ready to study exactly how the audio signal is superimposed on to the carrier.

There are many different methods of amplitude modulation. The most common method is to apply the audio-frequency modulating voltage to the plate of one of the RF amplifiers. This popular method is known as PLATE MODULATION. If the audio-frequency modulating voltage is applied to the control grid of the RF amplifier, we have what is called GRID MODULATION. If a pentode power amplifier is modulated by applying the audio-frequency modulating voltage to the suppressor grid, we have SUPPRESSOR MODULATION. SCREEN GRID MODULATION and CATHODE MODULATION can be similarly accomplished by applying the audio-frequency modulating voltage to the screen and cathode electrodes respectively. In other words, the method of modulation is determined by the electrode of the RF amplifier tube to which the audio frequency modulating voltage is applied.

Since there are several RF amplifier stages in a transmitter, a transmitter designer has his choice as to which stage shall be modulated. Modulating the final RF stage of a radiotelephone transmitter is known as HIGH LEVEL MODULATION. The term is derived from the fact that the modulation takes place at the highest power level of the transmitter. If the modulation process takes place in a stage preceding the final stage, the system is known as LOW LEVEL MODULATION. In low level modulation, the RF amplifiers which follow the modulated stage are operated as linear or Class A amplifiers, rather than Class C. A Class C amplifier will distort the audio component of the modulated signal, whereas a Class A amplifier will amplify all signal frequencies without distortion. If the audio component of the modulated wave is distorted, the receiver will, in turn, reproduce a distorted audio signal. In high level modulation, the final RF amplifier is always operated as a Class C amplifier. High level modulation is the most efficient modulation system, and is also much more popular than low level modulation.

Most commercial and amateur transmitters use either plate or control grid high level modulation. We will discuss these two systems in detail.

11-8 PLATE MODULATION

There are several methods of plate modulation. The simplest method of plate modulation is illustrated in Figure 11-6. The audio-frequency output of the modulator stage is coupled through transformer, T, to the plate circuit of the power amplifier. Transformer T is called the modulation transformer. The audio voltage across the secondary, S, of the modulation transformer is in series with the B+ voltage which is applied to the plate of the RF power amplifier stage. Figure 11-7A shows the audio voltage.

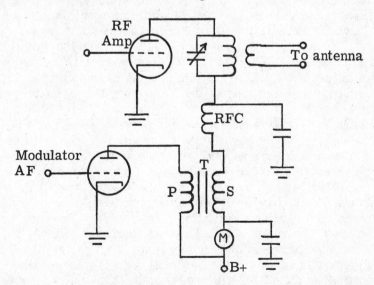

Figure 11-6. Transformer-coupled modulator circuit.

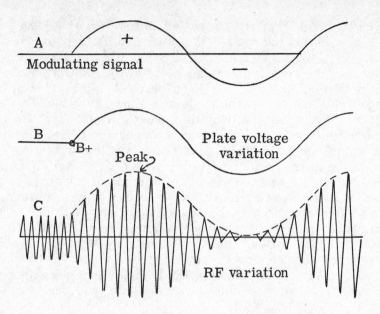

Figure 11-7. Amplitude modulation.

When the audio voltage causes the top of the transformer secondary, S, to go positive with respect to the bottom, the audio voltage
and the power supply voltage will aid each other in series. The plate
voltage of the RF amplifier stage will, therefore, be the sum of the
power supply voltage and the audio voltage. Figure 11-7B shows the
rise in the RF amplifier plate voltage above the B+ value during the
positive alternation of the audio. Since the plate power input to the
stage is directly dependent upon the plate voltage, the plate power
input will increase during the positive audio alternation. An increase
in plate power input will, in turn, cause the useful power output to
increase. The RF output, therefore, rises during the positive half
of the audio cycle. Figure 11-7C illustrates the RF output voltage
waveform before the modulating audio voltage is applied, and the resulting increase in amplitude of the RF during the positive peaks of
modulation.

During the negative half of the audio cycle, the top of the transformer secondary, S, is negative with respect to the bottom. Now
the audio voltage and the power supply voltage are in series opposing.
Therefore, the two voltages buck each other and the plate voltage of
the RF amplifier is the difference between the two voltages. Figure
11-7B shows the drop in the RF amplifier plate voltage below the B+
value during the negative alternation of the audio. The drop in plate
voltage causes the plate power input to decrease which, in turn,
causes the useful power output to decrease. Figure 11-7C shows the
resulting decrease in amplitude of the RF during the negative peaks
of the audio. Figure 11-7C also shows the RF output over a few cycles. Figure 11-1 illustrates the RF output from a transmitter that

has been modulated by speech or music, which is a complex audio signal.

11-9 PLATE CURRENT IN PLATE MODULATION

In Figure 11-6, "M" is a DC milliammeter which measures the DC plate current of the modulated RF stage. During normal modulation (100% or under), the DC plate current REMAINS CONSTANT. If the percent modulation does not increase beyond 100%, there will be no distortion of the RF wave. The instantaneous increase in plate current will, therefore, be exactly the same as the instantaneous decrease in the plate current. Therefore, the average plate current change is zero. The DC plate current meter, therefore, reads the same plate current when the power RF amplifier stage is either modulated or unmodulated.

11-10 THE PUSH-PULL MODULATOR

The single ended (one tube) modulator stage of Figure 11-6 is operated Class A so that there will be no distortion of the amplified modulating signal. The disadvantage of a one tube Class A amplifier is that it operates at low efficiency. A low efficiency tube cannot always deliver the power that is required of a modulator stage. A push-pull amplifier which is capable of delivering more power than a single tube is, therefore, to be preferred. Figure 11-8 illustrates a push-pull modulator circuit.

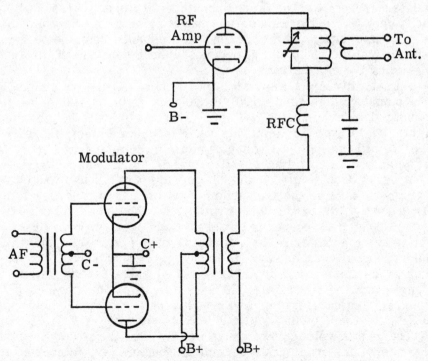

Figure 11-8. A push-pull modulator circuit.

201

The push-pull modulator may be operated either Class A or Class B, depending upon the power output requirements. A Class B push-pull amplifier is more efficient, but it does require a large driving power applied to its grid circuit. The positive peaks of the grid signal usually drive the grid into grid current. Flow of grid current causes power to be dissipated in the grid circuit. The driver stage must be able to supply the power dissipated in the grid circuit.

If the bias power supply of the modulator of Figure 11-8 became short-circuited, there would be no bias voltage on the grids. The plate current would rise and probably cause damage to the tubes.

A push-pull amplifier operated Class A does not operate in the grid current region and therefore, requires very little grid driving power from the driver stage. The Class A push-pull amplifier amplifies the audio modulating voltage without distortion. The Class B modulator introduces a slight amount of distortion into the modulating signal.

11-11 POWER RELATIONS IN A PLATE MODULATED TRANSMITTER

We can summarize the power relations that exist in a Class C modulated power amplifier by stating that the power required to generate the carrier wave is supplied from the RF amplifier DC plate supply, while the power required to generate the sidebands is supplied by the modulator. The amount of modulating power required to modulate a transmitter depends upon three factors. First of all, it depends upon the type of modulation that is being used (plate modulation, grid modulation, etc.). Secondly, it depends upon the percentage of modulation. Thirdly, it depends upon the nature of the audio that is doing the modulating.

An examination of Figure 11-3 will show that the peak modulated RF output voltage during 100% modulation is twice as high as the unmodulated output carrier voltage. This is also true for the plate current. The RF power amplifier when modulated must, therefore, be capable of handling peak voltages and currents that are twice as great as unmodulated voltages and currents. Since the voltage and current peaks double on 100% modulation, the power peaks will go up four times as high as the unmodulated power. This is because the power is equal to the product of the voltage and the current (2 x 2 = 4). We refer to the peak power as the Peak-Envelope Power or PEP. It is defined as the power in the modulator envelope at the instant the modulated signal reaches its peak (see Fig. 11-7). Thus, if the unmodulated carrier power input to the final stage is 200 watts, the PEP input will be 800 watts. If the efficiency of the stage is 70%, the unmodulated carrier output will be 140 watts (200 x .7 = 140) and the PEP output will be 560 watts (800 x .7 = 560).

The peak envelope power tells us only what the power is at the very peaks of the modulation envelope. We are also interested in knowing what the AVERAGE POWER is. The average power of a modulated signal is defined as the power averaged over several cycles of the modulating signal. By mathematical analysis, it is found that with 100% sine wave modulation, the average is 1.5 times the unmodulated carrier power. In other words, the average output or input power of a transmitter increases by 50% when it is modulated 100% by a sine wave signal. For example, if the unmodulated plate power input to the final RF power amplifier stage is 200 watts (refer to Lesson 6, Paragraph 6-8 for a discussion of plate power input), the modulator power output should be 100 watts for 100% modulation. The power input to the RF power amplifier stage has been increased by 50% ($\frac{100}{200}$ x 100 = 50) from 200 to 300 watts. If speech or music is used to modulate the carrier, the output modulator power that is required need be approximately one-fourth of the RF input power. In the above example, the average modulator power output for speech modulation would be about 50 watts. (1/4 of 200 = 50). This assures that the peaks of the speech modulation do not overmodulate the RF power amplifier. The power input to the RF power amplifier is increased by 25% ($\frac{50}{200}$ x 100 = 25%) from 200 to 250 watts.

It should be noted that while the average power increase for speech modulation is less than that for sine wave modulation, the peak envelope power is the same for both of them. Since 100% modulation increases the power to the modulated RF stage by 50%, the plate losses (refer to Lesson 6, Paragraph 6-9) are increased by 50%. The RF stage must be capable of handling this extra loss. Therefore, a transmitter which is designed for both CW and phone operation is adjusted for a lower plate voltage, with a resulting lower carrier power, in phone operation.

For 100% pure sine wave modulation, the modulator supplies an amount of power to the RF amplifier equal to 50% of the DC power input of the unmodulated RF amplifier stage. The total power increase in the modulated carrier is, therefore, 50%. This 50% increase in power is contained in the sidebands. The sidebands contain one-third of the total modulated carrier power for 100% modulation. For example, if the unmodulated carrier power is 200 watts, the 100% modulated carrier power would be 300 watts (50% increase in power). The increased 100 watts of power is contained in the sidebands. The sidebands, therefore, contain $\frac{100}{300}$ or one-third of the total modulated carrier power. Since the total sidebands contain one-third of the power, the upper and lower sidebands each contain one-sixth of the total power.

11-12 GRID MODULATION

Plate modulation requires a large amount of audio modulating power. Grid modulation, in comparison, requires very little audio modulating power.

Grid modulation operates by varying the bias to the grid of the RF power amplifier in accordance with the audio modulating voltage. The varying bias, in turn, causes the power output of the RF power amplifier to vary.

Grid modulation is illustrated in Figure 11-9. The primary of the modulation transformer T_2 is connected to the plate of the modulator. The secondary of T_2 is in series with the grid bias power supply of the RF amplifier. The grid bias power supply can either be supplied by a battery or a rectifier type power supply. The audio modulation varies the voltage across the secondary of transformer T_2 in polarity and amplitude. This varying voltage adds to or subtracts from the bias supply, resulting in a varying bias voltage on the grid of the RF power amplifier. The varying bias causes a varying RF output, which is the modulated carrier. The purpose of capacitor C is to by-pass the RF around the secondary of the modulator transformer.

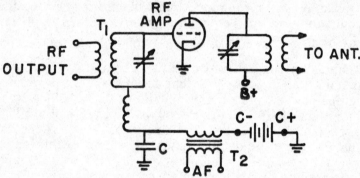

Figure 11-9. Grid modulation.

The last audio or modulator stage must be operated as a Class A amplifier if fidelity of reproduction is to be maintained. The comparatively low output of a Class A audio amplifier is sufficient for grid modulation because low power is required to vary the grid bias of the RF amplifier. The modulated carrier power of a grid modulated transmitter is about one-quarter of the output of a similar plate modulated transmitter. Because of the low efficiency and low power output, grid modulation is seldom used.

11-13 A TYPICAL RADIOTELEPHONE TRANSMITTER

Figure 11-10 illustrates a simple low power plate modulated radiotelephone transmitter. The power supplies have been omitted from the diagram for the sake of simplicity.

V_1 is a triode crystal controlled oscillator, and V_2 is the modulated RF amplifier. The details of the operation of these two stages have been adequately covered in Lesson 10. We will now discuss the audio section in detail.

V_3, the speech amplifier, is a high gain pentode which amplifies the weak audio voltage output of the high impedance crystal micro-

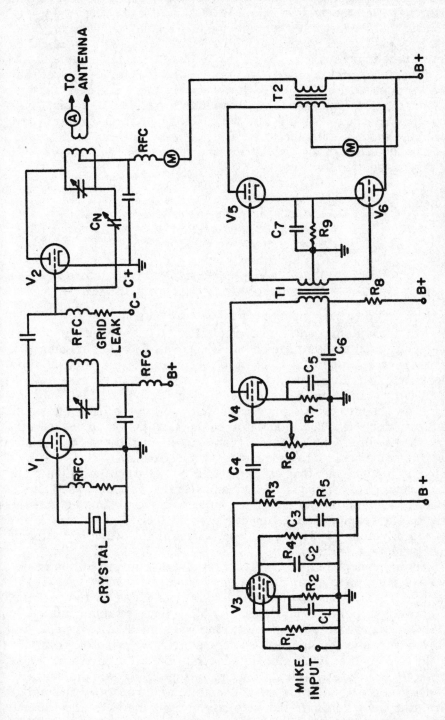

Figure 11-10. A typical radiotelephone transmitter.

phone. The output of V_3 is resistance coupled to a medium gain triode V_4, through R_6, the audio volume control. The setting of R_6 will determine the average percentage modulation of the carrier. The output of V_4 is transformer coupled by T_1 to V_5 and V_6. T_1 is called an interstage transformer. It serves to match the impedance of the plate of V_4 to the grids of V_5 and V_6. V_5 and V_6 may be operated in Class AB push-pull. Class AB is commonly used since it exhibits efficiency and fidelity characteristics which are midway between Class A and Class B operation. T_2 is the modulation transformer which couples the modulator stage to the RF power amplifier.

The function of the resistors and capacitors which have NOT been discussed are given below:

R_1 - Grid return resistor
R_2, R_7, R_9 - Cathode bias resistors
C_1, C_5, C_7 - Cathode by-pass capacitors
C_2 - Screen by-pass capacitor
R_4 - Screen dropping resistor
C_4 - Coupling capacitor
R_5, R_8 - Plate decoupling or isolating resistors
C_3, C_6 - Plate decoupling or isolating capacitors

11-14 CHECKING FOR PERCENT OF MODULATION

For maximum undistorted radiation of energy into space, a properly adjusted transmitter should be operated at 100% modulation. It is, therefore, important to be able to determine the point of 100% modulation of a transmitter.

A very simple method of determining the point of 100% modulation is to observe the DC plate current meter in the RF stage which is being modulated. The modulator output is adjusted up to the point where the needle of the plate current meter just begins to flicker. When this occurs, we are modulating at approximately 100%. It was previously pointed out that there should be no variation in the plate current reading of a modulated RF amplifier that is properly adjusted. A slight movement of the DC plate current meter indicates that the peaks of the speech modulation are driving the RF power amplifier stage slightly above 100% modulation. This slight overmodulation at the peak can be tolerated.

Another check on the proper point of 100% modulation is to observe the RF ammeter in the antenna circuit. (See Figure 11-10). When the transmitter is modulated, power is added to the carrier. The total output power is increased by 50% from the unmodulated to the 100% modulated condition (pure sine wave modulation). The antenna current should, therefore, rise approximately 22% from the unmodulated to the 100% modulated condition. If a pure sine wave audio note is not available to check for this 22% rise, the operator should whistle or hum a steady note into the microphone to simulate a pure sine wave note. If the antenna current meter reads 100 ma. with the transmitter unmodulated, the meter reading should increase about 22% to 122 ma. with the transmitter modulated 100% (22% of 100 ma. = 22 ma.).

A third way of checking modulation is by means of an instrument called a PEAK MODULATION MONITOR. The peak modulation monitor simply indicates when we are overmodulating. It does not tell us the percentage of modulation. Figure 11-11 shows a peak modulation monitor hooked up to a transmitter.

The monitor consists of a diode and a milliammeter in series across the modulation transformer. When overmodulation occurs, the plate voltage of the RF amplifier becomes negative with respect to ground during the negative peaks of the modulating wave. (During this time, the output of the transmitter drops to zero, as indicated by interval "C" of Figure 11-5). When the plate of the RF amplifier is negative with respect to ground, the diode will conduct because the cathode of the diode is connected to the plate of the RF amplifier, and the plate of the diode is connected to ground. This diode current will flow through the milliammeter, indicating a condition of overmodulation.

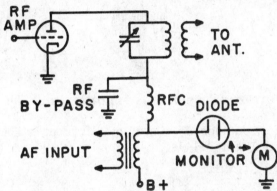

Figure 11-11. Peak modulation monitor connected to transmitter.

The fourth way to check modulation is by means of an instrument called the OSCILLOSCOPE or OSCILLOGRAPH. This instrument shows the graph or waveshape of the particular voltage waveform to be checked. By means of the oscilloscope, we can tell the approximate percentage of modulation, as well as a condition of overmodulation.

There are two ways in which the oscilloscope can be connected to the modulated RF amplifier to check modulation. Figure 11-12 shows one method.

The output of the transmitter is coupled directly to the vertical plates of the oscilloscope. The internal sweep of the oscilloscope is turned on. Figure 11-13 illustrates three possible patterns that would be seen on the screen of the oscilloscope for three different conditions of modulation. It is assumed that the modulating voltage is a pure sine wave. Figure 11-13A shows the waveshape for 50% modulation.

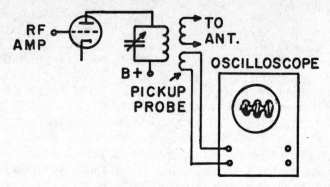

Figure 11-12.   Checking percentage modulation.

Figure 11-13B shows 100% modulation and Figure 11-13C shows over-modulation.

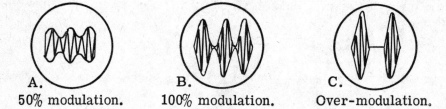

A.   B.   C.

50% modulation.   100% modulation.   Over-modulation.

Fig. 11-13. Wave-envelope modulation patterns on the oscilloscope.

The second method of using an oscilloscope to check modulation is illustrated in Figure 11-14.

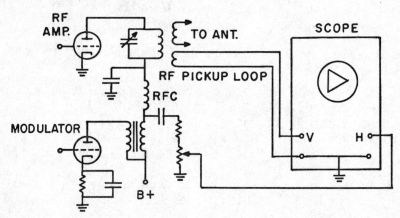

Figure 11-14.   Trapezoidal modulation patterns on oscilloscope.

The transmitter output is coupled to the vertical plates of the oscilloscope. The audio output of the modulator is connected to the horizontal deflecting plates. The internal sweep of the oscilloscope is turned off. As the amplitude of the audio signal applied to the hor-

208

izontal deflecting plates varies, the RF output of the transmitter also varies. This produces on the screen a wedge-shaped pattern called a TRAPEZOID. Figure 11-15 illustrates three trapezoidal patterns for three different conditions of modulation. Figure 11-15A shows the pattern for 50% modulation; Figure 11-15B shows the pattern for 100% modulation and Figure 11-15C shows the pattern for overmodulation.

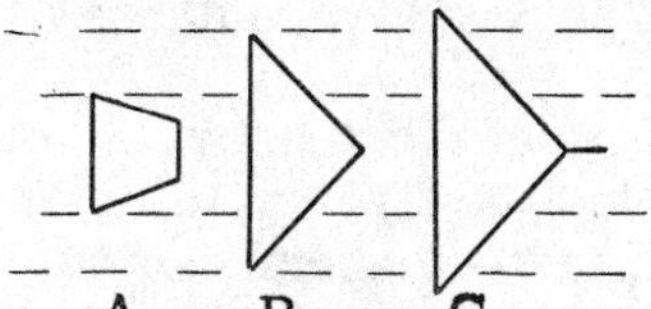

A. 50% modulation. B. 100% modulation. C. Over-modulation.

Figure 11-15. Trapezoidal modulation patterns on oscilloscope.

11-15 CHECKING THE QUALITY OF A TRANSMITTER'S EMISSIONS

It is important for an amateur to occasionally check the quality of his transmitter's emission. There are many ways that this can be accomplished. The simplest way is to listen to his sending on his receiver. While simple, this method has a serious drawback. A strong signal will overload a receiver's front end and may block it to a point where it is inoperative. To overcome this, we can remove the receiving antenna and reduce the receiver's gain control.

Another way to check the quality of a CW transmitter's output is to use a separate monitor. In this way, we do not disturb the receiver.

An oscilloscope is an extremely valuable aid in checking a phone transmitter. Paragraph 11-14 discusses its use in checking for modulation percentage. The oscilloscope, when used in conjunction with an audio generator, can be used to check for distortion.

A very practical way of checking a transmitter is to get an objective report from a ham located some distance away from the transmitter. Or better still, allow an amateur to operate your transmitter and listen to it on a receiver located some distance from the transmitter.

In addition to checking for the percentage of modulation in a radiotelephone transmitter, the radio operator should check for the following characteristics:

(1) The audio present in the output of the transmitter should be undistorted.

(2) The signal should not "splatter" or cause interference to neighboring frequencies.

(3) The signal should be free of background noise.

11-16 FACTORS CAUSING DECREASE IN ANTENNA CURRENT DURING MODULATION

We pointed out in Paragraph 11-14 that the antenna current should rise about 22% when the transmitter is being modulated. Some-

209

times the operator may find that the antenna current drops during modulation when it should be increasing. The operator should then immediately check the transmitter for one or more of the following troubles:

1. Insufficient RF excitation to the modulated amplifier.
2. Insufficient bias on the grid of the modulated amplifier.
3. Heavy overloading of the modulated Class C, RF amplifier.
4. Defective tube.
5. Poor voltage regulation of a power supply common to both the modulator and the RF amplifier.
6. Faulty or insufficient capacity of output filter capacitor in power supply of RF amplifier.

The decrease in antenna current during modulation is known as DOWNWARD MODULATION.

11-17 INTERFERENCE AND CONGESTION IN THE AMATEUR BANDS

An amateur must operate his transmitter in a manner so as not to cause interference to other amateurs. Also, some of the bands are quite congested and a good operator must avoid adding to this congestion. The following operating hints will minimize interference and congestion of the amateur bands:

(1) Before operating on a certain frequency, listen in on the frequency to see if it is being used. If the frequency is in use, wait till the parties have finished using the frequency or move on to a clear channel.

(2) When testing a transmitter, use a dummy antenna. Do not test "on the air". If "on the air" tests have to be made, do them on clear frequencies and during hours when there is little activity. Also, be brief.

(3) Use the minimum amount of power necessary to effect proper communications between the two stations.

(4) Do not overmodulate or splatter. This causes interference to adjacent frequencies. Also, make certain that no spurious or harmonic radiations are emitted from the transmitter.

(5) Use the minimum bandwidth necessary for good speech communications. The audio frequencies above 3 kHz should be elimimated to keep the bandwidth of the signal down.

(6) Use directional antennas. In this way, the signal is confined to fewer areas.

(7) In making CQ directional calls, give sufficient information to avoid useless answers.

(8) Use a recognized phonetic word list to avoid needless repetition and confusion. Also, use Q signal and other known abbreviations to cut down the length of the transmissions.

(9) Use less congested frequencies to make contacts where a choice is possible. For instance, don't use the 20 meter band to contact a local amateur where both of you have two-meter equipment. 20 meters is very crowded and 2 meters is not.

(10) Keep transmissions as brief as possible. Do not repeat words unless it is necessary. Also, in calling, use short calls with frequent breaks for listening.

11-18 TYPES OF TRANSMISSION

There are various types of transmissions that are used in radio communication. The two methods that we have studied are:

1. Continuous wave transmission in which the carrier is keyed according to the telegraph code.
2. Amplitude modulation transmission in which the carrier is amplitude modulated with audio.

The Federal Communications Commission has classified these and other types of emission according to letters and numbers, as follows:

Type A0 is the steady unmodulated emission of a CW transmitter. It is used only in special cases, such as radio beacon stations.

Type A1, TELEGRAPHY, is the keyed emission of a CW transmitter. It can only be picked up by special receivers.

Type A2, MODULATED TELEGRAPHY, is the keyed emission of a transmitter whose carrier is modulated by a pure audio note. It can be picked up by an ordinary receiver.

Type A3 RADIOTELEPHONY, is the emission of a transmitter whose carrier is amplitude modulated by voice, music, etc. An example of this type is the familiar broadcast transmitter.

Type A4, FACSIMILE, is the emission of a transmitter whose carrier is amplitude modulated by frequencies obtained by scanning a still picture or printed page.

Type A5, TELEVISION, is the emission of a transmitter whose carrier is amplitude modulated by frequencies obtained by scanning scenes, pictures, people, etc.

Type F0 is the steady unmodulated carrier of an FM transmitter.

Type F1 is carrier shift telegraphy.

Type F2 is audio frequency shift telegraphy.

Type F3 is frequency or phase-modulated telephony.

Type F4 is F.M. facsimile.

Type F5 is F.M. television.

FREQUENCY MODULATION

11-19 FUNDAMENTAL CONSIDERATIONS OF MODULATION

Modulation can be defined as the process wherein an audio voltage is superimposed upon an RF carrier wave in such a manner as to change one of the characteristics of the carrier. The characteristics of the carrier that can be changed are its amplitude, its frequency or its phase. In the system of amplitude modulation that has previously been discussed, the audio signal causes the amplitude of the carrier to vary. The variations in carrier amplitude follow the variations in the audio modulating voltage. At the receiver, the detector extracts the amplitude variations which represent the audio and pass them on to the audio amplifier.

The degree of modulation of an AM signal is directly dependent upon the strength of the audio modulating voltage. A larger audio signal causes a larger variation in carrier amplitude, and a smaller audio voltage causes a smaller variation in carrier amplitude.

11-20 AM DEFICIENCIES

If we modulate too heavily, we will have overmodulation. This, as we have previously seen, produces distortion. Another problem in AM is the fact that the frequency of the modulating system is limited. During modulation, sidebands are produced and they are equal to the carrier frequency, plus and minus the audio frequencies. Thus, if we modulate a carrier with high audio frequencies, the bandwidth occupied by the RF signal will be quite wide and will interfere with neighboring channels. In order to stay within the channel limits, the FCC has imposed a limit on the audio frequency that is used to modulate the carrier.

Interference, such as lightning, static, man-made, etc., generally causes the amplitude of a signal to vary. It impresses itself on the carrier as additional amplitude modulation. In the AM system of modulation, we therefore have the interference, as well as the audio, creating amplitude variations. When we detect the signal at the receiver, the interference will still be present.

These basic problems that are inherent in amplitude modulation are overcome in frequency modulation. In frequency modulation, the audio modulating signal causes the FREQUENCY of the carrier to vary in accordance with the strength of the audio signal. The amplitude of the RF carrier remains constant. This is shown in Figure 11-15A, where AM and FM are compared.

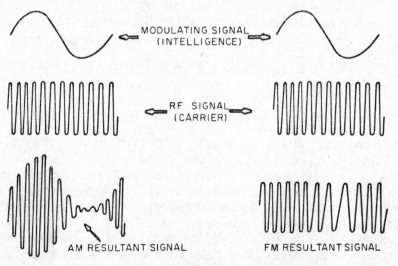

Figure 11-15A. AM and FM compared.

212

In FM, the frequency of the carrier varies in accordance with the amplitude of the audio signal. The higher the audio amplitude, the greater is the amount of frequency shift away from the center or resting frequency. The smaller the audio amplitude, the smaller is the frequency shift away from the center frequency. The amplitude of the carrier remains constant; only the frequency varies.

Note in Fig. 11-15A that the positive alternation of audio causes the carrier frequency to increase and the negative alternation causes the carrier frequency to decrease. The amount of frequency shift of the carrier above or below the resting frequency is known as the frequency deviation. The total variation between the minimum and maximum frequency values is known as the CARRIER SWING. While the extent of the frequency deviation is determined by the amplitude of the audio, the number of frequency deviations per second, or the rate of swing, depends upon the frequency of the modulating audio.

11-21 PERCENTAGE OF MODULATION

In AM, the percentage of modulation tells us the extent to which the audio has altered the amplitude of the carrier. We define 100% modulation as the point where the amplitude of the carrier rises to twice the normal amplitude at its maximum, and falls to zero at its minimum. Anything above 100% modulation is undesirable because it causes distortion.

The situation in FM is quite different. The FCC places a limit on the amount of frequency deviation, so that the band occupied by the station is not too great. In the case of FM broadcast stations, the maximum frequency deviation is ±75 kHz. When we modulate an FM carrier so that 75 kHz deviation is reached, we say we have 100% modulation. If we modulate above 100%, we will not cause distortion as in AM. We are merely exceeding the legal limit of 75 kHz. The lower the percentage of modulation, the lower is the amount of frequency swing or deviation. For instance, if we modulate 50%, the frequency deviation will be plus and minus 37.5 kHz (50% of 75 kHz is 37.5 kHz). Changing the frequency of the audio signal will not alter the frequency deviation. Only the amplitude of the audio modulating signal will control the frequency deviation of the carrier.

11-22 PHASE MODULATION

We have seen how frequency modulation can be produced by directly shifting the frequency of a carrier above and below a resting frequency. The amount of frequency shifting depended upon the amplitude of the modulating signal.

Frequency modulation can also be produced by shifting the phase of a signal. If we shift the phase of a signal, its frequency is automatically changed. This is shown in Fig. 11-16. Sine wave #1 represents the original frequency. Sine wave #2, the dotted line, represents the same signal which has been shifted 40° by the time it reaches point A. Since the sine wave #2 takes longer than #1, it is

213

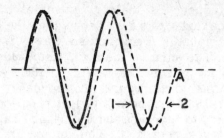

Figure 11-16. Shifting the phase.

obvious that the frequency has been reduced. If we shifted the phase angle in the opposite direction, the two cycles would be completed sooner and the frequency would have been increased. Thus, it is obvious that phase shift produces frequency changes.

In actual practice, an audio signal is used to alter the phase of a carrier. The higher the amplitude of the audio signal, the greater is the phase shift, resulting in a greater frequency swing. The lower the amplitude of the modulating signal, the lower is the phase shift, resulting in a reduced frequency swing of the carrier.

We refer to frequency modulation that results from the phase shift method as INDIRECT FM. The audio does not directly alter the frequency of the carrier; it changes the phase of the carrier which brings about the change in the frequency.

The frequency of the modulating signal determines the amount of shifting per second that the carrier will experience. However, if we shift the carrier faster or slower, this in itself also causes the carrier's frequency to vary. Thus we find that the frequency of the carrier is also affected by the frequency of the modulating signal.

To summarize; the amount of indirect FM produced as a result of phase modulation depends upon (1) the amplitude of the modulating signal and (2) the frequency of the modulating signal.

11-23 PREDISTORTION

A serious problem arises from the fact that the frequency deviation resulting from phase modulation depends upon the frequency as well as the amplitude of the audio modulating signal. We only want the amount of frequency deviation to be dependent upon the amplitude of the modulating signal. This is because the FM receiver produces amplitude variations that are dependent upon the frequency deviation. If the FM signal contained frequency deviations that were the result of frequency variations of the modulating signal, the FM receiver wouldn't know it. It would produce amplitude variations that never existed at the microphone of the transmitter.

To overcome this problem, a predistortion circuit is inserted in the audio stages of the transmitter. It distorts the audio signal so that its amplitude varies inversely with the frequency. In other words, when the frequency of the audio signal increases, the audio

214

amplitude is reduced, and vice versa. This compensates for the opposite effect that takes place during phase modulation. Thus, the output frequency deviation of a phase modulated transmitter varies only with the amplitude of the modulating signal.

11-24 NARROW-BAND AND WIDE-BAND FM

The terms "narrow-band" and "wide-band" refer to the amount of frequency deviation present for a given signal. This, in turn, determines the amount of bandwidth in the frequency spectrum that the signal will occupy.

In amateur use, wideband FM indicates that the FM signal has a deviation of approximately 15 kHz or a total frequency swing of approximately 30 kHz.

In amateur use, narrow band FM generally indicates a deviation of from 2.5 kHz to 5 kHz, or a total frequency swing of approximately 5 kHz to 10 kHz.

The FCC does not actually use the term "narrow-band FM". However, they do specify the bandwidth limit that can be used on certain frequencies. In the FCC Rules and Regulations, Paragraph 97.65 states that "on frequencies below 29.0 MHz and between 50.1 and 52.5 MHz, the bandwidth of an F3 emission shall not exceed that of an A3 emission (AM) having the same audio characteristics". In other words, if the maximum audio frequency is 3 kHz, the total AM bandwidth would be 6 kHz (2 x 3 kHz = 6 kHz). Therefore, if the same audio frequency is used in FM, the total bandwidth is limited to 6 kHz, or a maximum frequency deviation of approximately 3 kHz. Some amateurs use this rule as a definition of narrow-band FM.

Wideband FM can be used wherever F3 is permitted, except in those frequencies excluded by Paragraph 97.65 of the Rules and Regulations.

Some of the advantages of narrow-band FM over wide-band FM are:

(1) The equipment for receiving and transmitting is less expensive;

(2) for a given number of stages, the gain and selectivity of a narrow band receiver are greater;

(3) an AM detector can be used (when this is done, it is referred to as slope detection);

(4) the readable transmission distance is greater.

11-25 FM TRANSMISSION

There are a number of methods by which FM may be produced. One of the simplest is shown in Fig. 11-17.

The method used in Fig. 11-17 is a crude, elementary one. However, its action will help us understand how FM is produced.

An ordinary Armstrong oscillator is used and an additional capacitor is placed across the tuned circuit. The capacitor is actually a microphone with plate A free to move back and forth. Plate

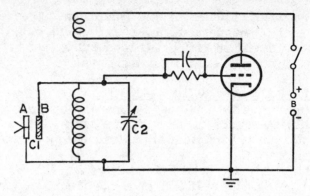

Figure 11-17. An elementary method of producing FM.

B is stationary. The frequency of the oscillator is primarily determined by the values of the inductance and the capacitance in the tank
circuit. The capacitance of the tank circuit is the sum of C2 and the
microphone capacitor C1.

Before speaking into the microphone, the oscillator produces
a steady output frequency. When we speak into the microphone, we
cause plate A of C1 to move back and forth in accordance with the
speech. This causes the capacitance of C1 to vary, which in turn
causes the output frequency of the oscillator to vary. If we speak
louder into the microphone, C1's capacitance will vary by larger
amounts and the output frequency will vary by larger amounts. If we
speak in a lower volume, C1's capacitance will vary slightly and the
output frequency will vary slightly. Thus, we have succeeded in converting audio into FM.

This method of frequency modulation is unsatisfactory because
of the varying response of the capacitor microphone to different
voices and because of the poor linearity of the microphone response.
Furthermore, the microphone must be close to the oscillator to prevent the pickup of stray signals by the microphone leads.

11-26 REACTANCE TUBE MODULATOR

The reactance tube modulator of Fig. 11-18 is a satisfactory
method of producing FM. V2 is the oscillator. L and C1 are the
inductance and capacitance of the tuned circuit of the oscillator. V1
is the reactance tube.

The reactance tube modulator operates in the following manner:
The resistance of R1 is very high, compared to the capacitive reactance of C2. The circuit R1C2 is therefore a resistive circuit.
The current, I1, that flows through R1C2, is practically in phase
with the voltage E, which is across R1C2. This is so because current and voltage tend to be in phase in a resistive circuit. However,
Ec, which is the voltage across C2, is out of phase with I1. In fact,
Ec lags behind I1 by 90° because the voltage across a capacitor lags
behind its current by 90°. This is shown vectorially in Fig. 11-19.

216

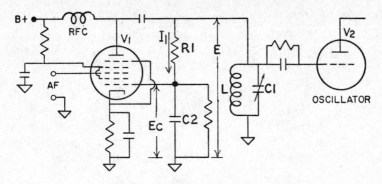

Figure 11-18.   Reactance tube modulator.

By looking at Fig. 11-18, we note that Ec also happens to be the grid voltage of V1. Since the plate current variations of a tube are the direct result of the grid voltage variations, we can say that the plate current Ip is in phase with the grid voltage Ec. This is also noted in Fig. 11-19 by drawing Ip alongside of Ec. We can put E on the same lines as I1, since we previously proved that I1 and E were practically in phase. By looking at the vectorial diagram, we note that Ip, the plate current of V1, is 90° behind E, the plate voltage of V1. Thus, we have a circuit in which the plate current lags behind the plate voltage by 90°. In our discussion of inductances, we learned that the current through an inductance lags behind the voltage across the inductance by 90°. Thus, V1 behaves the same as an inductance. As far as the tuned circuit of the oscillator is concerned, it "sees" V1 as an inductor.

If an audio signal is applied to grid #3 of V1, the plate current varies. This is the same as though the "acting" inductance were to vary because a varying inductance would also cause the current to vary. If the acting inductance varies, there will be a change in frequency. Thus, we see how FM can be produced in a very practical manner.

One important difference between AM and FM is that AM requires a considerable amount of audio power for proper modulation, whereas FM requires very little power. In an AM transmitter, the modulator must supply approximately 50% of the unmodulated carrier power for 100% modulation. In FM, the audio power required for 100% modulation is negligible. The FM modulation process involves a voltage imposition rather than power. During FM modulation, the transmission line current and the antenna current are the same as they were with no modulation present. Only the frequency is varied.

Figure 11-19. Vector
analysis of producing FM.

11-27 FM TRANSMITTER

Fig. 11-20 shows a block diagram of a reactance tube FM transmitter. For good stability, we start off with a low frequency oscillator that uses a well-regulated power supply. The FM output of the oscillator is passed through frequency multipliers to increase the frequency up to the desired output frequency of the broadcast station. Frequency multiplication of an FM signal does not destroy or distort the modulation, and the circuitry used is similar to that used in AM frequency multipliers. The output of the last frequency multiplier is then fed to a power amplifier to produce the correct output power.

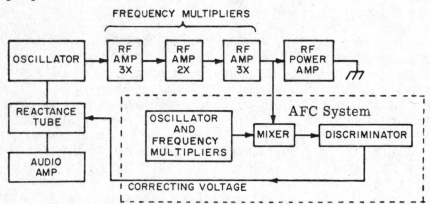

Figure 11-20. An FM transmitter.

If we wish to transmit an FM signal of 90 MHz, the oscillator would have to generate a 5 MHz signal. This is because the frequency multipliers multiply the oscillator signal a total of 18 times (3 x 2 x 3 = 18). 5 MHz x 18 = 90 MHz.

Not only will the center frequency be multiplied 18 times, but the carrier swing will also be multiplied 18 times. If we intend to modulate 100%, the transmitter's output will be 90 MHz ±75 kHz. The oscillator output will be 5 MHz ±75 kHz/18 or 5 MHz ±4.17 kHz.

Since the oscillator is not crystal controlled, we use an automatic frequency control system (AFC) to keep the carrier frequency constant. This is shown in Fig. 11-20. In the AFC system, the output of the frequency multiplier is compared with the output of a crystal oscillator. If the master oscillator has erroneously shifted, a voltage will be produced in the converter-discriminator stages, which is fed back to the reactance tube modulator. This, in turn, corrects the oscillator and sets it to its correct center frequency.

The FM transmitting antenna should be of the high gain type and it should be horizontally polarized. The FM broadcast band is from 88 to 108 MHz. Propagation at these frequencies is strictly via the ground wave. Any energy that travels upward is not reflected back to earth. It is therefore important that all the energy be radiated in a horizontal rather than vertical plane. High gain antennas should be used because the signal traveling in a horizontal plane along the ground is rapidly attenuated and absorbed by the ground.

11-28 SINGLE SIDEBAND

A complete discussion of single sideband transmission and reception is beyond the scope of this course. A sufficient amount of information is given, in the paragraphs below, to enable the student to be able to answer the few questions that may be asked on the examination. For the reader who desires more information on this subject, there are many excellent books on the market.

11-29 SINGLE SIDEBAND TRANSMISSION

The system of amplitude modulation that we have been discussing all along, is widely used. However, it does have a number of major drawbacks. For one thing, it occupies more of the frequency spectrum than is necessary. Both the upper and lower sidebands are transmitted. This is a waste since the same information that is transmitted in the upper sidebands is duplicated in the lower sidebands.

Another disadvantage of AM is that a tremendous amount of power is used at the transmitter in order to transmit a certain amount of information. It has been explained that two-thirds of the power is in the carrier and one-third in both sidebands. Thus, one-sixth of the power is in one-half of the sidebands (upper or lower). Since all of the information is contained in the upper or lower sidebands, five-sixths of the power delivered to the transmitter's antenna is unnecessary for communication.

The principle of single-sideband suppressed carrier (SSSC) transmission is to develop and transmit only one of the sidebands (upper or lower). Thus, a single sideband signal will occupy one half the bandwidth that an AM signal occupies.

Fig. 11-21 is a block diagram of a filter-type single-sideband suppressed carrier transmitter. The frequency components at the output of each block are indicated to the right of each block by the

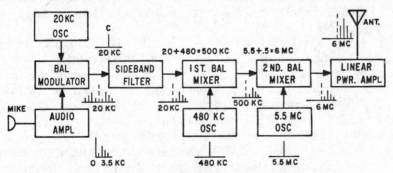

Figure 11-21. Block diagram of a single-sideband, suppressed carrier transmitter.

219

frequency and a sketch.

The 20 kHz oscillator generates the basic carrier and feeds it to a balanced modulator. Here, the carrier is modulated by the audio coming from the audio amplifier. The balanced modulator generates both the upper and lower sidebands, but it suppresses the basic carrier. The dotted line in the frequency sketch indicates the suppressed carrier. The double-sideband signal is passed on to a sideband filter which eliminates one of the sidebands. The signal leaving the sideband filter is now a single-sideband suppressed carrier signal.

In order to increase the frequency of the signal to the frequency to be transmitted, it is "heterodyned" or mixed up to the desired frequency. Two balanced mixers are used to do this. The first mixer beats the 20 kHz sideband with a signal from a 480 kHz oscillator to develop 500 kHz. The second mixer heterodynes the 500 kHz signal with 5.5 MHz to give a 6 MHz signal. The heterodyning process does not harm the audio. The reason for two mixers is to insure the suppression of the original 20 kHz.

The single sideband signal is now fed to a linear power amplifier which brings the signal up to the required power level. We use a linear amplifier because the signal contains audio and a linear amplifier does not distort the audio.

11-30 POWER RATINGS OF A SINGLE SIDEBAND TRANSMITTER

The peak-envelope power (PEP) has previously been defined as the power in the modulation envelope at the instant that the modulation signal reaches its peak. The peak-envelope power is significant is SSB transmitters because it is the basic SSB transmitter power rating. Unfortunately, the meters do not read peak values. The meters read average values. The ratio of the peak-envelope power to the average power is difficult to ascertain. It depends upon the characteristics of the modulating signal. One type of voice will have a different PEP-to-average ratio than another. From experience, however, it has been determined that a ratio of 2 to 1 is typical for the average voice. Therefore, when we speak of a legal DC input of 1 kilowatt, we accept a PEP input of 2 kilowatts for a single sideband transmitter.

The average plate current as read by the plate current meter multiplied by the plate voltage, gives us the DC plate power input. (This must never exceed 1 kilowatt). If it is 1 kilowatt, we can assume that, under normal conditions, the PEP input is 2 kilowatts. However, if your voice is such that the PEP-to-average ratio is 3 to 1 instead of 2 to 1, the PEP input will be 3 kilowatts. Since the final amplifier is probably rated for 2 kilowatts, you will exceed the capability of the equipment and get non-linearity with its subsequent spurious signals. In testing an SSB transmitter, an oscilloscope and the operator's voice should be used to check the linearity of the transmitter.

If the driver stage also supplies power to the antenna, as is the case of a grounded-grid amplifier, the input power to the driver stage must be added to the input power of the final stage in determining the total input power.

11-31 SIGNAL-TO-DISTORTION RATIO

Because of the heterodyning that takes place in a single sideband transmitter, a great many new frequencies are generated. The nonlinearity of the RF amplifiers gives rise to harmonics and all sorts of combinations (sums and differences) of these harmonics. We refer to many of these spurious frequencies as distortion products. We find that we can easily eliminate all distortion products except those that lie close to the desired frequencies. These are the odd-order products such as the third-order products, the fifth-order products, etc. These distortion products cause splatter or interference to neighboring frequencies and should be reduced to a point where they are insignificant.

In order to test for distortion products, we use a two-tone test signal as the audio source. The two-tone test signal contains two audio frequencies that are not harmonically related to each other. The two audio tones, which must be free of harmonics, are mixed together and fed to the transmitter. A spectrum analyzer is used to show the transmitter output on an oscilloscope. The amplitude of the test signal output, along with that of the distortion products, can be seen and measured on the oscilloscope. The performance of the transmitter, with regard to distortion elimination, is given by a ratio known as the "signal-to-distortion" ratio or simply "S/D" ratio. It is given in decibels and is defined as the ratio of the amplitude of one test tone to the amplitude of a third-order product. These amplitudes can be measured on the oscilloscope. S/D ratios should be at least 30 db down.

PRACTICE QUESTIONS - LESSON 11
(For answers, refer to Appendix 6)

11-1 Draw the trapezoidal type patterns showing 50% modulation and overmodulation as they would appear on the screen of an oscilloscope.

11-2 Draw a simple schematic diagram of a peak modulation monitor.

11-3 The average plate current in an amplitude modulated RF amplifier should:
    a. increase
    b. remain constant
    c. decrease
    d. increase on the positive peaks and decrease on the negative peaks

11-4* A Class B modulator as compared to a Class A modulator requires:
a. larger excitation voltage   c. no power to drive the grid
b. lower excitation voltage   d. zero bias operation

11-5 If the grid bias supply of a Class B modulator was suddenly short circuited:
a. the plate current would increase to excessively high values
b. grid current would increase
c. overmodulation would result
d. output power of the carrier would be in the sidebands

11-6* The ratio of modulator sine wave power output to Class C amplifier unmodulated plate power input is:
a. 100%   b. 25%   c. 125%   d. 50%

11-7* The ratio of modulator speech power output to Class C amplifier unmodulated plate power input is:
a. 125%   b. 100%   c. 25%   d. 50%

11-8* Define amplitude modulation.

11-9* What are sideband frequencies?

11-10 A downward deflection of the antenna RF current meter during modulation might indicate:
a. sufficient RF excitation to the modulated stage
b. proper filament emission of the modulated stage
c. excellent voltage regulation of power supply common to both modulator and RF stage
d. insufficient bias on grid of modulated stage

11-11 Show by a diagram the sinusoidal modulation envelope of an amplitude modulated wave at:
a. 50% modulation
b. 100% modulation
c. overmodulation

11-12* Phase modulated telephony is indicated by:
a. F1   b. F2   c. F3   d. F4

11-13* A two-tone test signal is used in determining:
a. SWR   c. modulation percentage
b. efficiency   d. S/D ratio

11-14* The sideband filter in an SSB transmitter:
a. removes the carrier
b. removes the lower sideband
c. removes a sideband
d. none of the above

11-15* SSB signals in a transmitter should be amplified by:
    a. RF amplifiers   c. phasing amplifiers
    b. linear amplifiers   d. a Class C amplifier

11-16* The PEP in a 100% sine wave modulated system is:
    a. lower than the average power
    b. 1.414 times the unmodulated power
    c. two times the unmodulated power
    d. four times the unmodulated power

11-17* The PEP-to-average power ratio in an SSB transmitter is primarily dependent upon the:
    a. characteristics of the modulating signal
    b. class of operation of the linear amplifier
    c. S/D ratio
    d. amount of unmodulated carrier power

11-18* FM can be produced by a:
    a. reactance tube modulator   c. pre-emphasis circuit
    b. predistortion circuit   d. AFC circuitry

11-19* What arrangement of multiplier stages is necessary to bring an oscillator frequency swing of 3 kHz up to an output carrier swing of 54 kHz?
    a. two doublers and a tripler
    b. a tripler and a quadrupler
    c. a doubler and two triplers
    d. a doubler, a tripler and a quadrupler

11-20* An advantage of narrow-band FM over wide-band FM is not:
    a. slope detection can be used
    b. greater audio frequency range can be utilized
    c. less expensive receiving equipment can be used
    d. allows for greater gain

11-21* The signal in a sideband transmitter is increased up to the desired frequency by means of:
    a. frequency multipliers   c. heterodyning
    b. frequency dividers   d. filtering

11-22* Which of the following will not minimize congestion in the Amateur bands?
    a. use a phonetic word list
    b. use a dummy antenna for testing
    c. use audio frequencies above 3 kHz
    d. use directional antennas

SECTION III — LESSON 12
ANTENNAS, FREQUENCY METERS, TYPES OF TRANSMISSION

12-1 ANTENNA RADIATION

Once the RF signal has been generated in the transmitter, some means must be provided for radiating this RF energy into space. The transmitting antenna provides the link or impedance matching device between the output stage of the transmitter and space. This energy, in the form of an electric field, travels through space and cuts across a receiving antenna, inducing a voltage in it. If the receiver is tuned to the same frequency as the transmitter, the signal will be received and heard.

12-1A PROPAGATION OF RADIO WAVES

The radio wave that leaves a transmitter takes two general paths. One path is along the surface of the earth and is called the GROUND WAVE. The other path is towards the sky and the radiated wave that travels along this path is called the SKY WAVE.

In traveling along the surface of the earth, the GROUND WAVE gradually loses its strength until it is completely diminished. On the other hand, the sky wave can travel for thousands of miles.

Some distance above the earth, the sky wave strikes a gaseous mass called the IONOSPHERE. Here, the wave is reflected back to the earth. (See Fig. 12-1). If a receiver is located between the end of the ground wave and the point where the sky wave returns to the earth, it will not pick up the transmitted signal. The area between the ground wave zone and the point where the sky wave hits the earth is called the SKIP ZONE. After the wave strikes the earth, it may again be reflected up to the ionosphere and back to the earth. In this way, a signal can travel all around the world.

Frequencies above 50 MHz. generally do not reflect from the

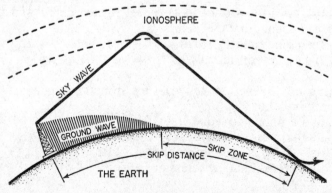

Figure 12-1. Propagation of radio waves.

ionosphere. They penetrate the ionosphere and never return to earth.

12-1B THE IONOSPHERE
As stated above, the ionosphere is a gaseous region in the upper atmosphere that extends approximately 30 to 300 miles above the earth. It consists of several layers of ionized particles. The ionization is caused by the air particles being bombarded by the sun's ultra violet rays and cosmic rays.

When a radio wave strikes the ionosphere, it is reflected or refracted back to the earth some distance away from the transmitter. The ability of the ionosphere to return a radio wave back to earth depends upon the ion density, the frequency of the signal, the angle of radiation and other factors.

The layers which form the ionosphere undergo considerable variations in altitude, density and thickness, due to the varying degrees of solar or sunspot activity. Every 11 years, the concentration of solar radiation (sunspot activity) into the earth's atmosphere reaches a peak. We refer to this as the sunspot cycle. During periods of maximum sunspot activity, the ionized layers are more dense and occur at higher altitudes. They allow for communication over greater distances. The opposite happens during minimum sunspot activity. See Figure 12-1A.

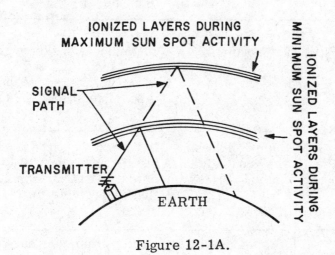

Figure 12-1A.

Following is a summary of radio wave propagation. Since there are many factors and variables that influence radio wave propagation, the following chart can only serve as an average guide. The first column lists the frequencies, the second column lists the propagation characteristics of the ground wave and the third column lists the propagation characteristics of the sky wave.

225

FREQUENCY	GROUND WAVE	SKY WAVE
Low Frequency (50 kHz - 500 kHz)	Communications are possible up to 1,000 or more miles, day or night, with high power transmitters.	Communications are generally reliable, day or night, over most of the band. They are slightly better at night. At the upper end of the band, the sky wave is useful only at night. Depending upon the time of day, the seasons and other factors, useful reception can be had for distances up to 8,000 miles.
Broadcast Frequencies (500 - 1600 kHz)	Reception can be had up to 50 to 100 miles, day or night.	There is no sky wave reception in the day time. At night, reception can be had up to 3,000 miles.
160 Meter Amateur Band (1.8 - 2.0 MHz)	Communications are reliable up to approximately 30 miles, day or night.	There is very little sky wave reception during the day. During the night, especially during winter season disturbances, communications can be had up to 2,500 miles.
80 Meter Amateur Band (3.5 - 4.0 MHz)	Communications are good only up to about 20 miles.	During the day time, useful communications are possible up to about 150 to 250 miles. At night time, communication is possible up to 2,000 to 3,000 miles.
40 Meter Amateur Band (7.0 - 7.3 MHz)	Communications are good only up to about 20 miles.	During the day, useful communication can be had up to 750 miles. At night, communication is possible up to 10,000 miles.
20 Meter Amateur Band (14.0 - 14.35 MHz)	Communications are good only up to about 20 miles.	During minimum sunspot activity, there is almost world wide communications during daylight hours and almost no communications at night. During medium sunspot activity, world wide reception is possible during the daylight hours and during the early evening hours. At the peak of sunspot

FREQUENCY	GROUND WAVE	SKY WAVE
		activity, excellent world wide reception is possible for almost 24 hours.
15 Meter Amateur Band (21.0 - 21.450 MHz)	Communications are good only up to about 20 miles.	World wide communications during day and night hours is possible during maximum sunspot activity. During minimum sunspot activity, there is no night time communication and some daylight communication.
10 Meter Amateur Band (28.0 - 29.7 MHz)	Communications are good only up to about 20 miles.	During maximum sunspot activity, excellent communication can be had during daylight hours and early evening hours. There is generally little communication at night. During minimum sunspot activity, the band is "dead" except for local communication.
Ultra High Frequency (30 - 300 MHz)	There is little or no ground wave propagation. The only communication is through the direct, line of sight wave, from the transmitter antenna to the receiver antenna.	There is generally very little reflection from the ionosphere, day or night. Occasionally, there is some sporadic reception for short periods of time in limited localities.

12-2 PRINCIPLES OF RADIATION

The currents flowing in the antenna, due to the excitation from the transmitter, set up magnetic and electrostatic fields which are pushed out from the antenna and fly off into space in all directions. The two fields, moving through space as an electromagnetic wave, contain the carrier and sideband energy and, as such, have quite definite characteristics. These characteristics are:

1.   The wave has a very definite frequency which is equal to the carrier frequency of the transmitter.

2.   The wave travels through space at a constant velocity, regardless of the frequency at which it is being transmitted. This ve-

locity is 186,000 miles per second or 3×10^8 meters per second.

$$3 \times 10^8 = 300,000,000$$

3. The wave has a certain wave length which is defined as the distance between adjacent peaks, or the distance the wave travels through space during one cycle of the antenna current. The wave length is measured in meters and is given the symbol "L".

L = wavelength in meters.

4. An equation which ties together wavelength, frequency and velocity of an electromagnetic wave is given below:

V = FL   Where: V is the velocity of the electromagnetic wave in free space which is constant.

$V = 3 \times 10^8$ meters per second.

F is the frequency of the wave in cycles per second.

L is the wavelength in meters.

If the frequency is in kilocycles per second, the formula becomes:

(2) F (kc) x L (meters) = 300,000

If we wish to solve for the wavelength, the formula becomes:

$$(3) \quad L \text{ (meters)} = \frac{300,000}{F \text{ (kc)}}$$

If we wish to solve for the frequency, the formula becomes:

$$(4) \quad F \text{ (in kc. per second)} = \frac{300,000}{L \text{ (meters)}}$$

FOR EXAMPLE:

(a) Find the wavelength of the distress frequency, 500 kc.

Solution: Use Formula No. 3

$$L \text{ (meters)} = \frac{300,000}{F \text{ (kc)}} = \frac{300,000}{500} = 600 \text{ meters}$$

(b) Find the wavelength of the frequency 1500 kc.

Solution: Use Formula No. 4

$$L \text{ (meters)} = \frac{300,000}{F \text{ (kc)}} = \frac{300,000}{1500} = 200 \text{ meters}$$

(c) Find the frequency of the signal whose wavelength is 300 meters.

Solution: Use Formula No. 4

$$F \text{ (kc)} = \frac{300,000}{L \text{ (meters)}} = \frac{300,000}{300} = 1000 \text{ kc.}$$

(d) Find the frequency of the signal whose wavelength is 500 meters.

Solution: Use Formula No. 4

$$F \text{ (kc)} = \frac{300,000}{L \text{ (meters)}} = \frac{300,000}{500} = 600 \text{ kc.}$$

Radio waves today are designated in frequency rather than in wavelength; for example, you talk about a 30 megacycle carrier frequency rather than a 10 meter carrier wavelength. However, wavelength figures are very convenient in the discussion of antenna systems because the wavelength gives some indication of the actual physical dimension of the wires. For example, a half wave antenna for 10 meter transmission is 5 meters long, or converting to yard units: 5-1/2 yards.

12-3 FUNDAMENTAL ANTENNA CONSIDERATIONS

Figure 12-1B shows an antenna or wire connected to an RF source. The alternating current travels out from point A and along the wire until it reaches point B. Since point B is free, the wave cannot continue farther and bounces back, or is reflected, from this point. The distance an RF wave travels during the period of one cycle is known as the wavelength. If the wave is to travel exactly the length of the wire and back, during the period of one cycle, it is evi-

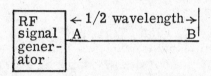

Figure 12-1B. Half-wave antenna.

dent that the wire must be equal in length to one half the wavelength of the voltage being applied. The wire is then said to be resonant to the frequency of the applied voltage. During the negative alternation of the RF generator, electrons will move along the wire away from point A towards point B. The electrons are stopped and accumulate at point B, which represents a high voltage point. During the positive alternation of the RF power source, electrons move away from point B and crowd together at point A, which also represents a high voltage point. In the center of the antenna there is, at all times, a maximum movement of electrons causing a high current or a low voltage point. Therefore, very little voltage will appear at the center of the antenna and no current will flow at the ends. Figure 12-2 illustrates the voltage and current distribution on a fundamental half wave antenna. This representation of a voltage and current distribution is known as a standing wave pattern. The points of minimum current and minimum voltage are known as current and voltage nodes respectively. An antenna is said to be resonant when there exist standing waves of voltage and current along its length. Since the waves traveling back and forth in the antenna reinforce each other, a maximum radiation of electro-magnetic waves into space results. When there is no res-

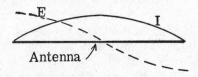

Figure 12-2. Distribution of voltage and current on half-wave antenna.

onance (no standing waves), the waves tend to cancel each other, thus dissipating their energies in the form of heat loss, rather than utilizing them to radiate the radio waves. Therefore, a resonant antenna connected to an RF generator can dissipate power because some of the energy leaves the antenna in the form of radiation.

12-4 ANTENNA IMPEDANCE

Since voltage and current vary along the length of the antenna, a definite impedance value must be associated with each point along the antenna. The impedance varies according to the relative crowding of the electrons as the ends are approached. The impedance existing at any point is simply the voltage at that point divided by the current at that point. Thus, the lowest impedance occurs where the current is highest; and the highest impedance occurs where the current is lowest.

12-5 PRACTICAL TRANSMITTING ANTENNAS

Most practical transmitting antennas come under one of two classifications, Hertz antennas or Marconi antennas. A Hertz antenna is operated some distance above the ground and may be either vertical or horizontal. A Marconi antenna operates with one end grounded (usually through the output of the transmitter or the coupling coil at the end of the feed line). Hertz antennas are generally used at higher frequencies, above about two megacycles, while Marconi antennas are used at lower frequencies.

12-6 THE HERTZ ANTENNA

A Hertz antenna is any length of wire far enough from ground so that it will not be influenced by grounded objects. Therefore, its physical length will directly determine the wavelength to which it will tune. A short length antenna will be resonant to a short wavelength or a high frequency; a long wavelength antenna will be resonant to a long wavelength or low frequency. Therefore, the resonant frequency of a Hertz antenna can be changed by varying its physical length.

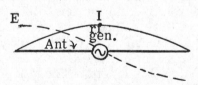

Figure 12-3. Center-fed Hertz antenna.

This is true because an antenna acts like a resonant circuit. Figure 12-3 illustrates a center-fed, half-wave Hertz antenna. The physical length of the antenna is one-half of the wavelength of the signal that it is radiating. This type of antenna is also referred to as a "dipole" (or "half-wave dipole") antenna.

Since the center of a half-wave antenna is a high current point (see Paragraph 12-3), we can say that this antenna is current-fed by the transmitter. The impedance at the center of this Hertz antenna is about 73 ohms. The impedance rises uniformly towards each end of the antenna where it is about 2400 ohms.

In order to find the approximate length of a half-wave antenna, we can use Formula 3 on Page 227 and divide the result by 2. However, due to end effects, diameter variation and other factors, the actual antenna should be about 5% less than the basic formula indicates. A more accurate and practical formula to use in finding the physical length of an antenna, if the frequency is known, is:

$$L = \frac{468}{f}$$

Where: L is the length in feet and f is the frequency in MHz.

For example:

Question: Find the length of a half-wave antenna for the middle of the 40 meter Novice ham band.

Answer: From the Rules and Regulations (Lesson 4), we find that the middle of the 40 meter ham band is 7.125 MHz. We then substitute in the formula.

$$L = \frac{468}{7.125} = 65.68 \text{ feet.}$$

12-7 THE MARCONI ANTENNA

If the lower half of a half-wave Hertz antenna is replaced by a conducting plane, such as illustrated in Figure 12-4, no disturbance is caused in the propagated wave from the upper half. The remaining quarter-wave will continue to radiate much in the same manner as a half-wave antenna, provided a large and extensive conducting plane is present (such as a good ground). The ground connection actually makes up the other half of the antenna's electrical length; you can look at it from the viewpoint that the antenna proper provides one-quarter wavelength; and the ground, or earth, supplies the additional one-quarter wavelength. A practical form of such a radiating system is the Marconi antenna, in which the lower terminal of the generator is connected to ground, and the earth's surface serves as the required extended conducting plane. The current and voltage distributions along the antenna length are as shown in Figure 12-5. Notice that the generator feed point is still a high current, low im-

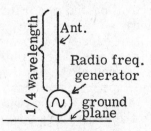

Figure 12-4.
Marconi antenna.

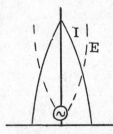

Figure 12-5. Distribution of voltage and current in a Marconi antenna.

pedance point, as in the case of the ungrounded Hertz antenna. The impedance at the feed point of the Marconi antenna is approximately 35 ohms. Since the Marconi antenna is only one-quarter wavelength in length, it is one-half the physical length of a Hertz antenna and therefore, is more practical for mobile operation.

12-7A DIRECTIONAL CHARACTERISTICS OF ANTENNAS

A horizontal transmitting antenna radiates well in the two directions broadside (at right angles) to the length of the antenna. It radiates poorly in the direction along the length of the antenna. Fig. 12-6A illustrates the directional transmitting pattern of a horizontal antenna as viewed from the top. The pattern is referred to as a "figure 8" pattern. A receiver, located at point A, would receive very little compared to one located at point B.

Fig. 12-6B shows the directional pattern of a vertical antenna as viewed from the top. It radiates well in all horizontal directions. We refer to this pattern as omnidirectional or non-directional.

The radiation patterns discussed above are for transmitting antennas. However, they hold true for receiving antennas as well.

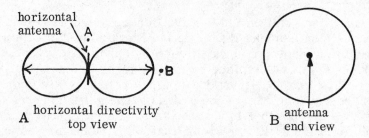

Figure 12-6. Directional transmitting patterns of a horizontal antenna.

12-8 ANTENNA LOADING

Since an antenna acts like a resonant circuit, it is resistive at its resonant frequency, and reactive at non-resonant frequencies. The antenna operates more efficiently when it presents a resistive load to the generator; in other words, when it is resonant. If the physical length of the antenna is too long at the wavelength which it is to radiate, it will act as an inductive load on the generator. We say that the electrical length of the antenna is too long. In this case, the electrical length of the antenna can be decreased by means of loading the antenna with a lumped capacitive reactance, which will counterbalance the effective inductive reactance of the antenna. The result is that the antenna is made to present a resistive load to the generator. Similarly, if the electrical length of the antenna is too short, it will present a capacitive load to the generator, resulting in inefficient radiation. Loading the antenna with an inductance of the right value will resonate the antenna.

TO SUMMARIZE:

(1) When an antenna is too LONG, it acts as an inductive load and requires a series capacitor to effectively shorten it.

(2) When an antenna is too SHORT, it acts as a capacitive load and requires a series inductance to effectively lengthen it.

(3) Increasing the electrical length of an antenna will decrease its resonant frequency.

(4) Decreasing the electrical length of an antenna will increase its resonant frequency.

12-9 RADIATION RESISTANCE

The action of the antenna as a resistance and as a power dissipator has resulted in a term called the RADIATION RESISTANCE. It is defined as that value of resistance which, if substituted for the antenna and connected in its place, would dissipate the same amount of power in heat as the antenna dissipates in radiation. As you can see, this is a rather fictitious term, since the antenna is not a resistance, but is simply acting like one. The radiation resistance at the center of a half-wave Hertz antenna is 73 ohms. For a Marconi antenna, the radiation resistance is roughly 35 ohms, or about half that of the Hertz. The radiation resistance can be used to determine the power input into an antenna by using the formula $P = I^2 R$, where I is the antenna current at the antenna input, and R is the radiation resistance. P is the power input to the antenna in watts.

12-10 DUMMY ANTENNA

When a transmitter is being tuned up for optimum operation, the antenna should be coupled to the final stage in order to insure correct settings of plate voltage and current (since the antenna is the load on the final stage). Coupling an antenna during the adjustment period is forbidden by law, since radiation will result which may cause interference. Most stations get around this difficulty by utilizing a dummy antenna which is nothing more than a resistive load of the correct power dissipation coupled to the tank coil of the final output tube in the same manner as the antenna is later to be coupled. An incandescent bulb of the proper wattage can readily be used. The brilliance of the lamp will give a rough idea of the transmitter power output. The peak brilliance of the lamp will indicate to the operator when the transmitter is tuned for maximum power output.

12-11 TUNING INDICATOR FOR THE ANTENNA CIRCUIT

The thermocouple ammeter is the standard antenna tuning indicator. The antenna circuit is tuned so that the ammeter reads a peak of RF antenna current. Auxiliary methods employ neon bulbs or low voltage incandescent lamps which can be connected to a loop of wire of several inches in diameter; the bulbs are then loosely coupled to the antenna inductor. The lamps will glow with a maximum brilliance when the antenna is tuned to resonance.

12-12 FADING

A signal picked up by a receiver may sometimes fade in and out of hearing. This variation in signal strength is due to the inter- action between two signals at the receiving antenna which vary in and out of phase with each other. These two signals are: (1) the directly received signal from the transmitter and (2) the same signal which has traveled to the receiver from a reflecting object. One way to overcome fading is to have two receiving antennas placed some dis- tance away from each other, with both feeding into the same receiver. Such a system is known as a diversity antenna receiving system.

12-13 TRANSMISSION LINES

In practically all transmitter installations, the antenna is lo- cated some distance from the transmitter. It may be 10 feet or it may be 200 feet. In all cases, some means must be used to carry the RF energy from the output of the transmitter to the antenna. The lines that are used to carry this energy are called **transmission lines.**

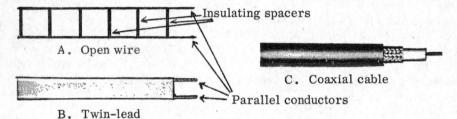

A. Open wire   Insulating spacers

B. Twin-lead   Parallel conductors   C. Coaxial cable

Figure 12-7. Transmission lines.

There are two basic types of transmission lines. One is called parallel line; the other is called coaxial cable. The parallel- line is further subdivided into two types. One is called the "open- wire" type. The other is the "twin-lead" type. Open-wire trans- mission line consists of two conductors in parallel separated by in- sulating spacers. Twin-lead insulation consists of two parallel con- ductors separated by flexible insulation. This type is commonly used in television installations. See Figure 12-7.

Coaxial cable consists of a conductor surrounded by a round flexible insulator. There is a concentric metallic covering made of flexible wire braid around this insulator. Surrounding this is a wea- therproof vinylite sheath. The outer conductor acts as a shield, pre- venting spurious and harmonic radiation from the transmission line.

The transmission line should carry the RF energy from the transmitter to the antenna with minimum losses. In order for this to occur, the impedance of the transmission line must be equal to the impedance of the transmitter's output and to the impedance of the antenna. Matching the impedances also cuts down on the radiation of spurious and harmonic signals.

The characteristic impedance of a parallel wire air insulated transmission line can be found with the aid of the following formula:

234

$$Z_O = 276 \log \frac{b}{a}$$

Where: Z_O is the characteristic impedance of the line
        b is the center to center spacing between conductors
        a is the radius of the conductors

The characteristic impedance of a coaxial transmission line is given by the following formula:

$$Z_O = 138 \log \frac{b}{a}$$

Where: b is the inside diameter of the outer conductor
        a is the outside diameter of the inner conductor

12-14 STANDING WAVE RATIO

It was seen in Section 12-3 of this chapter that a standing wave pattern occurs along the length of an antenna. These standing waves result in maximum radiation of the signal and they are desirable in an antenna. However, standing waves are undesirable on a transmission line. We do not want the transmission line to radiate; we only want it to transfer energy. We therefore do not want standing waves on a transmission line.

Standing waves occur on a transmission line when some of power that travels along the line to the antenna is reflected back to the transmitter instead of going into the antenna. This happens when the impedance of the line is not equal to the impedances of the transmitter and antenna.

The standing waves on a line give us maximum and minimum voltage and current points along the line. The ratio of the maximum current to minimum current or maximum voltage to minimum voltage, is called the STANDING WAVE RATIO (SWR). Expressed as a formula, it is:

$$SWR = \frac{I_{max.}}{I_{min.}} \text{ or } \frac{E_{max.}}{E_{min.}}$$

Where: SWR is the Standing Wave Ratio
        $I_{max.}$ and $E_{max.}$ are the maximum current and voltage points on the line.
        $I_{min.}$ and $E_{min.}$ are the minimum current and voltage points on the line.

In a transmission line, we want a minimum standing wave ratio. In other words, we want the current and voltage to be the same along the entire line.

One way to determine the standing wave ratio is to measure the voltage of the RF energy traveling to the antenna, and to compare it to the voltage of the RF energy being reflected back from the antenna. We can use these two voltages in the following formula to find the SWR:

$$SWR = \frac{E_F + E_R}{E_F - E_R}$$ where: E_F is the forward or incident voltage and E_R is the reflected voltage.

235

The ideal SWR occurs when the reflected voltage is zero. We can see from the formula that when E_R is zero, the SWR is $\frac{1}{1}$ or 1 to 1. As the reflected voltage rises, the SWR increases to 2 to 1, 3 to 1, etc.

An instrument, called an SWR bridge, reads the forward and reflected voltages and shows the SWR on the face of its meter.

12-14A MULTIBAND ANTENNAS

The most efficient antenna system is one where the antenna is cut for a certain frequency and is used for that one frequency, or band of frequencies. If an amateur wishes to operate efficiently on several bands, he must use several antennas. This would take up a considerable amount of space and be quite costly. An alternative would be to use a multiband antenna. There are several types of multiband antennas. We will discuss two of these types.

Fig. 12-8A illustrates a half-wave, fundamental antenna,

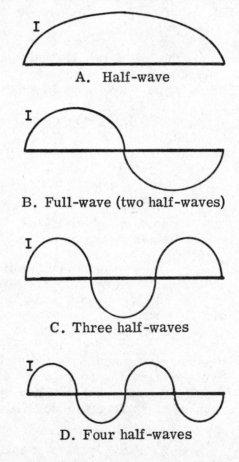

A. Half-wave

B. Full-wave (two half-waves)

C. Three half-waves

D. Four half-waves

Figure 12-8. Current graphs of various antenna lengths.

similar to the basic antenna shown in Figures 12-2 and 12-3. It was pointed out that a length of wire, that is one half of the wavelength of the signal fed to it, has standing waves on it and acts as an antenna. If we were to double the frequency of the signal (cutting the wavelength in half) the length of wire would also behave as an antenna for the new signal. This is because the wire is now a full wavelength long. It too, has standing waves on it, as shown in Fig. 12-8B. If we triple the signal frequency, the wire will behave as an antenna because it will be three half-wavelengths (see Fig. 12-7C). The rule is that, as long as the length of the wire is some integral multiple of a half wavelength, it will have standing waves on it and act as an antenna. Since the amateur band frequencies are harmonically related to each other, it is easy to see how a single length of wire can serve as an antenna for several amateur bands.

For instance, a half wave antenna for the 7 MHz (40 meter) band is approximately 20 meters long. This represents two half wavelengths on 14 MHz (20 meters) and four half wavelengths on 28 MHz (10 meters). Thus, the 20 meter length of wire can act as an antenna on the 7 MHz, 14 MHz and 28 MHz ham bands. A practical multiband antenna of this type would be fed at the center with open wire transmission line of a certain length. The antenna handbooks have tables giving various choices of feeder lengths that can be used. A "transmatch" (described below), must be used in a system of this type. It is placed between the transmitter and the transmission line.

A second type of multiband antenna uses "traps". The traps are parallel resonant circuits inserted into the antenna at different points. The operation of a multiband trap antenna can be understood by examining Fig. 12-9. Fig. 12-9 is a simple multiband trap antenna that works on 3 bands (7, 14 and 28 MHz). The two traps are resonant at 14 MHz. Therefore, they act as high impedances at 14 MHZ, and only sections B and C operate at this frequency. At 7 MHz, the traps behave as inductors and electrically lengthen the antenna so that the total length of sections A, B, C and D is resonant to 7 MHz. At 28 MHz, the antenna acts as a long wire or harmonic antenna. Its length becomes an integral multiple of a half-wave antenna for 10 meters.

While multiband antennas are practical, they do have draw-

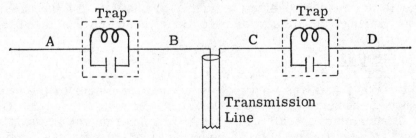

Figure 12-9. A multiband trap antenna.

backs. For one thing, they tend to radiate harmonics with its subsequent interference. Their efficiency and directivity are not as good as a single band antenna. It is also difficult to achieve a low SWR on all frequencies with a multiband antenna.

One way to reduce the emission of harmonics is to use a "Transmatch". A Transmatch is a device that is inserted between the transmitter and the transmission line leading to the antenna. It consists of one or more tuned circuits that selects the desired signal leaving the transmitter and rejects all others.

Another important function of the Transmatch is to match the impedance of the transmitter output to the input of the transmission line. Other advantages of the Transmatch are: it permits a transmitter to feed into almost any type of antenna, it permits a transmitter with an unbalanced output to feed a balanced transmission line and vice versa, and it permits maximum RF to be transferred from the transmitter to the antenna system.

Other ways of minimizing harmonic radiation from antennas are:

(1) Use a low-pass filter between the transmitter and the transmission line. This is described in Lesson 10.

(2) Make certain that all antenna joints are mechanically sound and free of corrosion. Corroded joints can act as rectifiers for harmonics and cause their radiation.

12-15 PROTECTING STATION EQUIPMENT FROM STATIC CHARGE AND LIGHTNING DISCHARGE ON ANTENNA

During an electric storm, an antenna may be hit by lightning which can damage the station equipment. A means must be provided to safely by-pass the lightning discharge to ground. What is usually done is to connect spark gaps of large current carrying capacity between the antenna and ground. The spark gap will provide an effective by-pass for the lightning surge. If an antenna is capacity coupled to the output of the transmitter, static charges of high potential may build up on the antenna because there is no direct leakage path to ground. In this case, static drain coils having a high resistance at the radiating frequency are connected from the base of the antenna to ground. They serve as the discharge path for any static charge on the antenna. An antenna grounding switch can also be used to discharge the atmospheric electricity that accumulates on the antenna system. During transmission or reception, the switch should be open.

12-15A GROUND

Cold water pipes are effective grounds since they make excellent contact with the earth. The ground terminals to the radio station and the antenna system should be connected by means of a heavy conductor to a cold water pipe. If there is no cold water pipe system, an effective ground can be made by driving a copper rod of at least 6 to 8 feet into the earth. We call this a "ground rod".

238

Even where a cold water system is used, it would help to use a ground rod in addition to the cold water pipe for ground. The ground rod could be located close to the antenna tower and connected to the ground of the antenna system. A heavy conductor could then be used to connect the ground rod to the cold water pipe and the ground terminals of the radio station.

12-16 THE MEASUREMENT AND DETERMINATION OF FREQUENCY

The FCC states that a station must maintain its exact operating frequency so that stations do not interfere with each other. Therefore, one of the most important duties of the transmitting engineer is to keep his station exactly on frequency. The FCC assigns definite frequencies or bands of frequencies to the various transmitting services. Operating "off frequency" represents a serious offense and must be avoided. Therefore, it is very important to be able to measure the frequency of a transmitter. The instrument which is used to measure frequency is called a frequency meter.

We will now discuss several frequency meters in detail.

12-17 THE ABSORPTION TYPE FREQUENCY METER OR WAVEMETER

A high "Q" tank circuit is resonant to only one frequency. If this tank circuit is placed in the vicinity of an RF field, it will absorb energy from this field and start to oscillate if the resonant frequency of the tank circuit is equal to the frequency of the radiation. This is the principle of the absorption type wavemeter. The circuit is illustrated in Figure 12-10. The absorption type wavemeter consists of a

Figure 12-10.
Frequency meter.

rigidly constructed, accurately calibrated coil and a variable capacitor combination. The coil is usually interchangeable with other coils to permit measurements to be taken over a large portion of the radio frequency spectrum. The resonance indicator may be a flashlight bulb for high intensity RF fields. A highly sensitive resonance indicator is a thermocouple ammeter which is placed in series with the tank circuit. A thermocouple ammeter can be used in place of the bulb. At resonance, the tank circuit will absorb maximum energy from the radiation and therefore, the circulating current in the series resonant loop will be at a maximum, as indicated on the ammeter or bulb. A set of calibration charts are provided with the instrument. These charts relate the dial reading of the instrument in terms of frequency. A separate chart is provided for each coil.

If we wish to determine the output frequency of a transmitter, the wavemeter, with the proper coil in place, is brought near the output tank coil of the transmitter. A knob which is geared to the capacitor, C, and the dial, is turned rapidly until a reading is noted on the bulb or ammeter. The dial is read and reference made to the calibration chart to determine the frequency of that particular dial setting.

A precaution to be followed in using the wavemeter is to place the instrument as far away as possible from the radiating source, consistent with a readable indication. The reason for this is that we do not want the wavemeter to change the operation of the radiating source by mutual coupling reaction.

12-17A THE GRID-DIP METER

A GRID-DIP METER is similar to a wavemeter in that it measures frequency. The grid-dip meter is an oscillator with a milliammeter in its grid circuit. The inductance of the oscillator's tuned circuit consists of plug-in coils. Each plug-in coil makes the oscillator resonant to a different band of frequencies. Fig. 12-11 illustrates a common form of grid-dip meter.

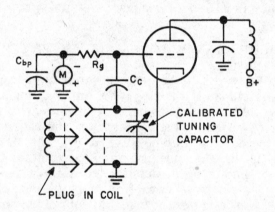

Figure 12-11. A grid-dip meter.

The purpose of the grid-dip meter is to measure the frequency of tuned circuits. In order to do this we must know the approximate range of the frequency to be measured. We then plug the correct coil into the meter. The coil with the meter is brought close to the tuned circuit being measured. The variable capacitor is rotated until the meter dips. This indicates that the grid dip oscillator is tuned to the same frequency as the tuned circuit being measured. The meter dips because the tuned circuit being measured draws energy from the meter. This reduces the amplitude of the oscillations and causes the grid current to drop. The calibrated dial, fastened to the tuning capacitor shield, indicates the frequency to which the oscillator is tuned.

The grid-dip meter can also be used as an absorption wave meter and it can be used to locate parasitic oscillations in transmitters.

240

12-18 PERCENTAGE ERROR

Suppose you want to determine the frequency of your transmitter, using your absorption type wavemeter. You would turn the tuning knob of your wavemeter until the indicating device indicates that the wavemeter is resonant to the transmitter frequency. At this point, you would stop and take a reading of the dial to determine the frequency. The reading that you get is not 100% accurate. There is a certain percentage error involved in the reading. This error involved in the reading is due to a number of factors. One factor is that it may be difficult to read the dial with complete accuracy. Another error is due to the limitations of the mechanical gearing system of the wavemeter. There may be some slack in the gears. Another factor is caused by the slight inaccuracies in the variable capacitor due to the limitations in manufacturing. All these factors contribute to a certain percentage error in a wavemeter reading. All wavemeters have their maximum percentage error listed under their characteristics. For example: a wavemeter is listed as having a maximum percentage error of 0.50%. What is the error involved in cycles at a reading of 1000 Kc. ?

Solution: The error in cycles per second is plus or minus 0.50% of 1000 Kc. or: $\frac{0.50}{100}$ x 1000 Kc. = 5 Kc. = $\pm$ 5000 cps.

The error in the reading $\pm$5000 cps. means that the actual frequency may be anywhere between 995 Kc. and 1005 Kc.

12-19 ERROR CALCULATIONS WHEN USING THE WAVEMETER

Suppose you wish to operate your transmitter close to the high frequency end of the 3500 - 4000 Kc. amateur band. You set your wavemeter dial to read 4000 Kc. and adjust your transmitter frequency until the wavemeter reads. Are you absolutely sure that the radio transmitter is radiating at 4000 Kc. ? You cannot be sure if you remember that the wavemeter reading has a tolerance, which means that there is a definite percentage error involved when a dial reading is indicated on a wavemeter. Returning to our example, if the wavemeter dial reads higher than the actual radiating frequency, you have nothing to worry about. However, if the dial reads lower than the actual radiating frequency (dial reading indicates 4000 Kc.), you are operating outside the band and are liable to be penalized by the FCC. If the wavemeter has a possible error of 0.60% at a reading of 4000 Kc., you should adjust the transmitter frequency to the wavemeter dial reading 3976 Kc.

0.60% of 4000 Kc. = 24 Kc.   4000 - 24 = 3976 Kc.

You can now be sure that if the wavemeter reading is low, the transmitter is in error by no more than 24 Kc. (to be exact: 0.60% of 3976 = 23.86 Kc.). Therefore, the most that the transmitter would be off from 3976 Kc. would be 3976 $\pm$23.86 or 3999.86 Kc.

Two problems are given:

(1) Using a frequency meter with a possible error of 0.75%,

241

on what whole number kilocycle frequency nearest the low frequency end of the 14,000 - 14,400 Kc. band could a transmitter safely be set?

Solution: The low frequency end of the band is 14,000 Kc.

$$0.75\% \text{ of } 14,000 \text{ Kc. is } \frac{.75}{100} \times 14,000 = 105 \text{ Kc.}$$

The transmitter should be set at: 14,000 Kc. + 105 Kc. = 14,105 Kc.

(2) Using a frequency meter with a possible error of 0.75%, on what whole number kilocycle frequency nearest the high frequency end of the 14,000 - 14,400 Kc. band could a transmitter safely be set?

Solution: The high frequency end of the band is 14,400 Kc.

$$0.75\% \text{ of } 14,400 \text{ Kc. is } \frac{.75}{100} \times 14,400 = 108 \text{ Kc.}$$

The transmitter should be set at: 14,400 Kc. - 108 Kc. = 14,292 Kc.

12-19A THE FREQUENCY MARKER

A simple method of checking one's frequency is to tune his signal in on his receiver. He must be careful not to overload the receiver. The operator then looks at his receiver dial to see what his transmitter frequency is. However, there is no assurance that the receiver dial is accurate. In order to correct the receiver calibration, we use a frequency marker. The frequency marker is a highly stable oscillator that is rich in harmonics. A popular frequency marker uses a 100 kHz crystal and produces signals, or "markers", every 100 kHz. With these marker frequencies, it is a simple matter to adjust the receiver so that the dial is accurate.

Many receivers and transceivers have a frequency marker built into them.

12-20 THE HETERODYNE FREQUENCY METER

The Heterodyne Frequency Meter is a rigidly constructed, accurately calibrated oscillator and detector. For stability, the oscillator is usually of the electron-coupled type. The oscillator is continuously variable and therefore, is not crystal controlled. An additional crystal oscillator can be incorporated in the frequency meter to check and calibrate the heterodyne oscillator at the crystal check points. Figure 12-12 illustrates a combination heterodyne frequency meter and monitor. The frequency meter incorporates a detector circuit into which is fed two RF signals. They are: (1) the transmitter signal picked up by an antenna circuit and (2) the signal from the heterodyne oscillator. These two signals mix in the grid of the detector and produce a beat note or difference frequency. If the beat note is in the audio range, it will be heard in the head sets.

To check the transmitter frequency, vary the frequency of the heterodyne oscillator frequency until the beat note becomes a zero beat. At zero beat, the transmitter and oscillator are producing exactly the same frequency. The frequency may now be read off directly from the frequency meter dial.

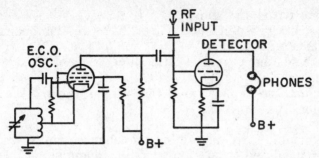

Figure 12-12. Combination heterodyne frequency meter and monitor.

A number of precautions to be observed in the use of the heterodyne type of frequency meters are as follows:

1. The heterodyne oscillator must be calibrated against the crystal oscillator check points for frequency accuracy.

2. When battery operated, check A and B battery voltages, as a change in battery voltage will affect the oscillator frequency.

3. Allow warm-up period before using.

PRACTICE QUESTIONS - LESSON 12

(For answers, refer to Appendix 6)

12-1* Which of the following cannot be used to determine that an emission from a transmitter is within an amateur band?
a. heterodyne frequency meter
b. grid-dip meter
c. wavemeter
d. thermocouple-type meter

12-2* An advantage of a Transmatch is not:
a. it reduces audio distortion
b. it brings about a good impedance match
c. it enables the transmitter to be used with several types of transmission lines
d. it reduces television interference

12-3* An important reason for using a dummy antenna is:
a. to minimize interference
b. it is the only way an FM transmitter can be tested
c. to measure the output power
d. to reduce splatter

12-4* If the voltage and current are the same on all points of a transmission line, the SWR is:
a. 1 to 1   b. 2 to 1   c. 1 to 2   d. .636 to 1

12-5* An antenna tuner will not:
   a. permit an antenna to be used on more than one frequency
   b. reduce RFI
   c. change the characteristic impedance of the transmission line
   d. match the impedance of the transmitter and the transmission line

12-6* The formula for determining the characteristic impedance of an air insulated parallel conductor transmission line is:
   a. $27 \log. ab$
   b. $\dfrac{276}{\log. ab}$
   c. $276 \log. \dfrac{b}{a}$
   d. $276 \dfrac{\log. a}{\log. b}$

12-7* A vertical Marconi antenna is:
   a. one-half wavelength long
   b. a full wavelength long
   c. one-quarter wavelength long
   d. an odd multiple of a half wavelength long

12-8* On which of the following ham bands is there maximum reception during daylight hours and during minimum sunspot activity?
   a. 160 meters
   b. 40 meters
   c. 20 meters
   d. 10 meters

12-9* What is the SWR on a line whose forward voltage is 5 volts and whose reflected voltage is 3 volts?
   a. 3 to 1
   b. 1 to 1
   c. 2 to 1
   d. 4 to 1

12-10* Ionization of the upper atmosphere is primarily dependent upon radiation from the:
   a. outer space
   b. sun
   c. moon
   d. earth

12-11* What is the approximate length of a half-wave antenna that is to transmit a frequency of 4850 kHz?
   a. 110 feet
   b. 96 feet
   c. 86 feet
   d. 79 feet

12-12* A precaution to be observed in the use of the absorption type frequency meter is to:
   a. loosely couple the frequency meter to the oscillator tank circuit
   b. calibrate the frequency meter
   c. check the B+ voltage of the frequency meter
   d. zero-beat the output of the wavemeter

12-13* A characteristic of a multiband antenna is:

a. low SWR   c. difficult to feed
b. high efficiency   d. high gain

12-14* The sky wave of a transmitter is refracted back to earth by the:

a. sun spots   c. antenna reflector
b. ionosphere   d. SWR

12-15* A transmitter is protected from damage from lightning by:

a. connecting spark gaps from the antenna base to ground
b. shorting the antenna
c. shunting the antenna with a low value resistance
d. opening up the antenna circuit

12-16* A precaution to be observed in the use of the battery operated heterodyne frequency meter is to:

a. check the crystal frequency
b. check the oscillator with a standard frequency
c. check the A and B battery voltages
d. check the tube filaments

SECTION III – LESSON 13
THE RADIO RECEIVER

13-1 FUNCTIONS OF A RADIO RECEIVER

Up to this point, we have covered the principles of the amplitude modulated transmitter in great detail. To complete the picture, we must consider the problem of the reception of radio waves by the radio receiver.

The radio receiver must be able to perform the following functions:

1. pick up radio frequency signals radiated by transmitters.
2. tune to one desired signal and reject the remaining signals.
3. amplify the desired radio frequency signal using radio frequency amplifiers.
4. detect or demodulate the desired signal (separate the audio intelligence from the radio frequency carrier).
5. amplify the detected audio signal and drive a speaker with it.

13-2 THE ONE TUBE RADIO RECEIVER

Figure 13-1 illustrates a block diagram of a one tube radio receiver.

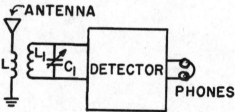

Figure 13-1. A simple one-tube receiver.

The antenna picks up any radiated signals that may be present in its vicinity and couples them to the tuned circuits L_1-C_1. The function of the tuned circuit is to select the station that is desired to be heard and at the same time, to reject the unwanted signals. This is accomplished by varying capacitor C_1, until the tuned circuit is resonant to the desired frequency. For a review of the theory of a tuned circuit, refer to Lesson 3, Paragraph 29 on series resonance. Once the signal has been selected, it is necessary to extract the audio-frequency intelligence from the radio-frequency carrier. This job is done by the detector, or demodulator, stage. A simple diode tube is generally used in the detector stage. The audio is then applied to the headphones.

13-3 THE TUNED RADIO-FREQUENCY RECEIVER

A radio signal diminishes in strength at a very rapid rate after it leaves the transmitting antenna. Therefore, it is seldom possible to use a detector circuit alone to obtain any useful output from the few microvolts of signal available at the receiving antenna. To remedy this, it is desirable to amplify the RF signal before it is detected. This is done by the use of an RF amplifier. The RF amplifier, like the detector, is provided with one or more tuned circuits so that it amplifies only the desired signal. The addition of an RF amplifier to the receiver gives not only greater sensitivity (ability to receive weak signals), but also greater selectivity (ability to separate signals). Audio amplifier stages usually follow the detector to amplify the audio signals before they are applied to the reproducer. The complete receiver, consisting of radio-frequency amplifiers, detector and audio amplifiers, is called the tuned radio frequency receiver or, as it is more commonly called, the TRF receiver.

A block diagram of a TRF receiver, showing the signal passing through the receiver, is illustrated in Figure 13-2.

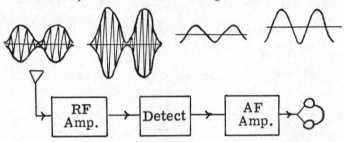

Figure 13-2. Block diagram of a TRF receiver.

13-4 THE RF AMPLIFIER

The RF amplifier, as indicated previously, gives us the desired selectivity and sensitivity required for satisfactory reception. Figure 13-3 illustrates an RF stage of amplification. The important operating characteristics of the amplifier shall be discussed at this time:

1. The RF amplifier tube is biased to operate as a Class A voltage amplifier. A Class A audio voltage amplifier differs from a Class A RF amplifier in that it does not have a tuned circuit and amplifies only audio frequencies. On the other hand, the RF amplifier has a tuned circuit which enables it to tune in, or select, only one signal frequency. Since this RF amplifier operates Class A, its fidelity is excellent.

2. The RF amplifier tube is always a pentode which has very low interelectrode capacities. If a triode with its high interelectrode capacities were used as an RF amplifier, there would be sufficient feedback from plate to grid at radio frequencies to cause the circuit to break into oscillations.

3. As in the audio amplifier, self-bias is almost always employed by using a cathode biasing resistor and a cathode by-pass capacitor.

4. The RF transformer consists of a primary coil and a secondary coil, L. L and C form a resonant circuit. The values of L and C are chosen so that when C is varied, the entire desired frequency range is covered. Resonant circuits, such as LC, provide much of the gain and selectivity of the RF amplifier. Without them, the signal would be shunted to ground by the capacitance between the tube's elements and ground. Most RF amplifier receivers use two

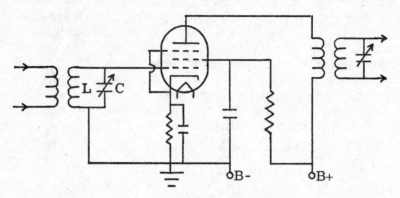

Figure 13-3. RF stage of a TRF receiver.

or three RF stages preceding the detector, with each stage tuned to the same frequency. It is, therefore, more convenient to have all of the tuning capacitors mounted on a common shaft so that all stages can be tuned simultaneously. These capacitors are called ganged variable capacitors. When these tuning circuits are ganged, the coils and the capacitors must be identical. This is necessary in order that all the circuits will tune to the same frequency for any dial setting. Since it is hardly likely that all the coils and capacitors of the tuned circuits will be identical (due to irregularities in manufacturing and the effects of stray capacity), the tuned circuits will not all tune to the same frequency, and decreased selectivity will result. These small differences are compensated for by providing small trimmer capacitors across each tuning capacitor. These trimmers are adjusted by means of a screwdriver so that each circuit may tune to the same frequency. This process is known as alignment. When all the stages tune to identical frequencies at all dial settings, they are said to be tracking and maximum gain and selectivity will be obtained from the receiver.

13-5 AF AMPLIFIERS

Since the signal output of a detector stage in a tuned radio frequency amplifier (TRF) receiver is low, it is usual to have at least one stage of AF amplification. The output of the first AF amplifier may be further amplified, if necessary, depending on the requirements of the receiver.

13-6 CAPABILITIES OF A TRF RECEIVER

Although the TRF receiver will give satisfactory results when covering the medium frequency band, such as the broadcast band, it has several disadvantages which makes it impractical for use in high frequency and multiband receivers. The chief disadvantage of the TRF receiver is that its selectivity does not remain constant over its tuning range. When a tuned circuit is made variable, as it must be in a TRF receiver, selectivity will decrease as the receiver is tuned to the high end of the band. If it were possible to design a receiver in which the selective circuits were fixed tuned, these circuits could very easily be designed for high gain and selectivity for the particular frequency at which they are to operate. This desirable effect is accomplished in the SUPERHETERODYNE RECEIVER.

13-7 THEORY OF SUPERHETERODYNE ACTION

The important difference between the TRF receiver and the superheterodyne receiver is that in the TRF, the RF signal is amplified at the frequency of the signal, while in the superheterodyne receiver, the RF signal is amplified at a new, lower, fixed frequency called the INTERMEDIATE FREQUENCY. The intermediate frequency (IF), though much lower in frequency than the original signal, retains all the modulation characteristics of the original signal. By amplifying this lower fixed frequency, it is possible to use circuits which are more selective and capable of greater amplification than the circuits used in TRF receivers.

13-8 THE HETERODYNE PRINCIPLE OF GENERATING A FIXED IF

In our study of the transmitter, we discussed the process of modulation, which is the mixing of two signals together to produce new frequencies called sidebands. (Refer to Lesson 11, Paragraph 5). In the superheterodyne receiver, the intermediate frequency is similarly generated by a mixing process called frequency conversion or HETERODYNING. The intermediate frequency in this case is the difference frequency. Suppose we were to mix a 1000 Kc. signal and a 1450 Kc. signal in a special mixing circuit. The output of the mixing circuit will contain the original frequencies (1000 Kc. and 1450 Kc.), the sum of the frequencies (2450 Kc.) and the difference frequency (450 Kc.). If the two original frequencies were varied by the same amount, the output difference frequency would remain fixed at 450 Kc. For example, if the two frequencies were increased by 1000 Kc. so that they became 2000 Kc. and 2450 Kc. respectively, the difference frequency would still be 450 Kc. As long as the two frequencies vary up or down by the same amount, the difference frequency (the IF) will always remain fixed at 450 Kc. If a modulated carrier is beat against a pure RF frequency, the modulation frequency will still remain present and unchanged in amplitude in the difference, or intermediate, frequency. For example, if a 1000 Kc. signal with a 400 cycle audio modulation is beat against a 1450 Kc. signal, the beat frequency will be a 450 Kc. RF wave with a 400 cycle audio modulation envelope. The process of mixing two frequencies to obtain a constant difference or intermediate frequency is utilized in the superheterodyne receiver.

13-9 THE SUPERHETERODYNE RECEIVER

The block diagram of a typical superheterodyne receiver, showing the signal passing through, is illustrated in Figure 13-4. The received modulated RF signal is first passed through an RF amplifier. A locally generated unmodulated RF signal is then mixed with the carrier frequency in the mixer stage. The mixer is called a converter and sometimes a first detector. This mixing action produces two new modulated RF signals in the output of the mixer, the sum and

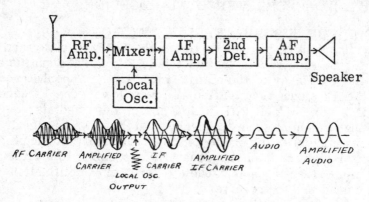

Figure 13-4. Block diagram of a superheterodyne receiver.

the difference, in addition to the original signals. It is the difference or intermediate frequency in which we are interested. A fixed tuned circuit in the plate of the mixer will reject all frequencies except the IF frequency to which it is tuned. This new IF frequency contains all the modulation characteristics of the original signal, but it is much lower in frequency. The intermediate frequency is usually set at some definite value. The frequency of the local oscillator must differ from that of the signal being received by an amount equal to the intermediate frequency. Thus, as the RF amplifier of the receiver is tuned to signals of various frequencies, the local oscillator must be tuned simultaneously, so that its frequency is always separated from that of the signal by the same amount. For example, if the IF is 450 kilocycles, a commonly used frequency, and the range of the receiver is from 500 to 1600 Kc., the oscillator would have to operate over a range of either 950 (450 + 500) to 2050 (450 + 1600) kilocycles or 50 (500 - 450) to 1150 (1600 - 450) kilocycles. Whether the oscillator frequencies are higher or lower than the signal, the difference is still 450 Kc. The intermediate frequency is then amplified in one or more fixed tuned stages called intermediate-frequency amplifiers, and is then fed into the second detector where it is detected or demodulated. The detected signal is amplified in the AF amplifier and then fed to the headset or loudspeaker. The reason why the detector is called the second detector is because the mixer tube is sometimes called the first detector. Because of this, the superheterodyne is sometimes called a double detector receiver. At this point, in order that you don't lose sight of the essential reason for designing the superheterodyne receiver, re-read Chapter 13-6 entitled "Capabilities of a TRF receiver".

13-10 FREQUENCY CONVERSION

The combined circuits of the oscillator stage and mixer stage form the frequency converter of the superheterodyne receiver. There are a large number of possible combinations of tubes and circuits which may be employed for frequency conversion.

The most popular circuits employ the Hartley, the Electron-Coupled or the Armstrong type of oscillator. The major requisite is stability rather than high output. The frequency of the oscillator is controlled by the coil constants and the variable capacitor which is ganged to the mixer tuned circuit.

The two most important types of conversion circuits are:

1. A separate oscillator and mixer, as illustrated in Figure 13-5.

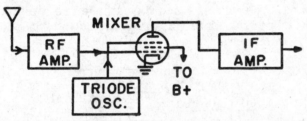

Figure 13-5. The pentode mixer.

2. Pentagrid converter: This circuit employs a single tube combining the oscillator and frequency mixer in the same envelope. The basic circuit of the pentagrid converter is illustrated in Figure 13-6. The cathode and the first two grids represent the oscillator section of the pentagrid converter tube.

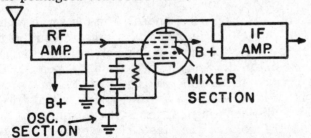

Figure 13-6. The pentagrid converter.

13-11 IF AMPLIFIERS

The intermediate-frequency amplifier is a high gain circuit

permanently tuned to the frequency difference between the local oscillator and the incoming signal. Pentode tubes are generally used as IF amplifiers because of their high gain and low interelectrode capacities. The IF section consists of one or more IF stages, with each stage adjusted to tune to the IF frequency. Since all incoming signals are converted to the same frequency by the frequency converter, the IF amplifier operates at only one frequency. The tuned circuits may, therefore, be permanently adjusted for maximum amplification and desired selectivity. It is in the IF voltage amplifier that practically all of the voltage amplification and selectivity of the superheterodyne are developed.

13-12 SECOND DETECTORS

The "second detector" of the superheterodyne is the actual detector of the receiver. It is here that we extract the audio intelligence from the RF carrier. We call it a "second detector" because we sometimes refer to the frequency converter as the "first detector".

Fig. 13-7 illustrates the diagram of a second detector used in most superheterodynes. The second detector and the first audio frequency amplifier are combined in one tube. This is done to save tubes and space. The plate P1 and the cathode are the diode detector portion of the tube. The plate P2, the grid and the cathode represent the first AF portion of the tube.

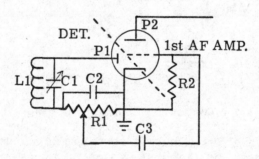

Figure 13-7. Second detector and first AF stage.

The detector of Fig. 13-7 operates in the same manner as all diode detectors. L1-C1 is the secondary tuned circuit of the last IF transformer. It is also the tuned circuit of the detector. R1 is the detector load resistor across which the audio appears. By using it as a voltage divider to tap off various amount of audio, we control the volume of the receiver. C2 is the capacitor that filters out the RF. C3 is an audio coupling capacitor that couples the audio from the detector to the grid of the first AF amplifier. R2 is the grid load resistor.

13-13 "S" METER

Many communications receivers have an "S" meter built into

252

them. The S meter indicates the relative signal strength of the received signal.

There are many types of S meter circuits. The simplest type consists of a rectifier and DC microammeter that reads the signal at the output of the last IF amplifier. Another type uses a high impedance voltmeter that reads the output of the last IF stage. In addition to being a signal strength indicator, the S meter can also be used as an output indicator in tuning up the receiver.

The lower half (left side) of the face of the S meter is calibrated in S units, from S-1 to S-9. Each S unit is approximately 5 to 6 db. Depending upon the receiver, an S-9 reading indicates a signal at the antenna of anywhere from 25 to 50 microvolts. The upper half of the meter is calibrated in db. over S-9, usually from 0 to 50 or 60 db.

It is important to keep in mind the fact that the S meter is not an accurate signal strength meter, but rather a means of obtaining relative signal strength indications.

13-14 THE WAVE TRAP

Broadcast receivers sometimes experience interference from a nearby amateur transmitter. The interfering station is usually

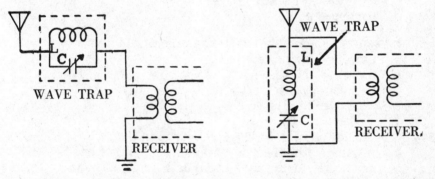

Fig. 13-8. Shunt-rejector wave trap.   Fig. 13-9. Series wave trap.

heard in the background over the entire tunable band of the receiver.

One way of reducing this interference is to place a tuned circuit in the antenna system which will either bypass the interfering station to ground, or else offer a high impedance to this frequency and prevent it from being developed across the antenna primary coil. The circuit used for this purpose is called a WAVE TRAP. Figure 13-8 illustrates a shunt rejector wave trap. The parallel circuit consisting of L and C is tuned until the interfering station frequency disappears. The parallel resonant circuit is a very high impedance at the interfering frequency. It thus blocks this signal from entering the antenna coil primary. Figure 13-9 is a diagram of a series wave trap. L and C are connected in a series circuit which is bridged across the primary of the antenna coil. The circuit is adjusted by varying capacitor C until the interfering station is eliminated. The wave trap acts as a short circuit at the interfering frequency, bypassing the signal to ground.

PRACTICE QUESTIONS - LESSON 13

(For answers, refer to Appendix 6)

13-1   Draw a schematic diagram of a filter for reducing amateur interference to broadcast reception, consisting of a series tuned circuit connected in shunt with the DC receiver input to bypass the interfering signal and a parallel tuned (trap) circuit in series with the receiver input to reject the interfering signal.

13-2   The function of the detector is to:
a. amplify the signal
b. demodulate the carrier
c. excite the speaker
d. bypass the AF

13-3   Increasing the number of tuned circuits in a receiver will:
a. increase the power output
b. increase the selectivity
c. decrease the selectivity
d. improve fidelity

13-4   The disadvantage of a TRF receiver is that:
a. sensitivity decreases towards high end of band
b. sensitivity decreases towards low end of band
c. selectivity decreases towards high end of band
d. it has poor fidelity

13-5   The Intermediate Frequency:
a. is the difference frequency between the carrier frequency and the local oscillator frequency
b. is always one-half the local oscillator frequency
c. depends upon the station tuned in
d. is twice the carrier frequency

13-6   If a superheterodyne receiver is tuned to 880 kHz and the intermediate frequency is 456 kHz, the local oscillator frequency is:
a. 1760 kHz   c. 912 kHz
b. 440 kHz   d. 1336 kHz

13-7 Fixed tuned IF stages mean:
    a. high fidelity
    b. variable IF
    c. high selectivity, high gain
    d. constant power output

13-8 A pentagrid converter is:
    a. a mixer oscillator tube
    b. an RF amplifier
    c. an AF amplifier
    d. an audio power amplifier

13-9 The object of frequency conversion in a superheterodyne is to:
    a. change the oscillator frequency
    b. double the IF
    c. obtain a fixed IF
    d. increase the fidelity

13-10 The way in which to eliminate broadcast interference by amateur transmission is to:
    a. tune to another channel
    b. use a directional antenna
    c. use a wave trap
    d. increase the IF

13-11*Removing a parallel resonant circuit from an RF amplifier:
    a. reduces its gain
    b. reduces its selectivity
    c. reduces its grid to ground capacitance
    d. a and b are correct

13-12*The purpose of an "S" meter is:
    a. to indicate relative signal strength
    b. to calibrate the receiver
    c. to measure the strength of the incoming signal
    d. to adjust the balanced modulator

SECTION III — LESSON 14
RULES AND REGULATIONS
GOVERNING AMATEUR RADIO SERVICE

The government of the United States does not license or interfere in any way with the RECEPTION of standard broadcast or short wave programs. Anyone can own and operate a radio receiver without a license. However, in the case of radio transmission, the situation is entirely different. All transmitting stations, whether Amateur or Commercial, are licensed by the Federal Communications Commission (FCC). Consequently, all operators of transmitting equipment must be licensed.

There are various rules and regulations which govern the operation of all radio transmissions. It is important that the radio amateur be familiar with the general rules and regulations of Communications as well as those rules which apply specifically to Amateur Radio. The examinations for the Amateur Operators Licenses contain questions based on the provisions of treaties, statutes and regulations affecting amateurs. Because it is important to know the laws regarding amateur radio transmission, we are reproducing excerpts from Part 97 of the FCC rules. Part 97 contains the rules and regulations that govern the Amateur Radio Service.

Violation of the rules and regulations of the Federal Communications Commission can result in a maximum penalty of up to $500.00 for each day during which the offense occurs. The penalty can also include suspension of the operator license and revocation of the station license.

97.1 BASIS AND PURPOSE
The rules and regulations in this part are designed to provide an amateur radio service having a fundamental purpose as expressed in the following principles:

(a) Recognition and enhancement of the value of the amateur service to the public as a voluntary noncommercial communication service, particularly with respect to providing emergency communications.

(b) Continuation and extension of the amateur's proven ability to contribute to the advancement of the radio art.

(c) Encouragement and improvement of the amateur radio service through rules which provide for advancing skills in both the communication and technical phases of the art.

(d) Expansion of the existing reservoir within the amateur radio service of trained operators, technicians, and electronics experts.

(e) Continuation and extension of the amateur's unique ability to enhance international good will.

97.3 DEFINITIONS

(a) Amateur radio service. A radio communication service of self-training, intercommunication, and technical investigation carried on by amateur radio operators.

(b) Amateur radio communication. Noncommercial radio communication by or among amateur radio stations solely with a personal aim and without pecuniary or business interest.

(c) Amateur radio operator. A person interested in radio technique solely with a personal aim and without pecuniary interest, holding a valid Federal Communications Commission license to operate amateur radio stations.

(e) Amateur radio station. A station licensed in the amateur radio service embracing necessary apparatus at a particular location used for amateur radio communication.

Control station. Station licensed to conduct remote control of another amateur radio station.

(m) Amateur radio operation. Amateur radio communication conducted by an amateur radio operator from an amateur radio station. May include one or more of the following:

Fixed operation. Radio communication conducted from the specific geographical land location shown on the station license.

Portable operation. Radio communication conducted from a specific geographical location other than that shown on the station license.

Mobile operation. Radio communication conducted while in motion or during halts at unspecified locations.

(n) Remote control. Control of transmitting apparatus of an amateur radio station from a position other than one at which the transmitter is located and immediately accessible, except that direct mechanical control, or direct electrical control by wired connections of an amateur radio transmitter from a point located on board any aircraft, vessel, vehicle, or on the same premises on which the transmitter is located, shall not be considered remote control within the meaning of this definition.

(p) Control operator. An amateur radio operator designated by the licensee of an amateur radio station to also be responsible for the emissions from that station.

(q) Control point. The operating position of an amateur radio station where the control operator function is performed.

(w) Third-party traffic. Amateur radio communication by or under the supervision of the control operator at an amateur radio station to another amateur radio station on behalf of anyone other than the control operator.

257

97.5 CLASSES OF OPERATOR LICENSES.
Amateur Extra Class.
Advanced Class (previously Class A).
General Class (previously Class B).
Conditional Class (previously Class C).
Technician Class.
Novice Class.

97.7 PRIVILEGES OF AMATEUR OPERATOR LICENSES. (See chart on Page 305 showing privileges of operator licenses for popular amateur bands.)

(a) Amateur Extra Class and Advanced Class. All authorized amateur privileges including exclusive frequency operating authority in accordance with the following table.

Frequencies	Class of license authorized.
3500-3525 kHz 3775-3800 kHz 7000-7025 kHz 14,000-14,025 kHz 21,000-21,025 kHz 21,250-21,270 kHz	Amateur Extra Only.
3800-3890 kHz 7150-7225 kHz 14,200-14,275 kHz 21,270-21,350 kHz 50-50.1 MHz	Amateur Extra and Advanced.

(b) General Class. All authorized amateur privileges except those exclusive operating privileges which are reserved to the Advanced Class and/or Amateur Extra Class.

(c) Conditional Class. Same privileges as General Class. New Conditional Class licenses will not be issued. Present Conditional Class licensees will be issued General Class licenses at time of renewal or modification.

(d) Technician Class. All authorized amateur privileges on the frequencies 50.1-54 MHz and 145-148 MHz and in the Amateur bands above 220 MHz. Such licenses also carry the full privileges of the Novice Class license.

(e) Novice Class. Radiotelegraphy in the frequency bands 3700-3750 kHz, 7100-7150 kHz (7050-7075 kHz when the terrestrial station location is not within Region 2), 21,100-21,200 kHz, and 28,100-28,200 kHz, using only Type A1 emission.

97.9 ELIGIBILITY FOR NEW OPERATOR LICENSE.
Anyone, except a representative of a foreign government, is eligible for an amateur operator license.

97.13 RENEWAL OR MODIFICATION OF AMATEUR OPERATOR LICENSE.

(a) An amateur operator license, except the Novice Class, may be renewed upon proper application.

(b) The Novice Class license will not be renewed.

(c) The applicant shall qualify for a new license by examination if the requirements of this section are not fulfilled.

(d) The renewal and/or modification (change of address, etc.) application of the amateur operator license shall be on FCC Form 610 and must be accompanied by the applicant's license. Unless the Commission directs otherwise, each application for the renewal of the license shall be filed only during the last 60 days of the license term or within a grace period of one year after the expiration date of the license. During the one year grace period, the expired license is not valid. Any license issued upon the basis of an application filed during the grace period will not be back-dated to the date of expiration of the license being renewed, but will be dated currently. In any case in which the licensee has, in accordance with the Commission's Rules, made timely and sufficient application for renewal of the license, no license with reference to any activity of a continuing nature shall expire until such application shall have been finally determined. A license for modification only will be dated to expire on the same date as the license being modified, in accordance with Section 97.59.

97.28 MANNER OF CONDUCTING EXAMINATIONS.

(a) Except as provided by 97.27, all examinations for Amateur Extra, Advanced, General and Technician Class operator licenses will be conducted by authorized Commission personnel or representatives at locations and times specified by the Commission. Examination elements given under the provisions of 97.27 will be administered by an examiner selected by the Commission. All applications for consideration of eligibility under 97.27 should be filed on FCC Form 610, and should be sent to the FCC field office nearest the applicant. (A list of these offices appears in Sec. 0.121 of the Commission's Rules and can be obtained from the Regional Services Division, Field Operations Bureau, FCC, Washington, D.C. 20554, or any field office.)

(b) Unless otherwise prescribed by the Commission, examinations for the Novice Class license will be conducted and supervised by a volunteer examiner selected by the applicant. The volunteer examiner shall be at least 21 years of age, shall be unrelated to the applicant, and shall be the holder of an Amateur Extra, Advanced or General Class operator license. The written portion of the Novice examination, Element 2, shall be obtained, administered, and submitted in accordance with the following procedure:

(1) Within 10 days after successfully completing telegraphy examination element 1(a), an applicant shall submit an application

(FCC Form 610) to the Commission's office in Gettysburg, Pennsylvania 17325. The application shall include a written request from the volunteer examiner for the examination papers for Element 2. The examiner's written request shall include (i) the names and permanent addresses of the examiner and the applicant, (ii) a description of the examiner's qualifications to administer the examination, (iii) the examiner's statement that the applicant has passed telegraphy element 1(A) under his supervision within the 10 days prior to submission of the request, and (iv) the examiner's written signature. Examination papers will be forwarded only to the volunteer examiner.

(2) The volunteer examiner shall be responsible for the proper conduct and necessary supervision of the examination. Administration of the examination shall be in accordance with the instructions included with the examination papers.

97.37 GENERAL ELIGIBILITY FOR STATION LICENSE

An amateur radio station license will be issued only to a licensed amateur radio operator, except that a military recreation station license may also be issued to an individual not licensed as an amateur radio operator (other than an alien or a representative of an alien or of a foreign government), who is in charge of a proposed military recreation station not operated by the U. S. Government but which is to be located in approved public quarters.

97.39 ELIGIBILITY OF CORPORATIONS OR ORGANIZATIONS TO HOLD STATION LICENSE

An amateur station license will not be issued to a school, company, corporation, association, or other organization, except that in the case of a bona fide amateur radio organization or society, a station license may be issued to a licensed amateur operator, other than the holder of a Novice Class license, as trustee for such society.

97.40 STATION LICENSE REQUIRED

(a) No transmitting station shall be operated in the amateur radio service without being licensed by the Federal Communications Commission.

(b) Every amateur radio operator must have a primary amateur radio station license.

(c) An amateur radio operator may be issued one or more additional station licenses, each for a different land location, except that repeater station, control station, and auxiliary link station licenses may also be issued to an amateur radio operator for land locations where another station license has been issued to the applicant.

(d) Any transmitter to be operated as part of a control link shall be licensed as a control station or as an auxiliary link station and may be combined with a primary, secondary, or club station license at the same location.

(e) A transmitter may only be operated as a repeater station under the authority of a repeater station license.

97.43 LOCATION OF STATION

Every amateur station must have one land location, the address of which is designated on the station license. Every amateur radio station must have at least one control point. If the control point location is not the same as the station location, authority to operate the station by remote control is required.

97.57 LICENSE TERM

Amateur operator licenses and station licenses are normally valid for a period of 5 years from the date of issuance of a new or renewed license, except the Novice Class which is normally valid for a period of 2 years from the date of issuance.

97.61 FREQUENCIES AND TYPES OF EMISSION FOR USE OF AMATEUR STATIONS

Subject to the limitations and restrictions set forth in these rules, the following frequency bands are available for amateur use:

(1) 1800 to 2000 kHz. Use of this band is on a shared basis with the Loran system of radio navigation. In any particular area, the Loran system operates either on 1800-1900 kHz or 1900-2000 kHz. In any area, the amateur service uses whichever bands, 1800-1825 and 1875-1900 kHz or 1900-1925 and 1975-2000 kHz, which are not required for Loran in that area. For instance, in most Eastern states, the Loran system operates in the 1900-2000 kHz band and the amateurs have the use of the 1800-1825 kHz and 1875-1900 kHz bands. In most Western states, the Loran system uses the 1800-1900 kHz band and the amateurs use the 1900-1925 kHz and the 1975-2000 kHz bands. Type A1* or A3* emission is used in the 1800-2000 kHz bands. The power used is 500, 200 or 50 watts, depending on the geographical area and the time of day. For exact information as to frequency and power in any particular state, write to the Federal Communications Commission.

(2) 3500 to 4000 Kc. Type A1 emission may be used in the entire band. Carrier-shift-telegraphy may be used on 3500-3775 Kc. Type A3 emission may be used on 3775 to 4000 Kc. Narrow band frequency modulation and phase modulation may also be used in the 3775 to 4000 Kc. portion of the band. The frequencies of 3900 to 4000 Kc. are not available to stations located within the following United States possessions in Region III as defined in the Atlantic City, 1947, Radio Regulations: Baker, Canton, Enderbury, Guam, Howland, Jarvis, Palmyra, American Samoa and Wake Islands. The phone

* The types of emission referred to in the Amateur rules are given on Page 211.

part of this band may be used by all amateurs except those of the Novice and Technician Classes. See Page 259 for the Novice use of this band.

(3) <u>7000 to 7300 Kc.</u> Type A1 emission may be used on the entire band. Carrier-shift-telegraphy may be used in the 7000 to 7150 Kc. portion of the band. Type A3 emission and narrow band frequency or phase modulation may be used in the 7150 to 7300 Kc. portion of the band.

(4) <u>14000 to 14350 Kc.</u> Type A1 emission may be used in the entire band. Carrier-shift-telegraphy may be used in 14000 to 14200 Kc. Type A3 emission or narrow band frequency or phase modulation for radiotelephony may be used in the 14200 to 14350 Kc. portion of the band.

(5) <u>21000 to 21450 Kc.</u> Type A1 emission may be used in the entire band. Carrier-shift-telegraphy may be used on 21000 to 21250 Kc. Type A3 emission may be used on 21250 to 21450 Kc.

(6) <u>28.0 to 29.7 Mc.</u> Type A1 emission may be used in the entire band. Type A3 emission and narrow band frequency or phase modulation may be used on 28.5 to 29.7 Mc. Carrier shift telegraphy may be used on 28.0 to 28.5 Mc.

(7) <u>50.0 to 54.0 Mc.</u> Type A1 emission may be used in the entire band. Type A2, A3, A4, A5 and narrow band F1, F3 and F5 emission on 50.1 to 54.0 Mc. Type AØ on 51.0 to 54.0 Mc.

(8) <u>144.0 to 148.0 Mc.</u> Type A1 emission may be used in the entire band. Types AØ, A2, A3, A4, A5, FØ, F1, F2, F3 and F5 may be used on 144.1 to 148 Mc.

(9) <u>220 to 225 Mc.</u> The entire band may be used for types AØ, A1, A2, A3, A4, A5, FØ, F1, F2, F3, F4 and F5 emission. The amateur service shall not cause harmful interference to the government radio-positioning service in this band. In portions of the states of Texas and New Mexico, the 220 to 225 Mc. band is not available for use by amateur stations engaged in normal amateur operation between the hours of 0500 and 1800 local time, Monday through Friday inclusive of each week.

(10) <u>420 to 450 Mc.</u> The whole band may be used for types AØ, A1, A2, A3, A4, A5, FØ, F1, F2, F3, F4 and F5 emission. In some areas of the Southeast and Southwest, the maximum DC plate power to the final shall not exceed 50 watts input. In this band, the amateur service shall not cause harmful interference to the government radio-positioning service.

(11) <u>1215 to 1300 Mc.</u> The entire band may be used for types AØ, A1, A2, A3, A4, A5, FØ, F1, F2, F3, F4 and F5 emission. In this band, harmful interference to the government radiopositioning service is not allowed.

(12) <u>2300 to 2450 Mc., 3500 to 3700 Mc. and 5650 to 5925 Mc.</u> These bands may use types AØ, A1, A2, A3, A4, A5, FØ, F1, F2, F3, F4, F5 and pulse emission. Operators in the frequency bands 2300 to 2450 Mc. and 5650 to 5925 Mc. are subject to such interference between 2400 and 2450 Mc. and between 5775 and 5925 Mc., respectively, as may result from emissions of industrial, scientific and medical devices on the frequencies 2450 and 5850 Mc. respectively. In these bands, the amateur service shall not cause harmful interference to the government radiopositioning service.

(13) <u>10,000 to 10,500 Mc.</u> Types AØ, A1, A2, A3, A4, A5, FØ, F1, F2, F3, F4 and F5 emission may be used in this band. In this band, the amateur service shall not cause harmful interference to the government radiopositioning service.

(14) <u>21,000 to 22,000 Mc. and any frequency or frequencies above 30,000 Mc.</u> Types AØ, A1, A2, A3, A4, A5, FØ, F1, F2, F3, F4, F5 and pulse emission may be used in the entire bands.

97.65 <u>TYPES OF EMISSION</u>

(c) On frequencies below 29.0 MHz and between 50.1 and 52.5 MHz, the bandwidth of an F3 emission (frequency or phase modulation), shall not exceed that of an A3 emission having the same audio characteristics; and the purity and stability of emissions shall comply with the requirements of 97.73.

97.73 <u>PURITY AND STABILITY OF EMISSIONS</u>

.... In the case of A3 emission, the amateur transmitter shall not be modulated to the extent that interfering spurious radiation occurs, and in no case shall the emitted carrier wave be amplitude-modulated in excess of 100 percent. Means shall be employed to insure that the transmitter is not modulated in excess of its modulation capability for proper technical operation...........When using amplitude modulation on frequencies below 144 megaHertz, simultaneous frequency modulation is not permitted, and when using frequency modulation on frequencies below 144 megaHertz, simultaneous amplitude modulation is not permitted. The frequency of the emitted carrier wave shall be as constant as the state of the art permits.

97.75 <u>FREQUENCY MEASUREMENT AND REGULAR CHECK</u>

The licensee of an amateur station shall provide for measurement of the emitted carrier frequency or frequencies and shall establish procedure for making such measurements regularly. The measurement of the emitted carrier frequency or frequencies shall be made by means independent of the means used to control the radio frequency or frequencies generated by the transmitting apparatus and shall be of sufficient accuracy to assure operating within the amateur frequency band used.

97.77 PRACTICE TO BE OBSERVED BY ALL LICENSEES

In all respects not specifically covered by these regulations, each amateur station shall be operated in accordance with good engineering and good amateur practice.

97.79 CONTROL OPERATOR REQUIREMENTS

(a) The licensee of an amateur station shall be responsible for its proper operation.

(b) Every station when in operation shall have a control operator at an authorized control point. The control operator may be the station licensee or another amateur radio operator designated by the licensee. Each control operator shall also be responsible for the proper operation of the station.

(c) An amateur station may only be operated in the manner and to the extent permitted by the operator privileges authorized for the class of license held by the control operator, but may exceed those of the station licensee provided proper station identification procedures are performed.

(d) The licensee of an amateur radio station may permit any third party to participate in amateur radio communication from his station, provided that a control operator is present and continuously monitors and supervises the radio communication to insure compliance with the rules.

97.83 AVAILABILITY OF OPERATOR LICENSE

The original license of each operator shall be kept in the personal possession of the operator while operating an amateur station. When operating an amateur station at a fixed location, however, the license may be posted in a conspicuous place in the room occupied by the operator. The license shall be available for inspection by an authorized government official whenever the operator is operating an amateur station and, at other times, upon request made by an authorized representative of the Commission, except when such license has been filed with application for modification or renewal thereof, or has been mutilated, lost or destroyed, and application has been made for a duplicate license in accordance with 97.57. Photo copies of the license can be made but cannot be used in lieu of the original as required by this section.

97.85 AVAILABILITY OF STATION LICENSE

The original license of each amateur station or a photocopy thereof shall be posted in a conspicuous place in the room occupied by the licensed operator while the station is being operated at a fixed location, or shall be kept in his personal possession. When the station is operated at other than a fixed location, the original station license or a photocopy thereof shall be kept in the personal possession of the station licensee (or a licensed representative) who shall be present at the station while it is being operated as a portable or mobile station. The original station license shall be available for inspection by any authorized Government official at all times while that station is being operated, and at other times upon request made by an authorized representative of the Commission, except when such license has been filed with application for modification or renewal thereof, or has been mutilated, lost or destroyed, and application has been made for a duplicate license in accordance with 97.57.

97.87 STATION IDENTIFICATION

(a) An amateur station shall be identified by the transmission of its call sign at the beginning and end of each single transmission or exchange of transmissions and at intervals not to exceed 10 minutes during any single transmission or exchange of transmissions of more than 10 minutes duration. Additionally, at the end of an exchange of telegraphy (other than teleprinter) or telephony transmissions between amateur stations, the call sign (or the generally accepted network identifier) shall be given for the station, or for at least one of the group of stations, with which communication was established.

(b) When an amateur station is operated as a portable or mobile station, the operator shall give the following additional identification at the end of each single transmission or exchange of transmissions:

(1) When identifying by telegraphy, immediately after the call sign, transmit the fraction-bar $\overline{DN}$ followed by the number of the call sign area in which the station is being operated.

(2) When identifying by telephony, immediately after the call sign, transmit the word "portable" or "mobile", as appropriate, followed by the number of the call sign area in which the station is being operated.

(d) Under conditions when the control operator is other than the station licensee, the station identification shall be the assigned call sign for that station. However, when a station is operated within the privileges of the operator's class of license but which exceeds those of the station licensee, station identification shall be made by following the station call sign with the operator's primary station call sign (i.e. WN4XYZ/W4XX).

(e) A repeater station shall be identified by radio-telephony or by radio telegraphy when in service at intervals not to exceed 5 minutes at a level of modulation sufficient to be intelligible through the repeated transmission.

(f) A control station must be identified by its assigned station call sign unless its emissions contain the call sign identification of the remotely controlled station.

(g) An auxiliary link station must be identified by its assigned station call sign unless its emissions contain the call sign of its associated station.

(h) The identification required by paragraphs (a), (b), (c), (d), (e), (f), and (g) of this section shall be given on each frequency being utilized for transmission and shall be transmitted either by telegraphy using the international Morse code, or by telephony, using the English language. If by an automatic device only used for identification by telegraphy, the code speed shall not exceed 20 words per minute. The use of a national or internationally recognized standard phonetic alphabet as an aid for correct telephone identification is encouraged.

97.89 POINTS OF COMMUNICATIONS

An amateur station may be used to communicate only with other amateur stations, except that in emergencies or for test purposes, it may also be used temporarily for communication with other classes of stations licensed by the Commission, and with the United States Government stations. Amateur stations may also be used to communicate with any radio station other than amateur which is authorized by the Commission to communicate with amateur stations. Amateur stations may be used also for transmitting signals, or communications, or energy, to receiving apparatus for the measurement of emissions, temporary observation of transmission phenomena, radio control of remote objects, and for similar experimental purposes set forth in Section 97.91 of these rules. (Third party messages may be handled by amateur stations of different countries if such communication is authorized by a special agreement between the countries involved).

97.91 ONE-WAY COMMUNICATIONS

In addition to the experimental one-way transmission permitted by Section 97.89, the following kinds of one-way communications, addressed to amateur stations, are authorized and will not be construed as broadcasting:

(a) Emergency communications, including bonafide emergency drill practice transmissions;

(b) Information bulletins consisting solely of subject matter having direct interest to the amateur radio service as such;

(c) Round-table discussions or net-type operations where more than two amateur stations are in communication, each station taking a turn at transmitting to other station(s) of the group; and

(d) Code practice transmissions intended for persons learning or improving proficiency in the International Morse Code.

97.95, 97.97 REQUIREMENTS FOR PORTABLE AND MOBILE OPERATION - NOTICE OF OPERATION

Within the continental limits of the United States, its territories or possessions, an amateur station may be operated as either a portable or a mobile station on any frequency authorized and available for the amateur radio service. Whenever portable operation is, or is likely to be, for an over-all period in excess of 15 days, away from the fixed transmitter location designated in the station license, the licensee shall give prior written notice to the FCC Engineer-In-Charge of the radio inspection district in which such portable operation is intended. (This applies to operation on any amateur band). A new notice is required whenever there is any change in the particulars of a previous notice or whenever operation away from the authorized station continues for a period in excess of one year. The notice required for either portable or mobile operation shall state the station call sign, authorized fixed transmitter location, the name of the licensee, the date or dates of proposed operation and the contemplated portable station locations or mobile station's itinerary, as specifically as possible. Also, the address at which, or through which, the licensee can be readily reached. In the case of mobile operation, the official name, registry number or license number (including the name of the issuing state or territory, if any) of the aircraft, vessel or land vehicle in which the mobile station is installed and operated, must be given.

97.99 STATIONS USED ONLY FOR RADIO CONTROL OF REMOTE MODEL CRAFTS AND VEHICLES

An amateur transmitter when used for the purpose of transmitting radio signals intended only for the control of a remote model craft or vehicle and having mean output power not exceeding one watt may be operated under the special provisions of this section provided an executed Transmitter Identification Card (FCC Form 452-C) or a plate made of a durable substance indicating the station call sign and licensee's name and address is affixed to the transmitter.

(a) Station identification is not required for transmissions directed only to a remote model craft or vehicle.

(b) Transmissions containing only control signals directed only to a remote model craft or vehicle are not considered to be codes or ciphers in the context of the meaning of 97.117.

(c) Notice of operation away from authorized location is not required where the portable or mobile operation consists entirely of transmissions directed only to a remote model craft or vehicle.

(d) Station logs need not indicate the times of commencing and terminating each transmission or series of transmissions.

97.103 STATION LOG REQUIREMENTS

An accurate legible account of station operation shall be entered in a log for each amateur radio station. The log shall bear the call sign of the station and the signature of the licensee. The following information shall be recorded as a minimum:

(a) Written entries for all stations which are required only once, or when there is a change thereto.

(1) The signature of the control operator on duty and the call sign of his primary station, if he is other than the station licensee.

(2) The location of the station. Stations in mobile operation may enter the word "local" for amateur radiocommunication conducted within 100 statute miles of the address shown on the station license, otherwise the location of the first and last radiocommunication of each day. Stations in mobile or portable operation shall

make an entry showing compliance with 97.97, if required.

(3) The input power to the transmitter final amplifying stage.

(4) The type of emission used.

(5) The frequency or frequency subband used for transmitting.

(b) Other entries for all stations which may be recorded in a form other than written but which can readily be transcribed by the licensee into written form:

(1) The dates of operation.

(2) Except for repeater stations, names of persons other than the control operator using the station, either directly or indirectly, for amateur radiocommunication.

(3) A notation of third party messages sent or received, including names of all participants and a brief description of the message content.

(4) The call sign of each station actually contacted, or other purpose of the transmission, i.e., those set forth in 97.89. Stations in mobile operation and repeater stations may omit this entry. Control stations shall enter the call sign(s) of each station in the control link. An auxiliary link station shall enter the call sign of its associated station(s).

(5) All stations shall enter the times the station is put into, or taken out of, service. Stations other than those in mobile operation, control station, auxiliary link stations, and repeater stations shall enter the times of commencing and terminating each exchange of radiocommunication.

97.105 RETENTION OF LOGS

The station log shall be preserved for a period of at least 1 year following the last date of entry and retained in the possession of the licensee. Copies of the log, including the sections required to be transcribed by 97.103, shall be available to the Commission for inspection.

97.108 OPERATION OF A REMOTELY CONTROLLED STATION

(a) An amateur radio station may be operated by remote control only from an authorized control point, and only where there is compliance with the following:

(1) The license for the remotely controlled station must list the authorized remote control point(s). A photocopy of the remotely controlled station license must be posted in a conspicuous place at the authorized control point(s), and at the remotely controlled transmitter location. A copy of the system network diagram on file with the Commission must be retained at each control point. The transmitting antenna, transmission line, or mast, as appropriate, associated with the remotely controlled transmitter must bear a durable tag marked with the station call sign, the name of the station licensee and other information so that the control operator can readily be contacted by Commission personnel.

(2) The control link equipment and the remotely controlled station must be accessible only to persons authorized by the licensee. Protection against both inadvertent and unauthorized deliberate emissions must be provided. In the event unauthorized emissions occur, the station operation must be suspended until such time as adequate protection is incorporated, or there is reasonable assurance that unauthorized emissions will not recur.

(3) A control operator designated by the licensee must be on duty at an authorized control point while the station is being remotely controlled. Immediately prior to, and during the periods the remotely controlled station is in operation, the frequencies used for emission by the remotely controlled transmitter must be continuously monitored by the control operator. The control operator must terminate transmission upon any deviation from the rules.

(4) Provisions must be incorporated to automatically limit transmission to a period of no more than 3 minutes in the event of malfunction in the control link.

(5) A remotely controlled station may not be operated at any location other than that specified on the license without prior approval of the Commission except in emergencies involving the immediate safety of life or protection of property.

(6) A repeater station may be operated by radio remote control only where the control link utilizes frequencies other than the repeater station receiving frequencies.

97.113 BROADCASTING PROHIBITED

Subject to the provisions of 97.91 of these rules, an amateur station shall not be used to engage in any form of broadcasting, that is, the dissemination of radio communications intended to be received by the public directly or by the intermediary of relay stations, nor for the retransmission by automatic means of programs or signals emanating from any class of station other than amateur. The foregoing provision shall not be construed to prohibit amateur operators from giving their consent to the rebroadcast by broadcast stations of the transmissions of their amateur stations, provided, that the transmissions of the amateur stations shall not contain any direct or indirect reference to the re-broadcast.

97.114 THIRD PARTY TRAFFIC

The transmission or delivery of the following amateur radio-communication is prohibited:

(a) International third party traffic except with countries which have assented thereto;

(b) Third party traffic involving material compensation, either tangible or intangible, direct or indirect, to a third party, a station licensee, a control operator, or any other person.

(c) Except for an emergency communication as defined in this part, third party traffic consisting of business communications on behalf of any party. For the purpose of this section business communication shall mean any transmission or communication the purpose of which is to facilitate the regular business or commercial affairs of any party.

97.115 MUSIC PROHIBITED

The transmission of music by an amateur station is forbidden. However, single audio frequency tones may be transmitted for test purposes of short duration for the development and perfection of amateur radiotelephone equipment.

97.116 AMATEUR RADIOCOMMUNICATION FOR UNLAWFUL PURPOSES PROHIBITED

The transmission of radiocommunication or messages by an amateur radio station for any purpose, or in connection with any activity, which is contrary to Federal, State, or local law is prohibited.

97.117 CODES AND CIPHERS PROHIBITED

The transmission by radio of messages in codes or ciphers in domestic and international communications to or between amateur stations is prohibited. All communications, regardless of type of emission employed, shall be in plain language except that generally recognized abbreviations established by regulation or custom and usage are permissible, as are any other abbreviations or signals where the intent is not to obscure the meaning, but only to facilitate communications.

97.119 OBSCENITY, INDECENCY, PROFANITY

No licensed radio operator or other person shall transmit communications containing obscene, indecent or profane words, language or meaning.

97.121 FALSE SIGNALS

No licensed radio operator shall transmit false or deceptive signals or communications by radio or any call letter or signal which has not been assigned by proper authority to the radio station he is operating.

97.123 UNIDENTIFIED COMMUNICATIONS

No licensed radio operator shall transmit unidentified radio communications or signals.

97.125 INTERFERENCE

No licensed radio operator shall willfully or maliciously interfere with or cause interference to any radio communication or signal. (The penalty for violation of this rule is as follows: A fine of up to $500.00 for each day during which the offense occurs, and suspension of the operator's license. In case the interference is in connection with distress communications, the penalty may be a maximum fine of

$10,000.00 or imprisonment up to one year, or both, and the revocation of the station license).

Extracts From Radio Regulations Annexed to the International Telecommunication Convention (Geneva, 1959)

ARTICLE 41—AMATEUR STATIONS

Section 1. Radiocommunications between amateur stations of different countries[1] shall be forbidden if the administration of one of the countries concerned has notified that it objects to such radiocommunications.

Sec. 2. (1) When transmission between amateur stations of different countries are permitted, they shall be made in plain language and shall be limited to messages of a technical nature relating to tests and to remarks of a personal character for which, by reason of their unimportance, recourse to the public telecommunications service is not justified. It is absolutely forbidden for amateur stations to be used for transmitting international communications on behalf of third parties.

(2) The preceding provisions may be modified by special arrangements between the administrations of the countries concerned.

Sec. 3. (1) Any person operating the apparatus of an amateur station shall have proved that he is able to send correctly by hand and to receive correctly by ear, texts in Morse code signals. Administrations concerned may, however, waive this requirement in the case of stations making use exclusively of frequencies above 144 MHz.

PRACTICE QUESTIONS - LESSON 14
(for answers, refer to Appendix 6)

14-1* One of the fundamental purposes of amateur radio is not:
    a. enhancing international good will.
    b. expanding the reservoir of electronics experts.
    c. advancing technical skills of radio.
    d. encouraging others to become radio amateurs.

14-2* In the event of a violation of the Rules at a transmitter operated by a control operator other than the station licensee, who is responsible?
    a. the licensee.   b. the control operator.
    c. the licensee and the control operator.
    d. the owner of the station.

---

1. As may appear in public notices issued by the Commission.

14-3 *Radio communication conducted while in motion or during halts at unspecified locations, is called:
a. mobile operation
b. fixed operation
c. portable operation
d. repeater operation

14-4 *Which one of the following types of one-way communication is not prohibited?
a. music
b. broadcasting
c. round table discussions
d. unidentified communications

14-5 *For how long must a log be preserved?
a. 6 months   b. 12 months   c. 2 years   d. 3 years

14-6 *A notice of operation away from the authorized location is required if the operator is to be away for a period exceeding:
a. 15 days   b. 48 hours   c. 30 days   d. 6 months

14-7* If a Conditional Class licensee fails to pass a Commission supervised examination, and has his license cancelled, he may:
a. take another Commission supervised examination for the Conditional Class after 30 days.
b. not apply for a General Class operator license.
c. apply for a Conditional Class operator license after six months.
d. not apply for a Conditional Class license.

14-8* An amateur radio station may be operated by a person if:
a. he holds a 1st or 2nd Class Commercial radio operator license.
b. he holds any Commercial radio operator license with a broadcast endorsement.
c. he held an amateur license prior to 1921.
d. none of the above.

14-9* The control operator:
a. is designated by the FCC.
b. may be designated by the station licensee.
c. must have a higher class of license than the station licensee
d. is not responsible for the emissions from the station.

14-10*A log need not contain:
a. the type of emission used.
b. the input power to the transmitter final.
c. the operating frequency.
d. dates of operation.

STUDY GUIDE — SECTION III

Section III is the most important section of the course for the following reasons:

1. 50% or more of the license examination questions are based upon the material in this section.

2. It contains a detailed discussion of transmitter theory and operation, which is of major importance to an amateur radio operator.

3. It contains Government rules and regulations concerning amateur radio operation, which every amateur is required to know.

You must, therefore, study Section III very carefully. Make sure that you understand every lesson thoroughly and can answer the practice questions without difficulty, before you proceed to take the FCC-type examination.

It is suggested that before you take the official license examination, you should go over all of the practice questions of the course, as well as all FCC-type examinations. If you find that you have forgotten an answer or simply cannot answer the question, go back to the lesson material and review those points on which you are hazy. Only in this way will you build up your confidence to successfully pass the license examination and gain your Radio Amateur's License.

A. <u>LESSON 9 - OSCILLATORS</u>

(1) You must be thoroughly familiar with the INTRODUCTION TO TRANSMISSION AND RECEPTION at the beginning of the lesson. You should know how to draw the block diagrams of a receiver and a transmitter and be able to explain the function of each part.

(2) You should know the explanation for the operation of a basic oscillator. You should also know how each of the other oscillators function.

    (a) Review Paragraphs 9-1 through 9-6.

    (b) Review Practice Question 9-10.

(3) You should be familiar with the crystal controlled oscillator and the electron-coupled oscillator.

    (a) Review Practice Questions 9-2, 9-5, 9-6 and 9-7.

B. <u>LESSON 10 - CW TRANSMITTERS</u>

(1) You should know the designation for CW operation.

    (a) Refer to Paragraph 10-2.

    (b) Refer to Page 211 for a complete list of symbols that are used to designate the various types of emissions from a transmitter.

(2) You should be familiar with Class C operation, its use in RF amplifiers and its efficiency.

    (a) See Paragraph 10-5.

    (b) Review Practice Question 10-18.

(3) You must be completely familiar with the subject of har-

monic radiation and you should know the various methods that are used to eliminate it.

    (a) Review Paragraph 10-6.

    (b) Review Practice Question 10-11.

  (4) You must be familiar with the neutralization of RF amplifiers. You must know the various methods of neutralization and the actual steps required to neutralize an RF amplifier.

    (a) Refer to Paragraphs 10-12 through 10-16.

    (b) Review Practice Questions 10-3, 10-4, 10-5, 10-6 and 10-9.

  (5) You should be familiar with the operation and use of the grounded grid amplifier.

    (a) Review Paragraph 10-16.

    (b) Review Practice Question 10-19.

  (6) You should be familiar with the characteristics of good quality keying.

    (a) Review Paragraph 10-19.

  (7) You should be familiar with the power supplies of a transmitter, especially the methods used to minimize the danger of electrical shock.

    (a) Review Paragraph 10-22.

    (b) Review Practice Question 10-15.

  (8) You must know the maximum power permitted to a Novice Class transmitter, as well as to the other classes of transmitters. You must know how to calculate the power input to the final stage of a transmitter.

    (a) Review Paragraph 10-28.

  (9) You must be thoroughly familiar with the schematic of a pi-network output circuit, and you must know how to tune up the pi-network circuit.

    (a) Refer to Paragraph 10-29.

    (b) Review Practice Question 10-13.

  (10) You must be familiar with Radio Frequency Interference (RFI), especially Television Interference (TVI). You must know the methods used to prevent interference to other services.

    (a) Study Paragraphs 10-30 and 10-31.

    (b) Review Practice Question 10-17.

  (11) You must know how to choose an operating frequency.

    (a) Review Paragraph 10-32.

C. <u>LESSON 11 - THE MODULATED TRANSMITTER</u>

  (1) You should be familiar with the method by which a carrier is amplitude modulated. You should know the maximum percentage of modulation permitted by the FCC rules and regulations.

    (a) Review Paragraphs 11-2, 11-3 and 11-4.

    (b) Refer to Practice Question 11-8.

  (2) You should be able to draw trapezoidal patterns and you should be familiar with the sinusoidal modulation envelope.

(a) Review Paragraph 11-14.

(b) Refer to Practice Questions 11-1, 11-6 and 11-11.

(3) You should know the definition of the term "occupied band-width of a transmission" and know how to use it.

(a) Review Paragraph 11-5.

(4) You should be thoroughly familiar with the power relations in a plate modulated transmitter. You should know the meanings of Peak Envelope Power (PEP) and Average Power. You should know how to calculate them.

(a) Review Paragraph 11-11.

(b) Refer to Practice Question 11-16.

(5) You should know how to use the oscilloscope in checking the modulation of a transmitter.

(a) Review Paragraph 11-14.

(6) You should know how to check for the quality of a transmitter's emissions.

(a) See Paragraph 11-15.

(7) You should be familiar with the symbols used to designate the various types of transmission.

(a) Review Paragraph 11-18.

(8) You should know how to minimize interference and congestion in the amateur bands.

(a) Refer to Practice Question 11-22.

(9) Be familiar with the methods used to accomplish frequency modulation and phase modulation. You should know how a reactance modulator tube operates. You should be able to draw a block diagram of an FM transmitter.

(a) Refer to Paragraphs 11-19 through 11-23 and 11-25 through 11-27.

(b) Review Practice Questions 11-18 and 11-19.

(10) You should know the definition of Narrow-Band and Wide-Band FM as they pertain to amateur use.

(a) Refer to Paragraph 11-24.

(b) Review Practice Question 11-20.

(11) You should know the general operation of a single side-band transmitter. You must be thoroughly familiar with the power ratings of a single sideband transmitter. You should know the definition of Signal-to-Distortion Ratio (S/D).

(a) Refer to Paragraphs 11-29 through 11-31.

(b) Review Practice Questions 11-14 through 11-17.

D. LESSON 12 - ANTENNAS, FREQUENCY METERS AND TRANSMISSION LINES

(1) You should be familiar with the principles of radio wave propagation through space. You should be thoroughly familiar with the chart on Pages 225 and 226. You must know how to work out problems using the formula involving frequency and wave length on Page 227.

(a) Review Paragraphs 12-1 and 12-2.

(b) Review Practice Questions 12-10, 12-16 and 12-17.

(2) You should know the characteristics of the Hertz antenna and the Marconi antenna. You should know the differences between the two antennas. You should be able to work out problems of finding the length of an antenna when the frequency is given, and vice versa.

(a) Review Paragraphs 12-6 and 12-7.

(b) Review Practice Questions 12-9, 12-12 and 12-14.

(3) You should know the two basic types of transmission lines and how to figure out their characteristic impedances.

(a) Review Paragraph 12-13.

(b) Review Practice Question 12-8.

(4) You should know what standing wave ratio is and be able to figure out the standing wave ratio of an antenna system.

(a) Refer to Paragraph 12-14.

(b) Review Practice Questions 12-11 and 12-13.

(5) You will be responsible for the basic principles involved in multiband antennas. You should know how a multiband antenna is constructed. You should also know the advantages and disadvantages of multiband antennas. You should be familiar with the uses of an antenna tuner and a transmatch. You must know the methods used to minimize harmonic radiation from an antenna.

(a) Review Paragraph 12-14A.

(b) Review Practice Questions 12-5, 12-7 and 12-15.

(6) You must be familiar with the methods used to measure frequency. You should know how to determine exactly how close you are to a band's edge.

(a) Refer to Paragraphs 12-16 through 12-20.

(b) Review Practice Questions 12-2, 12-3 and 12-4.

E. LESSON 13 - THE RADIO RECEIVER

There are very few questions asked on the official examination concerning radio receivers. As an amateur radio operator, however, you should have a fairly good working knowledge of receiver theory and operation.

(1) You should be familiar with the RF amplifier and the resonant circuits used in an RF amplifier.

(a) Refer to Paragraph 13-4.

(b) Refer to Practice Questions 13-3 and 13-11.

(2) You should be familiar with the "S" meter that is used in the receiver.

(a) Refer to Paragraph 13-13.

(b) Review Practice Question 13-12.

F. LESSON 14 - RULES AND REGULATIONS OF THE AMATEUR RADIO SERVICE

The applicants for both the Novice and the General Class licenses should be thoroughly familiar with the entire chapter. At one time, it was necessary to know all of Part 97. However, effective July 1, 1973, the prospective amateurs were held responsible only for those Rules given in Chapter 14. This simplifies matters since it narrows down the number of "Rules and Regulations" that must be memorized.

1. Radio messages having top priority are:
   a. relief or emergency messages
   b. messages sent to foreign amateurs
   c. ordinary calls   d. ship to shore messages

2.* The maximum voltage, divided by the minimum voltage along a transmission line, is called the:
   a. forward voltage   c. incident voltage
   b. standing wave ratio   d. reflected voltage

3.* The maximum input power permitted to the final stage of a transmitter, owned and operated by a Novice operator, is:
   a. 50 watts   b. 75 watts   c. 100 watts   d. 250 watts

4. The penalty for willful interference with other radio communications is:
   a. restricting operating to the 20 meter band
   b. restricting operator to key operation
   c. fine and suspension of license
   d. restriction to local calls

5. A state of emergency affecting amateur communications becomes effective when:
   a. an emergency occurs   b. so ordered by the FCC
   c. at the discretion of the operator
   d. 3 hours after an emergency has started

6.* The following restriction applies to the holder of a Novice Class license:
   a. electron-coupled oscillator must be used
   b. grid modulation must be used
   c. may not operate a phone transmitter
   d. rice neutralization must be used

7.* Which of the following is not used as a transmission line in an amateur transmitting antenna system?
   a. TV twin lead
   b. RF waveguide line
   c. parallel conductors separated by insulators
   d. coaxial cable

8.* What can be determined with a two-tone test signal applied to an SSB transmitter, and an oscilloscope at the transmitter's output?
   a. the SWR   b. the S/D ratio
   c. the efficiency of the final stage
   d. the phase of the audio signal

9.* Which of the following frequencies may be used exclusively by Extra Class and Advanced Class operators?
a. 14, 033 kHz.
b. 7160 kHz.
c. 50.15 MHz.   d. 3.51 MHz.

10. The purpose of using a center-tap return connection on the secondary of a transmitting tube's filament transformer is to:
a. allow the filaments to heat up   b. permit power output
c. prevent modulation of the RF by the AC filament supply
d. prevent radiation of spurious harmonics

11.* What is the highest percentage modulation of an amateur radio-telephone transmitter permitted by the FCC?
a. 75%   b. 50%   c. 25%   d. 100%

12. A separate power supply is used for the oscillator stage of a transmitter:
a. because the filaments require a separate heating source
b. because a lower B+ voltage is required
c. to prevent frequency instability due to load variations being fed back through a common power supply
d. to increase the frequency bandwidth radiated due to a common power supply

13.* A triode radio frequency power amplifier must be neutralized:
a. to increase power output   b. to prevent self-oscillations
c. to eliminate second harmonic radiation
d. when used as a frequency doubler

14.* What is the maximum permissible plate power input to the final stage of an amateur transmitter on all bands except 420 - 450 MHz and 1800 - 2000 kHz?
a. 850 watts   b. 1000 watts   c. 10 kilowatts   d. 1000 kilowatts

15.* The result of operating an unneutralized RF triode power amplifier is:
a. decreased output   c. decrease in harmonic content
b. spurious radiation   d. varying load condition

16.* One of the characteristics of an RF frequency doubler amplifier is NOT:
a. high negative grid bias   b. large excitation signal
c. high impedance plate circuit
d. low impedance plate circuit tuned to the same frequency as the excitation voltage

17.* What are the requirements for portable operation in excess of 15 days from the fixed location?
a. maximum power output is limited to 500 watts
b. operation permitted only in the 10 meter band

c. prior notification to FCC Engineer-in-Charge of district
d. single sideband transmission

18. In order to obtain optimum power output from an RF power amplifier:
   a. the antenna system should be matched to the rated tube load impedance
   b. a directional array antenna should be used
   c. link coupling is required
   d. Class B push-pull operation should be employed

19. A power output RF amplifier SHOULD NOT:
   a. be coupled to the antenna system
   b. have minimum plate current at resonance
   c. couple high harmonics to the antenna
   d. be matched to the output circuit impedance

20.* An amateur operating at 1 kilowatt, 100% modulated power output:
   a. must get permission from the FCC
   b. is operating illegally
   c. must have means of adequately checking percent modulation and power output
   d. can only operate on certain bands

21.* The principle purpose of using door interlock switches is that they:
   a. eliminate the need of turning off transmitter
   b. act as an on-off switch
   c. protect equipment against mishandling by incompetent personnel
   d. prevent personnel from being accidentally shocked by dangerous voltages when cage to transmitter is open

22. The circuit condition which WILL NOT minimize harmonic components in the output circuit of an RF amplifier is:
   a. low L/C ratio
   b. improper neutralization
   c. push-pull operation
   d. proper bias voltage

23.* What is the meaning of "QRM"?
   a. I am being interfered with
   b. stop sending
   c. the strength of your signal is _____.
   d. change to transmission on another frequency

24.* In determining the input power to a grounded-grid final amplifier stage of an SSB transmitter, we must consider:
   a. the input power to the plate of the final stage
   b. the input power to the plate and screen of the final stage
   c. the input power to the plates of the driver stage and final stage
   d. the drive power to the control grid and the input power to the plate and screen of the final stage

25.* In which of the following modulation systems does the amplitude of the wave remain constant?
   a. amplitude modulation
   b. phase modulation
   c. frequency modulation
   d. b and c

26. The average plate current in an amplitude modulated RF amplifier should:
   a. increase on the positive peaks and decrease on the negative peaks
   b. remain constant
   c. decrease
   d. increase

27.* Which of the following is true for a Novice license?
   a. it is valid for 5 years
   b. it is valid for 1 year
   c. it may not be renewed
   d. it is valid for 3 years

28.* What is the exact wavelength of a 21,180 kHz signal?
   a. 51.18 meters
   b. .0706 meters
   c. 14.1 meters
   d. 70.6 meters

29.* A Class B modulator, compared to a Class A modulator, requires:
   a. larger excitation voltage
   b. lower excitation voltage
   c. no power to drive the grid
   d. zero bias operation

30.* A notice of operation away from the authorized location of an amateur radio station must be given if the operator is to be away for a period in excess of:
   a. 24 hours
   b. 48 hours
   c. 15 days
   d. 1 year

31. If the grid-bias supply of a Class B modulator was suddenly short-circuited:
   a. the plate current would increase to excessively high values
   b. grid current would increase
   c. overmodulation would result
   d. output power of the carrier would be in the sidebands

32.* Using a frequency meter with a possible error of 0.75%, on what whole number kiloHertz frequency nearest the low frequency end of the 14,000-14,400 kHz band could a transmitter safely be set?
   a. 14,000 kHz
   b. 13,985 kHz
   c. 14,200 kHz
   d. 14,105 kHz

33.* In the cathode-follower, the output is taken from the:
   a. cathode
   b. control grid
   c. screen grid
   d. plate

FINAL GENERAL CLASS "FCC-TYPE" EXAMINATION

1.* A tetrode has
   a. one grid   b. two grids   c. three grids   d. four grids
2.* Power is measured by:
   a. a voltmeter b. an ammeter c. a wattmeter d. an ohmmeter
3.* The second harmonic of 150 cycles is:
   a. 75 cycles   b. 150 cycles   c. 300 cycles   d. 450 cycles
4.* The DC power input to the plate of a tube having a plate voltage of 750 volts and a plate current of 50 milliamperes is:
   a. 3,750 watts b. 37,500 watts c. 375 watts d. 37.5 watts
5.* The DC power input to the plate of a tube having a plate voltage of 500 volts and a plate current of 60 milliamperes is:
   a. 30 watts   b. 560 watts   c. 300 watts   d. 3000 watts
6.* Radio communication conducted from a specific geographical location other than that shown on the station license, is called:
   a. portable operation   c. fixed operation
   b. mobile operation   d. geographical operation
7. The purpose for a filter in a power supply is to:
   a. get rid of the excess DC   b. increase the output voltage
   c. take the place of the rectifier tube
   d. smooth out the AC ripple component
8.* A tetrode is superior to a triode as a radio frequency amplifier because of:
   a. lower plate resistance   b. increased grid resistance
   c. reduced possibility of oscillation
   d. increased cathode emission
9.* Transmissions between amateurs of different countries:
   a. are not permitted
   b. must be of a technical nature
   c. must be in plain language
   d. must be limited to third party traffic
10.* An important step in neutralizing an RF amplifier is:
   a. remove the plate voltage of the stage to be neutralized
   b. remove the filament voltage of the oscillator
   c. remove the plate coil   d. lower the plate voltage
11. Maximum plate dissipation means maximum:
   a. current to the filament   b. power output to the tube
   c. heat the plate can safely radiate in watts
   d. current the plate can absorb
12. If a transformer were connected to a source of DC:
   a. the primary current would be zero
   b. the secondary current would exceed the normal rating
   c. rectification would be easier
   d. excessive current would flow in the primary
13.* What is the db gain of an amplifier that puts out a 2 volt signal with an input of 200 microvolts?
   a. 10,000 db   b. 10 db   c. 80 db   d. 8 db

14.* Neutralization of a triode RF amplifier is necessary in order to prevent:
    a. self oscillation   c. loss of power
    b. reduced amplification   d. damped oscillation

15.* What is the meaning of F3?
    a. amplitude tone-modulated telephony
    b. amplitude modulated telephony
    c. frequency modulated telephony
    d. phase modulated telephony

16.* In a CW signal, the PEP is:
    a. twice the average power
    b. four times the average power
    c. the same as the average power
    d. 1.414 times the average power

17.* Frequency modulation of an amplitude modulated wave:
    a. causes no output signal   b. doubles the output power
    c. causes spurious sidebands and interference
    d. causes undesired harmonics

18. Push-pull operation:
    a. introduces harmonics into the grid circuit
    b. improves the signal strength
    c. cancels the third harmonic
    d. eliminates the second harmonic in the plate circuit

19. An electron-coupled oscillator:
    a. has very good frequency stability
    b. has very good efficiency   c. has low output power
    d. is more stable than a crystal-controlled oscillator

20. Optimum power output from an RF amplifier can be obtained:
    a. when the stage is a frequency doubler
    b. when the output circuit impedance matches the tube load impedance
    c. when the plate impedance is equal to the grid load impedance
    d. when the plate circuit is slightly off resonance

21.* Which of the following requires neutralization?
    a. a triode RF amplifier
    b. a tetrode RF amplifier
    c. a grounded-grid amplifier
    d. an RF frequency multiplier

22.* An advantage of a cathode-follower is:
    a. its excellent frequency response
    b. its low input impedance
    c. its high output impedance
    d. its high amplification factor

23. Full wave rectification is better than half wave rectification because:
    a. its output is easier to filter
    b. its output contains a lower ripple frequency
    c. a choke input filter may be used
    d. a swinging choke may be used

24.* A third party may participate in amateur radio communications:
    a. if a control operator is present
    b. if a control operator is present and continuously monitors the radio communication to insure compliance with the rules
    c. if an advanced or extra class licensee is the control operator
    d. third party communications are forbidden in the United States and its possessions
25.* The N-type material of a semiconductor has:
    a. an excess of protons
    b. an excess of neutrons
    c. an excess of electrons
    d. an excess of holes
26.* What determines the operator privileges at an amateur station where the control operator is other than the station licensee?
    a. the class of license issued to the station licensee
    b. the class of license issued to the station licensee or the control operator, whichever has the lesser privileges
    c. the class of license held by the control operator
    d. none of the above
27.* What range of audio frequencies should be used for communications systems?
    a. 20 Hz to 300 Hz   c. 200 Hz to 6,000 Hz
    b. 60 Hz to 15,000 Hz   d. 200 Hz to 3,000 Hz
28.* An amateur Novice Class License is good for:
    a. 6 months   b. 2 years   c. 3 years   d. 5 years
29.* The owner of a Novice Class license may NOT operate his station in the following band:
    a. 3700 - 3750 Kc.   c. 7200 Kc. - 7250 Kc.
    b. 21.10 Mc. - 21.20 Mc.   d. 28.1 Mc. - 28.2 Mc.
30.* The owner of a General Class license may NOT operate a radio-telephone station in the following band:
    a. 1800 Kc. - 2000 Kc.   c. 28.5 Mc. - 29.7 Mc.
    b. 28.0 Mc. - 28.5 Mc.   d. 50.1 Mc. - 54.0 Mc.
31.* What is the FCC regulation regarding the transmission of music by an amateur station?
    a. it is permitted only on frequencies above 28 Mc.
    b. it is permitted only during the hours of 6:00 AM - 11:00 AM
    c. it is permitted only on frequencies above 116 Mc.
    d. it is not permitted
32.* The ratio of modulator sine wave power output to Class C amplifier unmodulated plate power input is:
    a. 100%   b. 25%   c. 125%   d. 50%
33.* The ratio of modulator speech power output to Class C amplifier unmodulated plate power input is:
    a. 125%   b. 100%   c. 25%   d. 50%
34.* A precaution to be observed in the use of the battery operated heterodyne frequency meter is to check the:
    a. crystal frequency   b. tube filaments
    c. "A" and "B" battery voltages

d. oscillator with a standard frequency

35. A downward deflection of the antenna RF current meter during modulation might indicate:
    a. sufficient RF excitation to the modulated stage
    b. proper filament emission of the modulated stage
    c. excellent voltage regulation of the power supply common to both the modulator and the RF stage
    d. insufficient bias on the grid of the modulated stage

36.* A precaution to be observed in the use of the absorption type frequency meter is to:
    a. loosely couple the frequency meter to the oscillator tank circuit
    b. calibrate the frequency meter
    c. check the B+ voltage of the frequency meter
    d. zero beat the output of the wavemeter

37.* Third party traffic consisting of business communications:
    a. must be logged in a separate log book
    b. cannot be supervised by a control operator other than the station licensee
    c. cannot be performed at other than standard commercial rates
    d. is forbidden

38.* When removing an unconscious person from contact with a high voltage circuit, the first thing to do is:
    a. call a doctor   b. try to revive the person
    c. open main switch of high voltage power supply
    d. attempt to move the person

39.* If the power output of an amplifier is decreased from 500 watts to 5 watts, what is the power reduction expressed in decibels?
    a. -2 db   b. -10 db   c. -100 db   d. -20 db

40.* The highest modulation percentage permitted is:
    a. 50%   b. 75%   c. 100%   d. 125%

41.* The maximum power input to the final stage is:
    a. 100 watts b. 500 watts c. 1000 watts   d. 10 kilowatts

42.* The value of the bias voltage of Figure 1 is:
    a. 6.25 volts   b. 5 volts
    c. 1.25 volts   d. 50 volts

43.* The value of R_2 of Figure 1 is:
    a. 60,000 ohms b. 60 ohms
    c. 6000 ohms   d. 300 ohms

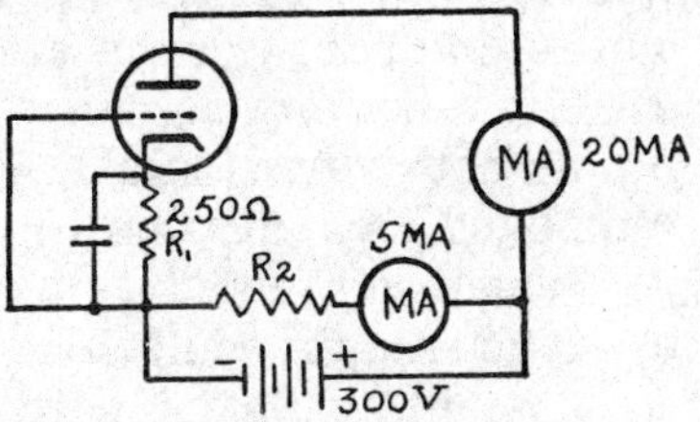

Figure 1.

44.* What is the SWR if the forward voltage is 8 volts and the reflected voltage is 2 volts?
    a. 4 to 1   b. 1 to 4   c. 1.6 to 1   d. 3 to 1

45.* The final amplifier of an SSB transmitter must be:
    a. Class A   c. Class C
    b. Class B   d. linear

285

46.* Which of the following types of one-way transmission is prohibited?
   a. round-table discussions
   b. code practice transmission
   c. dissemination of radio communications to be received by
   the public
   d. information bulletins consisting of information having interest to amateurs
47.* Which of the following types of one-way transmission is permitted?
   a. music transmission
   b. radio control of remote objects
   c. unidentified transmission
   d. broadcasting
48.* The operating position of an amateur radio station where the
control operator function is performed, is called the:
   a. operating position   c. operating point
   b. remote control point   d. control point
49.* How often must an amateur radio station be identified during a
single lengthy transmission?
   a. every 10 minutes
   b. every 15 minutes
   c. every 20 minutes
   d. at the beginning and end of the transmission
50.* To whom must a notice of operation away from the authorized
radio station location be sent?
   a. the engineer-in-charge of the FCC radio district office in
   which operation is intended
   b. the engineer-in-charge of the FCC radio district where the
   original authorized location is located
   c. the FCC in Washington, D. C.
   d. a and b
51.* Which of the following is not employed to minimize congestion
and interference of the amateur bands?
   a. use a dummy antenna   c. utilize band's edges
   b. do not overmodulate   d. use Q signals
52.* Wideband F3 indicates:
   a. frequency modulation with a swing of 10 kHz
   b. frequency modulation with a swing of 30 kHz
   c. phase modulation with a swing of 200 to 3,000 Hz
   d. frequency modulation containing 99 percent of the total radiated power
53.* The term "narrow-band FM" indicates an FM signal:
   a. whose bandwidth does not exceed that of an AM signal having the same audio characteristics
   b. whose frequency swing is limited to 3000 Hz
   c. whose frequency swing is limited to 30 kHz
   d. a and b are correct

54.* In an SSB transmitter, the PEP-to-average power ratio is determined chiefly by the:
   a. characteristics of the audio modulating signal
   b. input power to the final RF stage
   c. class of operation of the final RF amplifier
   d. efficiency of the modulator stage
55.* The best way to eliminate TVI is by using:
   a. a high-pass filter at the receiver and a high-pass filter at the transmitter
   b. a low-pass filter at the transmitter and a high-pass filter at the receiver
   c. a low-pass filter at the transmitter and a low-pass filter at the receiver
   d. a high-pass filter at the transmitter and a low-pass filter at the receiver
56.* An advantage of a grounded-grid amplifier, compared to a grounded cathode amplifier, is not:
   a. lower noise figure
   b. lower output capacity
   c. can be used in a linear amplifier
   d. requires less driving power
57.* The voltage gain of a cathode-follower is:
   a. less than 1
   b. 1
   c. between 1 and 10
   d. above 10
58.* The base of a transistor is similar to which element in a vacuum tube?
   a. cathode
   b. filament
   c. plate
   d. control grid
59.* A doughnut-shaped coil is characteristic of:
   a. a swinging choke
   b. a smoothing choke
   c. a toroidal coil
   d. a high frequency RF coil
60.* Which of the following is not characteristic of a length of wire being used as a multiband antenna?
   a. a transmatch is used
   b. an antenna tuner is used
   c. the length of the antenna is one-half the wavelength of the lowest frequency being used
   d. the bands to be used cannot be harmonically related to each other
61.* A Marconi antenna is not:
   a. 30 ohms at its feed point
   b. one-quarter wavelength long
   c. fed at its end
   d. fed at a low current point
62.* Which of the following is the most useful instrument in adjusting a radiotelephone transmitter?
   a. grid-dip meter
   b. peak-modulation meter
   c. oscilloscope
   d. frequency meter

63.* The characteristic impedance of a coaxial type of transmission line is equal to:

a. $276 \log \frac{b}{a}$

c. $\log 30,000 \frac{b}{a}$

b. $138 \log \frac{b}{a}$

d. $\frac{300,000}{f}$

64.* Which pattern do we get when we couple the output of a transmitter to the vertical plates of an oscilloscope, and the audio output of the modulator to the horizontal plates?
a. sine wave envelope
c. parallelogram
b. toroid
d. trapezoid

65.* In a filter-type SSB transmitter, the output of the balanced modulator contains:
a. both sidebands and the carrier
b. both sidebands
c. one sideband and the carrier
d. one sideband

66.* In a filter-type SSB transmitter, the output of the sideband filter contains:
a. the upper or lower sidebands
b. the upper or lower sidebands and the carrier
c. the upper and lower sidebands
d. the upper and lower sidebands and the carrier

67.* Two mixers are employed in an SSB transmitter in order to:
a. amplify both the upper and lower sidebands
b. insure elimination of one of the sidebands
c. insure adequate image rejection of the original carrier frequency
d. increase the frequency up to its proper value

68.* In which stage of an FM transmitter does the modulation take place?
a. mixer
c. audio amplifier
b. reactance tube
d. discriminator

69.* A door interlock switch, a bleeder resistor, connecting cabinets to a common ground, are all factors in:
a. neutralizing an RF amplifier stage
b. preventing parasitic and spurious output
c. preventing electric shock
d. improving the SWR

70.* A notice of operation away from the authorized location of an amateur radio station must be given if the operator is to be away for a period in excess of:
a. 24 hours
c. 15 days
b. 48 hours
d. 1 year

FINAL NOVICE CLASS "FCC-TYPE" EXAMINATION

1.* What part of the FCC rules govern the Amateur Radio Service?
   a. 95   b. 97   c. 73   d. 74

2.* In what two phases of the radio art do the FCC rules encourage improvement?
   a. technical and communications
   b. speech and communications
   c. technical and international good will
   d. legal and communications

3.* A control operator of a station:
   a. must be designated by the FCC
   b. must be designated by the engineer-in-charge of the local FCC radio district office
   c. may be designated by the station licensee
   d. must hold a General Class or higher grade of license

4.* An amateur radio station license may not be issued to the following:
   a. a licensed radio amateur operator
   b. an individual, not licensed, in charge of a proposed military recreation station
   c. a licensed radio amateur operator who also operates commercial radio equipment at the same premises
   d. a Novice class licensee in charge of a school amateur radio station

5.* For how long must a station log be preserved?
   a. 1 year   b. 2 years   c. 3 years   d. 5 years

6.* Which of the following frequencies cannot be used by a Novice class operator?
   a. 3741 kHz   c. 21,101 kHz
   b. 7152 kHz   d. 28,101 kHz

7.* The holder of a Novice Class license may operate an amateur radiotelephone station in the following band:
   a. 145 MHz - 147 MHz   c. 28.5 MHz - 29.7 MHz
   b. 147 MHz - 149 MHz   d. none of the above

8.* Which of the following indicates the end of the entire transmission?
   a. K   b. SK   c. DE   d. AR

9.* Which of the following reports indicates a moderately strong signal that is readable, but with considerable difficulty?
   a. R2S8   b. R2S7   c. R4S8   d. R3S7

10.* What is the meaning of QRS?
   a. shall I transmit more slowly?
   b. am I being interfered with?
   c. what is your location?
   d. what is your signal strength?

11.* What is the unit of capacitance?
   a. henry   b. farad   c. ohm   d. volt

12.* The abbreviation for kiloHertz is:
   a. kT   b. kH   c. kZ   d. kHz
13.* The unit of inductance is the:
   a. ohm   b. farad   c. henry   d. joule
14.* Continuous Wave is abbreviated by:
   a. CW   b. CN   c. CS.WV.   d. CU
15.* AC is changed to DC by means of a
   a. rectifier   c. filter
   b. transistor   d. transformer
16.* Which of the following stores electrostatic charges?
   a. inductance   c. resistance
   b. capacitance   d. storage battery
17.* The internal resistance of a battery:
   a. is in parallel with the load on the battery
   b. decreases as the battery ages
   c. is generally large with relation to its load
   d. opposes the current flow in the circuit
18.* In a pi-network circuit, the variable capacitor closest to the plate of the amplifier tube:
   a. is much larger than the antenna loading capacitor
   b. is tuned for a plate current dip
   c. is also tuned to neutralize the RF amplifier stage
   d. is tuned for a dip in the RF antenna current
19.* What is the input power to a final RF amplifier stage having a plate voltage of 300 V, a plate current of 70 ma, a screen voltage of 150 V, a screen current of 10 ma, a driving power of .4 watts, a filament voltage of 6.3 volts and a filament current of 300 ma?
   a. 22.9 W   b. 22.5 W   c. 21 W   d. 24.79 W
20.* What is the input power to a final RF amplifier stage having a plate voltage of 400 V, a plate current of 80 ma, a screen voltage of 125 V, a screen current of 5 ma, a driving power of .6 watts, a filament voltage of 12.6 V and a filament current of 150 ma?
   a. 32 W   b. 34.49 W   c. 35.115 W   d. 33.225 W
21.* A heterodyne frequency meter contains, among other components:
   a. two crystal controlled oscillators
   b. a mixer and an AF amplifier
   c. an electron-coupled oscillator and two detectors
   d. a variable oscillator and a detector
22.* What is the value of a resistor having a current of 3 amperes flowing through it and 30 volts across it?
   a. 10 ohms   b. .1 ohm   c. 90 ohms   d. 270 ohms
23.* By injecting a small quantity of arsenic into silicon, we can make a:
   a. high frequency conductor   c. resistor
   b. high frequency insulator   d. semiconductor

24.* An advantage of a transmatch is not:
   a. a reduction of harmonics
   b. matches transmitter to antenna system
   c. amplifies RF from final amplifier
   d. feeds maximum energy to antenna
25.* Which of the following cannot be used to determine that an emission from a transmitter is within an amateur band?
   a. heterodyne frequency meter
   b. grid-dip meter
   c. thermocouple-type meter
   d. wavemeter
26.* An advantage of a multiband antenna is:
   a. low SWR
   b. high efficiency
   c. high directivity
   d. several bands can be operated with one antenna
27.* A Novice Class operator may operate an amateur radio station in the following band:
   a. 3700 kHz - 3750 kHz   c. 21.0 MHz - 21.25 MHz
   b. 50.0 MHz - 54.0 MHz   d. 145.0 MHz - 147.0 MHz
28.* The maximum input power permitted to the final stage of a transmitter, owned or operated by a Novice Class operator, is:
   a. 50 W   b. 250 W   c. 100 W   d. 1000 W
29.* The term of a Novice Class license is:
   a. 1 year   b. 2 years   c. 3 years   d. 5 years
30.* A Novice Class license is renewable under the following conditions:
   a. upon application by the Novice operator
   b. if the Novice operator can show proof of still being able to pass the original examination
   c. proof must be given of 3 actual contacts with radio amateurs
   d. the Novice Class license is not renewable under any conditions
31.* The log of an amateur station must be preserved for:
   a. 6 months   b. 1 year   c. 2 years   d. 3 years
32.* The log of an amateur station is:
   a. a special type of radio calendar
   b. the rules and regulations of the FCC pertaining to the amateur operator
   c. a written record of transmissions made by the amateur operator
   d. a copy of the frequencies that an amateur can use under his class of license
33.* The second harmonic of 400 kHz is:
   a. 400 c   b. 800 c   c. 800 kHz   d. 1200 kHz
34.* One kiloHertz is equal to:
   a. 1000 Hertz   c. 1000 megaHertz
   b. 10,000 Hertz   d. 100,000 Hertz

35.* Interference due to sparking at the telegraph key contacts can be eliminated by a:
a. spark suppressor   c. key-click filter
b. resistor spark plug   d. spark gap device
36.* The method of frequency control required in a station licensed to the holder of a Novice Class license is:
a. automatic frequency control
b. crystal control
c. electron-coupled oscillator must be used
d. any standard method
37.* An amateur shall establish a procedure for measuring his carrier frequency:
a. when so ordered by the FCC
b. once a year
c. at regular intervals
d. when asked to do so by another amateur
38.* The means by which an amateur measures his emitted frequency shall be:
a. sufficiently accurate to assure operation within the amateur band being used
b. accurate within 2% of the dial calibrations
c. accurate within 5% of the dial calibrations
d. crystal controlled
39.* The third harmonic of 2 MHz is:
a. 6 MHz   b. 8 MHz   c. 12 kHz   d. 12 MHz
40.* A transmatch is used to:
a. match the impedance of a microphone to the impedance of the first AF tube
b. match the impedance of the transmitter to the impedance of the antenna system
c. increase the flow of harmonics to the antenna
d. tune the final amplifier stage of the transmitter
41.* One MegaHertz is equal to:
a. 100,000 Hertz   c. 1,000 Hertz
b. 1,000,000 Hertz   d. 100 kiloHertz

APPENDIX I
RADIO ABBREVIATIONS

Group	Abbreviation	Meaning
Ampere	a, or amp.	ampere
	μa	microampere
	ma.	milliampere
Farad	fd or f	farad (rarely used alone)
	μf	microfarad
	$\mu\mu$f or pf	micromicrofarad or picofarad
Frequency	f	frequency
	c*(or)	cycles
	cps	cycles per second
	kc.	kilocycles per second
	Mc.	Megacycles per second
Henry	h	henry
	mh	millihenry
	μh	microhenry
Impedance	X_L	inductive reactance (in ohms)
	X_C	capacitive reactance (in ohms)
Ohm	Ω (Omega)	ohm resistance
	$M\Omega$	megohm (one million ohms)
Volt	v	volt
Watt	w	watt
	p	power (in watts)
Current	AC	alternating current
	DC	direct current
Frequency	AF	audio frequency
	RF	radio frequency
	IF	intermediate frequency
	TRF	tuned radio frequency
Miscellaneous	CW	continuous wave
	AM	amplitude modulation
	FM	frequency modulation
	EMF	electromotive force (in volts)
	MOPA	master oscillator power amplifier
	EST	Eastern Standard Time
	GMT	Greenwich Mean Time

*The term "Hertz" has been used in place of cycles in recent years. The abbreviation for Hertz is Hz. We can, therefore, also use the terms kiloHertz and MegaHertz.

The abbreviation for kiloHertz is kHz.
The abbreviation for MegaHertz is MHz.

APPENDIX 2
COMMON RADIO SYMBOLS

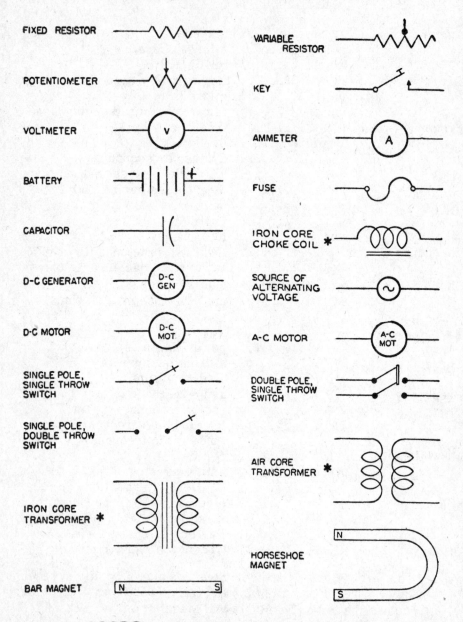

FIXED RESISTOR

VARIABLE RESISTOR

POTENTIOMETER

KEY

VOLTMETER

AMMETER

BATTERY

FUSE

CAPACITOR

IRON CORE CHOKE COIL *

D-C GENERATOR

SOURCE OF ALTERNATING VOLTAGE

D-C MOTOR

A-C MOTOR

SINGLE POLE, SINGLE THROW SWITCH

DOUBLE POLE, SINGLE THROW SWITCH

SINGLE POLE, DOUBLE THROW SWITCH

AIR CORE TRANSFORMER *

IRON CORE TRANSFORMER *

HORSESHOE MAGNET

BAR MAGNET

*Either (coil) or (coil) may be used to represent coils of wire on chokes or transformers.

APPENDIX 2
COMMON RADIO SYMBOLS

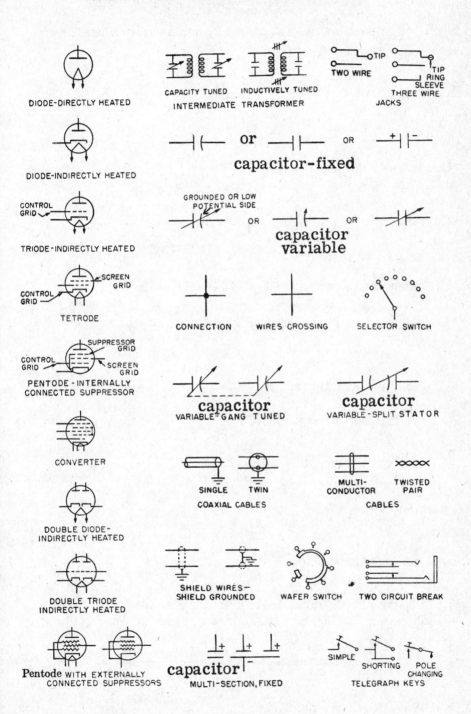

DIODE-DIRECTLY HEATED

DIODE-INDIRECTLY HEATED

CONTROL GRID
TRIODE-INDIRECTLY HEATED

SCREEN GRID
CONTROL GRID
TETRODE

SUPPRESSOR GRID
CONTROL GRID
SCREEN GRID
PENTODE - INTERNALLY CONNECTED SUPPRESSOR

CONVERTER

DOUBLE DIODE- INDIRECTLY HEATED

DOUBLE TRIODE INDIRECTLY HEATED

Pentode WITH EXTERNALLY CONNECTED SUPPRESSORS

CAPACITY TUNED   INDUCTIVELY TUNED
INTERMEDIATE TRANSFORMER

TWO WIRE
TIP
TIP
RING
SLEEVE
THREE WIRE
JACKS

or   OR   +   —
capacitor-fixed

GROUNDED OR LOW POTENTIAL SIDE
OR   OR
capacitor variable

CONNECTION   WIRES CROSSING   SELECTOR SWITCH

capacitor
VARIABLE-GANG TUNED

capacitor
VARIABLE-SPLIT STATOR

SINGLE   TWIN
COAXIAL CABLES

MULTI-CONDUCTOR   TWISTED PAIR
CABLES

SHIELD WIRES— SHIELD GROUNDED   WAFER SWITCH   TWO CIRCUIT BREAK

capacitor
MULTI-SECTION, FIXED

SIMPLE
SHORTING   POLE CHANGING
TELEGRAPH KEYS

APPENDIX 3
RADIO FORMULAS

(Explanations of letters and symbols are on Page 297).

1. Ohm's Law: $I = \dfrac{E}{R}$ $E = IR$ $R = \dfrac{E}{I}$

2. Power: $P = EI$ $P = I^2 R$ $P = \dfrac{E^2}{R}$

3. Resistors in Series: $R_T = R_1 + R_2 + R_3 \ldots\ldots\ldots$

4. TWO Resistors in Parallel: $R_T = \dfrac{R_1 \times R_2}{R_1 + R_2}$

5. Resistors in Parallel: $R_T = \dfrac{1}{\dfrac{1}{R_1} + \dfrac{1}{R_2} + \dfrac{1}{R_3} \ldots\ldots\ldots}$

6. Inductors in Series: $L_T = L_1 + L_2 + L_3 \ldots\ldots\ldots\ldots$

7. Inductors in Parallel: $L_T = \dfrac{1}{\dfrac{1}{L_1} + \dfrac{1}{L_2} + \dfrac{1}{L_3} \ldots\ldots\ldots}$

8. Inductive Reactance: $X_L = 2\pi f L$

9. Capacitors in Parallel: $C_T = C_1 + C_2 + C_3 \ldots\ldots\ldots$

10. Capacitors in Series: $C_T = \dfrac{1}{\dfrac{1}{C_1} + \dfrac{1}{C_2} + \dfrac{1}{C_3} \ldots\ldots\ldots\ldots}$

11. Capacitive Reactance: $X_C = \dfrac{1}{2\pi f C}$

12. Resonant Frequency of a Tuned Circuit: $f_r = \dfrac{1}{2\pi\sqrt{LC}}$

13. Characteristic Impedance of an Air Insulated Parallel Conductor Transmission Line: $Z = 276 \log \dfrac{b}{a}$

14. Standing Wave Ratio of a Transmission Line: $SWR = \dfrac{I_{max}}{I_{min}}$ or $\dfrac{E_{max}}{E_{min}}$

15. Wavelength of Radio Waves: $= \dfrac{300,000,000}{f}$

APPENDIX 3
RADIO FORMULAS

In the Radio Formulas given on Page 296, Appendix 3, note the following:

I is current in Amperes
E is voltage in volts
R is resistance in ohms
P is power in watts
L is inductance in henries
T stands for total
X_L is inductive reactance in ohms
f is frequency in cycles
C is capacity in farads
X_C is capacitive reactance in ohms
"a" is the radius of the conductor
"b" is the center to center distance between conductors
λ is the wavelength in meters
π is called "pi" and is equal to 3.14

APPENDIX 4
ABBREVIATIONS IN THE AMATEUR RADIO SERVICE
Q SIGNALS

"Q signals" are widely used abbreviations. Their use saves time in transmitting commonly used expressions and questions. When a Q signal is followed by a question mark, it takes the form of a question. When not followed by a question mark, a Q signal is either a reply to a Q signal question, or a direct statement. For instance, "QRA?" means "What is the name of your station?" "QRA" without the question mark means "The name of my station is......" Commonly used Q signals are listed below:

QRG? - What is my frequency?
QRM? - Are you being interfered with?
QRQ - Send faster.
QRS? - Shall I send slower?
QRT - I am closing down my station.
QRU? - Do you have anything for me?
QRX - Wait or stand by.
QRZ? - Who is calling me?
QSB? - Is my signal fading?
QSL? - Can you acknowledge receipt?
QSY? - Shall I change frequency?
QSZ? - Shall I send each group twice?
QTH? - What is your location?

The following abbreviations are commonly used by amateurs in telegraphy:

CQ - A general inquiry call. It is used when an amateur wishes to make a contact.
DE - means "from". It is followed by the call letters of the station doing the sending.
K - means "go ahead". It is used after a CQ or at the end of a transmission.
AR - indicates the end of a message unit or transmission.
SK - indicates the end of the entire transmission.

RST REPORTING SYSTEM

The RST reporting system is a means of rating the quality of a signal on a numerical basis. In this system, the R stands for readability and is rated on a scale of 1 to 5. The S stands for signal strength and it is rated on a scale of 1 to 9. The T indicates the quality of a CW tone and its scale is also 1 to 9. The higher the number, the better the signal.

APPENDIX 4
ABBREVIATIONS IN THE AMATEUR RADIO SERVICE

READABILITY

1. Unreadable
2. Barely readable; occasional words distinguishable
3. Readable with considerable difficulty
4. Readable with practically no difficulty
5. Perfectly readable

SIGNAL STRENGTH

1. Faint; signals barely perceptible
2. Very weak signals
3. Weak signals
4. Fair signals
5. Fairly good signals
6. Good signals
7. Moderately strong signals
8. Strong signals
9. Extremely strong signals

TONE

1. Extremely rough, hissing tone
2. Very rough AC note; no trace of musicality
3. Rough, low-pitched AC note; slightly musical
4. Rather rough AC note; moderately musical
5. Musically modulated note
6. Modulated note; slight trace of whistle
7. Near DC note; smooth ripple
8. Good DC note; just a trace of ripple
9. Purest DC note (If note appears to be crystal controlled, add letter X after the number indicating tone)

EXAMPLE: Your signals RST 599X. (Your signals are perfectly readable, extremely strong, have purest DC note, and sound as if your transmitter is crystal-controlled.)

APPENDIX 5
STUDY MATERIAL FOR NOVICE LICENSE PREPARATION

Section I   Introduction to Radio. Page 5.

Lesson 1.   Entire lesson. All Practice Questions.

Lesson 2.   Paragraphs 2-1, 2-2, 2-5, 2-7, 2-8, 2-11.

Lesson 3.   Paragraphs 3-1 through 3-4, 3-8, 3-9, 3-12, 3-16 through 3-19, 3-30 through 3-33, 3-38 through 3-42, 3-45.

Practice Questions 1, 2, 5, 9, 12, 21.

FCC-type exam. Page 68. Questions 1 through 4, 6, 12, 15, 16, 19, 28.

Section II   Lesson 4.   Paragraphs 4-1 through 4-7, 4-10 through 4-13.

Practice Questions 1 through 3, 9 through 13.

Lesson 5.   Paragraphs 5-1 through 5-3.

Practice Question 1.

Lesson 6.   Paragraphs 6-1 through 6-3, 6-6, 6-17, 6-20.

Practice Questions 7 through 10, 12.

Lesson 7.   Paragraphs 7-1 through 7-4.

Lesson 8.   Paragraphs 8-1, 8-2, 8-6, 8-7 through 8-10, 8-15, 8-16.

Practice Questions 2 through 5.

FCC-type exam. Page 142. Questions 2, 9 and 10.

Section III   Introduction to Transmission and Reception. Page 145.

Lesson 9.   Paragraphs 9-1 through 9-5.

Lesson 10.   Paragraphs 10-1 through 10-5, 10-19 through 10-22, 10-28, 10-29.

Practice Questions 13, 15.

Lesson 11.   Paragraphs 11-1 through 11-3, 11-15, 11-17, 11-18.

Practice Question 22.

Lesson 12.   Paragraphs 12-1 through 12-7, 12-10, 12-13, 12-14A, 12-15, 12-15A, 12-16, 12-17, 12-19A, 12-20.

Practice Questions 1, 2, 3, 6, 8, 10 through 14.

Lesson 13.   Paragraphs 13-1 and 13-2.

Lesson 14.   Introduction. Page 256.

Paragraphs 97.1, 97.3, 97.5, 97.7, 97.9, 97.13, 97.37, 97.40, 97.57, 97.75, 97.79, 97.83, 97.85, 97.103, 97.105.

Practice Questions 1, 2, 5, 9, 10.

FCC-type exam. Page 278. Questions 6, 7, 21, 25, 27, 28, 32.

Final Novice FCC-type exam. Page 289. Entire exam.

APPENDIX 6
ANSWERS TO PRACTICE QUESTIONS

LESSON 1.

1. c	7. d	13. 6.67 ohms	19. b
2. b	8. c	14. 0.5 A.	20. a
3. b	9. a	15. 25 V.	21. a
4. d	10. b	16. b	22. d
5. c	11. 14.06 W	17. c	23. c
6. b	12. 100 V.	18. b	

LESSON 2.

1. b	4. b	7. d	10. c
2. c	5. a	8. b	
3. b	6. c	9. d	

LESSON 3.

1. b	8. d	15. c	22. a
2. c	9. b	16. b	23. b
3. b	10. a	17. c	24. b
4. d	11. b	18. a	25. a
5. c	12. d	19. b	
6. c	13. b	20. c	
7. c	14. a	21. c	

SECTION I FCC-TYPE EXAM.

1. c	9. a	17. a	25. a
2. a	10. d	18. a	26. c
3. b	11. d	19. c	27. c
4. c	12. c	20. b	28. a
5. c	13. a	21. d	29. b
6. c	14. c	22. c	30. d
7. b	15. b	23. d	31. d
8. c	16. d	24. a	

LESSON 4.

1. b	5. a	9. c	13. a
2. d	6. b	10. d	
3. a	7. a	11. b	
4. d	8. b	12. a	

LESSON 5.

1. b	5. d	9. a	13. c
2. c	6. b	10. b	14. c
3. b	7. c	11. d	15. a
4. a	8. d	12. b	16. c

APPENDIX 6
ANSWERS TO PRACTICE QUESTIONS

LESSON 6.

1. c	7. d	13. a	19(a). 7 V.
2. a	8. c	14. d	19(b). 100 V.
3. a	9. a	15. b	19(c). 107 V.
4. d	10. d	16. d	20(a). 75 V.
5. b	11. a	17. b	20(b). 150 V.
6. b	12. c	18. d	20(c). 225 V.
			21. a

LESSON 7.

1. See Fig.	4. a	8. b	11. b
7-5	5. c	9. See Figs.	12. a
2. d	6. c	7-5, 7-6	13. a
3. b	7. a	10. d	14. a

LESSON 8.

1. b	4. d	7. a	10. d
2. a	5. d	8. a	11. c
3. c	6. c	9. c	12. a

SECTION II FCC-TYPE EXAM.

1. c	8. d	15. a	22. d
2. c	9. a	16. c	23. a
3. d	10. d	17. b	24. d
4. c	11. c	18. b	25. b
5. 79.5 V.	12. a	19. c	26. c
6. a	13. b	20. c	27. c
7. c	14. a	21. a	28. a

LESSON 9.

1. d	4. d	7. d	9. 28.003
2. d	5. a	8. See Fig.	MHz
3. b	6. b	9-13	10. c

LESSON 10.

1. c	6. b	11. c	16. b
2. c	7. d	12. a	17. c
3. a	8. See P.	13. c	18. d
4. See P.	10-18	14. See Figs.	19. c
10-16	9. a	10-7, 10-14	
5. b	10. b	15. d	

APPENDIX 6
ANSWERS TO ALL QUESTIONS

LESSON 11.
1. See P. 11-14
2. See P. 11-14
3. b
4. a
5. a
6. d
7. c
8. See P. 11-2
9. See P. 11-5
10. d
11. See Fig. 11-13
12. c
13. d
14. c
15. b
16. d
17. a
18. a
19. c
20. b
21. c
22. c

LESSON 12.
1. d
2. a
3. a
4. a
5. c
6. c
7. c
8. c
9. d
10. b
11. b
12. a
13. c
14. b
15. a
16. c

LESSON 13.
1. See Figs. 13-8 and 13-9
2. b
3. b
4. c
5. a
6. d
7. c
8. a
9. c
10. c
11. d
12. a

LESSON 14.
1. d
2. c
3. a
4. c
5. b
6. a
7. d
8. d
9. b
10. c

SECTION III FCC-TYPE EXAM.
1. a
2. b
3. d
4. c
5. b
6. c
7. b
8. b
9. b
10. c
11. d
12. c
13. b
14. b
15. b
16. d
17. c
18. a
19. c
20. b
21. d
22. b
23. a
24. c
25. d
26. b
27. c
28. c
29. a
30. c
31. a
32. d
33. a

APPENDIX 6
ANSWERS TO ALL QUESTIONS

FINAL GENERAL CLASS FCC-TYPE EXAM.

1. b	19. a	37. d	55. b
2. c	20. b	38. c	56. d
3. c	21. a	39. d	57. a
4. d	22. a	40. c	58. d
5. a	23. a	41. c	59. c
6. a	24. b	42. b	60. d
7. d	25. c	43. a	61. d
8. c	26. c	44. c	62. c
9. c	27. d	45. d	63. b
10. a	28. b	46. c	64. d
11. c	29. c	47. b	65. b
12. d	30. b	48. d	66. a
13. c	31. d	49. a	67. c
14. a	32. d	50. a	68. b
15. c	33. c	51. c	69. c
16. c	34. c	52. b	70. c
17. c	35. d	53. a	
18. d	36. a	54. a	

FINAL NOVICE CLASS FCC-TYPE EXAM.

1. b	12. d	23. d	34. a
2. a	13. c	24. c	35. c
3. c	14. a	25. c	36. d
4. d	15. a	26. d	37. c
5. a	16. b	27. a	38. a
6. b	17. d	28. b	39. a
7. d	18. b	29. b	40. b
8. b	19. a	30. d	41. b
9. d	20. d	31. b	
10. a	21. d	32. c	
11. b	22. a	33. c	

FREQUENCY ALLOCATIONS FOR POPULAR AMATEUR BANDS
All in Megacycles.   "X" indicates no privileges.

CLASSES →	NOVICE		TECHNICIAN		GENERAL AND CONDITIONAL		ADVANCED		EXTRA	
BANDS ↓	CW	PHONE	CW	PHONE	CW	PHONE	CW	PHONE	CW	PHONE
80 METERS	3.7 to 3.75	X	X	X	3.525 to 3.775 and 3.89 to 4.0	3.89 to 4.0	3.525 to 3.775 and 3.8 to 4.0	3.8 to 4.0	3.5 to 4.0	3.775 to 4.0
40 METERS	7.1 to 7.15	X	X	X	7.025 to 7.15 and 7.225 to 7.3	7.225 to 7.3	7.025 to 7.3	7.15 to 7.3	7.0 to 7.3	7.15 to 7.3
20 METERS	X	X	X	X	14.025 to 14.2 and 14.275 to 14.35	14.275 to 14.35	14.025 to 14.35	14.2 to 14.35	14.0 to 14.35	14.2 to 14.35
15 METERS	21.1 to 21.2	X	X	X	21.025 to 21.25 and 21.35 to 21.45	21.35 to 21.45	21.025 to 21.25 and 21.27 to 21.45	21.27 to 21.45	21.0 to 21.45	21.25 to 21.45
10 METERS	28.1 to 28.2	X	X	X	28.0 to 29.7	28.5 to 29.7	28.0 to 29.7	28.5 to 29.7	28.0 to 29.7	28.5 to 29.7
6 METERS	X	X	50.1 to 54.0	50.1 to 54.0	50.1 to 54.0	50.1 to 54.0	50.0 to 54.0	50.1 to 54.0	50.0 to 54.0	50.1 to 54.0
2 METERS	X	X	145.0 to 148.0	145.0 to 148.0	144.0 to 148.0	144.1 to 148.0	144.0 to 148.0	144.1 to 148.0	144.0 to 148.0	144.1 to 148.0

INDEX

Boron, 77
Bridge rectifier, 87

C

"C" battery, 169
Cable, coaxial, 234
  open wire, 234
  twin-lead, 234
Capacitance, 42, 43
Capacitance, interelectrode, 105
Capacitive reactance, 47
Capacitor coupling, 121
Capacitor in an AC circuit, 47
Capacitor input filter, 85
Capacitor voltage rating, 44
Capacitors, electrolytic, 88
  ganged, 44
  transmitter filter, 89
  variable, 43
Capacitors in parallel, 46
Capacitors in series, 45
Capacity coupling, 176
Carbon microphone, 128
Carbon resistor, 10
Care of crystals, 160
Carrier swing, 213
Cascade stages, 116
Cathode, 72
Cathode bias, 118
Cathode, directly heated, 72
  indirectly heated, 72
Cathode follower, 137
Cell, 11
  internal resistance of, 16
Characteristic impedance of
  transmission line, 234
Charge, 8
Charge, space, 71, 75
Choke, 40
  filter, 90
  swinging, 90
Choke input filter, 90
Circuits, electrical, 12
  magnetic, 24
  open, 12
  parallel, 16, 18
  pi-network, 186
  series, 14

Circuits, series, parallel, 18
  short, 12
  tank, 148
  transistor, 111
  tuned, 146
Class A amplifier, 117
Class A amplifier distortion, 122
Class A power amplifier, 132
Class B amplifier, 117
Class B power amplifier, 133
Class B push-pull amplifier, 134
Class C amplifier, 117, 167
Class C amplifier efficiency, 167
Click, keying, 177
Cloud, electron, 74
Coaxial cable, 234
Coil, tickler, 149
Collector, 111
Colpitts oscillator, 153
Compass, 23
Complete circuit, 12
Conductance, 10
Conductor, diode as a, 74
Conductors, 8
Continuous wave transmitter,
    165, 181
Control grid, 96
Copper losses, 59
Copper wire, 9
Core, air, 58
  laminated, 60
Coulomb, 11
Counter-EMF, 48
Coupling capacitor, 121
Coupling, capacity, 176
  inductive, 176
  link, 176
CPS (cycles per second), 33
Crystals, AT-cut, 159, 160
  X-cut, 159
  Y-cut, 159
  care of, 160
  resonant frequency of, 159
Crystal controlled oscillator, 157
Crystal microphone, 130
Crystal set, 76
Current, 11
Current, alternating, 31

Micromho, 11
Microphone, 128
   carbon, 128
   crystal, 130
   ribbon, 129
   velocity, 129
Microphone transformer, 129
Milliammeter, 11
Milliampere, 11
Millihenry, 37
Modulated transmitter, 193
Modulation, amplitude, 193
   frequency, 211
   grid, 203
   high-level, 199
   low-level, 199
   phase, 213
   plate, 199, 202
   push-pull, 201
Modulation percentage, 194, 206, 213
Modulation percentage, checking, 208
Modulator, reactance tube, 216
Morse code, 165
Multiband antennas, 236
Multipliers, frequency, 175
Mycalex, 8

N

N-type material, 77
Narrow-band frequency modulation, 215
Negative temperature coefficient, 159
Neutralization, 170
   Ballantine, 172
   criss-cross, 172
   grid, 172
   Hazeltine, 172
   plate, 171
   Rice, 172
Nichrome, 9
North pole, magnetic, 23
N-P-N transistor, 110

O

Oersted, 28

Ohm, 9
Ohm's Law, 13
Ohm's Law problems, 14
Ohmmeter, 9
One tube receiver, 225
One tube transmitter, 165
Open circuit, 12
Open wire transmission line, 234
Operating frequency, choosing an, 190
Operating voltage, filament, 73
Oscillation, 105
   parasitic, 175
Oscillator, 146-163
   Armstrong, 149
   Colpitts, 153
   Crystal controlled, 157
   electron coupled, 156
   Hartley, 153
   parallel-fed, 152
   shunt-fed, 152
   tuned-grid, 149
   tuned-plate, tuned-grid, 153
Oscillator frequency, 151
Oscilloscope, 207
Out of phase, 35
Overmodulation, 196, 208

P

P-type material, 77
Parallel capacitors, 46
Parallel circuits, 16, 18
Parallel-fed oscillator, 152
Parallel inductances, 38
Parallel resonance, 53
Parallel resistances, 16
Parallel resonant circuit impedance, 54
Parasitic oscillations, 175
Peak amplitude, 33
Peak-Envelope-Power, 202
Peak modulation monitor, 207
Peak value, 36
Pentode, 107
PEP (see Peak-Envelope-Power)
Percentage of modulation, 194
Period, 33

APPENDIX 7

ADDITIONAL FCC RULES AND REGULATIONS

97.45 <u>LIMITATIONS ON ANTENNA STRUCTURES</u>.

(a) Except as provided in paragraph (b) of this section, an antenna for a station in the Amateur Radio Service which exceeds the following height limitations, may not be erected or used unless notice has been filed with both the FAA on FAA Form 7460-1 and with the Commission on Form 714 or on the license application form, and prior approval by the Commission has been obtained for:

(1) Any construction or alteration of more than 200 feet in height above ground level at its site (Sec. 17.7(a) of this chapter).

(2) Any construction or alteration of greater height than an imaginary surface extending outward and upward at one of the following slopes (Sec. 17.7(b) of this chapter);

(i) 100 to 1 for a horizontal distance of 20,000 feet from the nearest point of the nearest runway of each airport, with at least one runway more than 3,200 feet in length, excluding heliports and seaplane bases without specified boundaries, if that airport is either listed in the Airport Directory of the current Airman's Information Manual or is operated by a Federal military agency.

(ii) 50 to 1 for a horizontal distance of 10,000 feet from the nearest point of the nearest runway of each airport with its longest runway no more than 3,200 feet in length, excluding heliports and seaplane bases without specified boundaries, if that airport is either listed in the Airport Directory or is operated by a Federal military agency.

(iii) 25 to 1 for a horizontal distance of 5,000 feet from the nearest point of the nearest landing and takeoff area of each heliport listed in the Airport Directory or operated by a Federal military agency.

(3) Any construction or alteration on an airport listed in the Airport Directory of the Airman's Information Manual (Sec. 17.7(c) of this chapter).

(b) A notification to the Federal Aviation Administration is not required for any of the following construction or alteration:

(1) Any object that would be shielded by existing structures of a permanent and substantial character or by natural terrain or topographic features of equal or greater height, and would be located in the congested area of a city, town, or settlement where it is evident beyond all reasonable doubt, that the structure so shielded will not adversely affect safety in air navigation. Applicants claiming such exemption shall submit a statement with their application to the Com-

mission explaining the basis in detail for their finding (Sec. 17.14(a) of this chapter).

(2) Any antenna structure of 20 feet or less in height, except one that would increase the height of another antenna structure (Sec. 17.14(b) of this chapter).

(c) Further details as to whether an aeronautical study and/or obstruction marking and lighting may be required, and specifications for obstruction marking and lighting when required, may be obtained from Part 17 of this chapter, "Construction, Marking and Lighting of Antenna Structures". Information regarding the inspection and maintenance of antenna structures requiring obstruction marking and lighting, is also contained in Part 17 of this chapter.

97.49 COMMISSION MODIFICATION OF STATION LICENSE.

(a) Whenever the Commission shall determine that public interest, convenience and necessity would be served, or any treaty ratified by the United States will be more fully complied with, by the modification of any radio station license either for a limited time, or for the duration of the term thereof, it shall issue an order for such licensee to show cause why such license should not be modified.

(b) Such order to show cause shall contain a statement of the grounds and reasons for such proposed modification, and shall specify wherein the said license is required to be modified. It shall require the licensee against whom it is directed to appear at a place and time therein named, in no event to be less than 30 days from the date of receipt of the order, to show cause why the proposed modification should not be made and the order of modification issued.

(c) If the licensee against whom the order to show cause is directed does not appear at the time and place provided in said order, a final order of modification shall issue forthwith.

97.67 MAXIMUM AUTHORIZED POWER.

(a) Except for power restrictions as set forth in Sec. 97.61, each amateur transmitter may be operated with a power input not exceeding 1 kilowatt to the plate circuit of the final amplifier stage of an amplifier-oscillator transmitter or to the plate circuit of an oscillator transmitter. An amateur transmitter operating with a power input exceeding 900 watts to the plate circuit shall provide means for accurately measuring the plate power input to the vacuum tube or tubes supplying power to the antenna.

(b) Notwithstanding the provisions of paragraph (a) of this section, amateur stations shall use the minimum amount of transmitter power necessary to carry out the desired communications.

(c) Within the limitations of paragraphs (a) and (b) of this section, the effective radiated power of a repeater station shall not exceed that specified for the antenna height above average terrain in the following table:

Antenna height above average terrain	Maximum effective radiated power for frequency bands above:			
	52 MHz	146 MHz	442 MHz	1215 MHz
Below 50 feet	100 watts	800 watts	Paragraphs (a) and (b)	----------
50 to 99 feet	100 watts	400 watts	--- do ---	----------
100 to 499 feet	50 watts	400 watts	800 watts	Paragraphs (a) and (b)
500 to 999 feet	25 watts	200 watts	800 watts	--- do ---
Above 1,000 feet	25 watts	100 watts	400 watts	--- do ---

97.109 OPERATION OF A CONTROL STATION.

(a) Amateur frequency bands above 220 MHz, excepting 435 to 438 MHz, may be used for emissions by a control station. Frequencies below 225 MHz used for control links must be monitored by the control operator immediately prior to, and during, periods of operation.

(b) Where a remotely controlled station has been authorized to be operated from one or more remote control stations, those remote control stations may be operated either mobile or portable.

97.131 RESTRICTED OPERATION.

(a) If the operation of an amateur station causes general interference to the reception of transmissions from stations operating in the domestic broadcast service when receivers of good engineering design including adequate selectivity characteristics are used to receive such transmissions, and this fact is made known to the amateur station licensee, the amateur station shall not be operated during the hours from 8 p.m. to 10:30 p.m., local time, and on Sunday for the additional period from 10:30 a.m. until 1 p.m., local time, upon the frequency or frequencies used when the interference is created.

(b) In general, such steps as may be necessary to minimize interference to stations operating in other services may be required after investigation by the Commission.